FEEDBACK SYSTEMS:
INPUT-OUTPUT PROPERTIES

ELECTRICAL SCIENCE
A Series of Monographs and Texts

Editors: Henry G. Booker and Nicholas DeClaris
A complete list of titles in this series appears at the end of this volume

FEEDBACK SYSTEMS: INPUT-OUTPUT PROPERTIES

C. A. DESOER
DEPARTMENT OF ELECTRICAL ENGINEERING
AND COMPUTER SCIENCES
UNIVERSITY OF CALIFORNIA
BERKELEY, CALIFORNIA

M. VIDYASAGAR
DEPARTMENT OF ELECTRICAL ENGINEERING
CONCORDIA UNIVERSITY
MONTREAL, CANADA

ACADEMIC PRESS New York San Francisco London 1975

A Subsidiary of Harcourt Brace Jovanovich, Publishers

ACADEMIC PRESS, INC.
111 Fifth Avenue, New York, New York 10003

United Kingdom Edition published by
ACADEMIC PRESS, INC. (LONDON) LTD.
24/28 Oval Road, London NW1

Library of Congress Cataloging in Publication Data

Desoer, Charles A
Feedback systems.

(Electrical science series)
Bibliography: p.
1. Feedback control systems. I. Vidyasagar, M., joint author. II. Title.
TJ216.D42 629.8'312 74-5694
ISBN 0-12-212050-7

PRINTED IN THE UNITED STATES OF AMERICA

CONTENTS

II Norms

III General Theorems

IV Linear Systems

V Applications of the Small Gain Theorem

VI Passivity

Appendixes

A Integrals and Series

B Fourier Transforms

C Convolution

D Algebras

PREFACE

During the last 15 years the subject of nonlinear feedback systems has undergone considerable development. On the one hand, the theory of Lyapunov functions has evolved rapidly: It is, in fact, the subject of three authoritative treatises by Zubov, Yoshizawa, and Hahn, respectively. For this reason, this book does not cover the theory of Lyapunov functions. On the other hand, the techniques of functional analysis, pioneered by Sandberg and Zames, have developed equally rapidly and generated a large number of results concerning the input–output properties of nonlinear feedback systems. The principal advantage of the latter technique is that it covers *distributed* systems almost as easily as *lumped* systems and that it deals with multiinput–multioutput systems in the same framework as the single-input–single-output systems. This is also true for the continuous-time and discrete-time systems. The thrust of this book is, therefore, on the multiinput–multioutput feedback system made of distributed subsystems with attention principally focused on continuous-time systems. Our purpose has been to develop the main techniques that led to the basic input–output properties of feedback systems; we have not even attempted to present an encyclopedic coverage of all problems solved by such methods. Rather, we have tried to maintain a happy medium between illustrating the techniques by treating simple cases and developing the best and most esoteric results.

Our audience consists of mathematically inclined engineers interested in feedback systems. Most of the subject matter in this book has been taught at Berkeley to engineering students at the Master's level. Experience has shown that engineering students with a good junior course in "mathematical analysis" and an undergraduate course in "control" experience little difficulty with the material covered here. With such an audience in mind, the first two chapters slowly develop special material which is constantly used in the remaining four chapters. Useful mathematical facts whose proofs would take us too far from our main path are collected in the five short appendixes. On the other hand, our audience allows us to motivate many approaches by analogies from conservation of energy and reference to standard reasonings of circuit theory and control theory. This audience would also understand without further explanation terms such as "positive feedback," "feedforward," "transfer function," and "impulse response."

In the first chapter we develop a few simple facts about feedback systems and exhibit simple examples of nonlinear systems which illustrate the important distinction that has to be maintained between the questions of existence, uniqueness, continuous dependence, and boundedness, roughly, in the sense of bounded-input–bounded-output. The second chapter develops a number of useful properties of norms and induced norms and of normed spaces, which are used later. Several theorems are presented in Chapter III at a very general and abstract level; to compensate for this, numerous exercises point to useful applications. Chapter IV covers the main results concerning linear systems. Chapter V uses these results to illustrate the use of the small gain theorem: Each of the nine sections applies the small gain theorem to a different class of systems. Finally, Chapter VI develops the framework necessary to discuss passivity and the applications of the passivity theorem. In short, our purpose is to present the main results and the main techniques so that the reader can easily follow the current literature on the subject.

A few words about the nature of collaborative effort. Desoer laid down the plan of the book and had the first three chapters and the appendixes almost complete by the winter of 1973. At that time rough drafts of the remaining three chapters were rendered obsolete by recent developments. Vidyasagar, who had indicated an interest in writing a book of this sort, joined in the effort to revise the first three chapters and to rewrite completely the last three chapters. This was done at Berkeley during the summer of 1973. Both authors are responsible for any errors.

ACKNOWLEDGMENTS

In writing a book that presents a unified view of a large number of results obtained by many researchers over a decade or more, the authors faced the difficult problem of acknowledging the contributions of individual researchers. At one time Desoer attempted to collect a reasonably complete bibliography, but soon the size of the list became so overwhelming that the attempt was abandoned. We finally settled on referring specific results to those papers which we believed taught us a particular approach or solved a particular problem. Thus when we refer a particular item to a specific author, we do not purport to settle claims of priority. We leave such questions of priority and of distinguishing individual contributions to the professional historians. If in the process we have committed some injustices, we apologize and assure the authors involved that the mistake was unintentional.

The preparation of this book involved a great amount of preliminary research that would have been impossible without support and encouragement from several agencies and institutions. The first author gratefully acknowledges the National Science Foundation, the National Aeronautics and Space Administration, the Joint Services Electronics Program, and the University of California. It is a pleasure to acknowledge the contributions of the many discussions, clarifications, and hard work of colleagues, visitors, and former students in the seminar on nonlinear feedback systems. In the words of E. A. Guillemin, he "cannot name one without naming them all, and he cannot name them all because he can't be sure that he won't miss one or two." They are not nameless, because they have made a name for themselves. The second author gratefully acknowledges the generous policies of Sir George Williams University (Concordia University), which made possible his stay at Berkeley, as well as research support from the National Research Council of Canada.

NOTE TO THE READER

The chapter number and chapter title are shown at the top of each *left* page, e.g., "II Norms." The section number and the section title are shown at the top of each *right* page, e.g., "2 Equivalent Norms."

Within each section, comments, definitions, equations, facts, theorems, remarks, and so forth, are numbered by means of a numeral appearing in the left-hand margin. These numerals constitute within each section a strictly increasing sequence. From time to time, the numerals are not consecutive: This will not cause problems since these numerals are used like street numbers for houses; they merely identify, within the sequence, one specific item.

In referring to an item within the *same* section, we use only the item number, e.g., "Definition (3)," "Fact (11)." In references within the *same* chapter but referring to an item in *another* section, we use the section and item number, e.g., "Definition (2.3)," "Theorem (7.1)." In referring to items in *another* chapter we use the chapter, section, and item number, e.g., "Eq. (II.3.2)," "Theorem (III.2.1)."

The figures are numbered consecutively within a chapter; e.g., "Fig. III.1" means the first figure of Chapter III.

Every technical term is printed boldface in its defining sentence.

For convenience the abbreviations u.t.c. for "under these conditions" and s.t. for "so that" are used throughout.

LIST OF SYMBOLS

$\mathscr{A}$ convolution algebra

$\mathscr{A}_2$ two-sided convolution algebra

$[a, b]$ closed interval: $\{x \in \mathbb{R} \mid a \leq x \leq b]$

$(a, b]$ interval: $\{x \in \mathbb{R} \mid a < x \leq b\}$

boldface denotes operators, typically maps from $\mathscr{L}_e \to \mathscr{L}_e$

$B(x; r)$ open ball of center x and radius r $\{x \mid \|x\| < r\}$

$\bar{B}(x; r)$ closed ball of center x and radius r

$\mathbb{C}$ field of complex numbers

$\mathbb{C}_+$ closed right half plane, i.e., $\{z \in \mathbb{C} \mid \text{Re } z \geq 0\}$

$\mathbb{C}^n$ linear space of ordered n-tuples in $\mathbb{C}$

$\mathbb{C}^{n \times m}$ ring of matrices with n rows and m columns with elements in $\mathbb{C}$

$\mathscr{H}$ inner product function space $\{f: \mathscr{T} \to \mathscr{V} \mid \langle f \mid f \rangle < \infty\}$

$\mathscr{H}_e$ extended inner product function space

$\mathscr{L}$ normed function space $\{f: \mathscr{T} \to \mathscr{V} \mid \|f\| < \infty\}$

$\mathscr{L}_e$ extended normed function space

$L^p(\mathbb{R})$, $(L^p(\mathbb{R}_+))$ space of functions $\{f: \mathbb{R} \to \mathbb{R}\}$ such that $t \mapsto |f(t)|^p$ is integrable over $\mathbb{R}$ ($\mathbb{R}_+$, resp.); typically $p = 1, 2, \infty$

l^p space of sequences $z = (z_0, z_1, \ldots)$ such that $\sum_0^\infty |z_k|^p$ is summable

$\mathbb{R}$	field of real numbers
$\mathbb{R}_+$	set of nonnegative real numbers $\{x \in \mathbb{R} : x \geq 0\}$
$\mathbb{R}^n$	linear space of ordered n-tuples in $\mathbb{R}$
$\mathbb{R}^{n \times m}$	ring of matrices with n rows and m columns with elements in $\mathbb{R}$
$\mathbb{R}[s]$	commutative ring of polynomials in s
$\mathbb{R}(s)$	commutative field of rational functions in s
sgn	"signum" function: sgn x is 1, 0, or -1, resp., according as $x > 0$, $x = 0$, $x < 0$
$\mathbb{Z}$	ring of integers: $\{\ldots, -1, 0, 1, \ldots\}$
$\mathbb{Z}_+$	set of nonnegative integers: $\{0, 1, 2, \ldots\}$
$\lvert\ \rvert$	denotes the absolute value of a real or complex number. the norm of a vector in $\mathbb{R}^n$ or $\mathbb{C}^n$
$\lVert\ \rVert$	denotes a norm (in a general context); the norm of a function, e.g., $\lVert f \rVert$, or the induced norm of a linear operator $\lVert A \rVert$
$\lVert g \rVert_{\mathscr{A}}$	$\mathscr{A}$-norm of g
$\lVert f \rVert_p$	norm of f as an element of L^p
$\nearrow$	$f: R \to R$ is "$\nearrow$" means that $t_1 > t_2 \Rightarrow f(t_1) \geq f(t_2)$

I MEMORYLESS NONLINEARITIES

The purpose of this chapter is to direct the reader's attention to some fundamental features of nonlinear problems. Most *linear* problems encountered in engineering have the feature that to any reasonable input, a solution exists and it is unique, and in most cases, it depends continuously on the input. In some cases (extremely important in practice), a bounded input produces a bounded output. We show below that in the nonlinear problems, these four properties—existence, uniqueness, continuous dependence, and finite gain—need not be fulfilled in even some very simple examples, namely, memoryless nonlinear systems with linear feedback.

We also use this chapter to introduce some extremely useful classes of nonlinearities. Only memoryless systems are considered in this chapter. In Section 1, nonlinearities satisfying sector conditions are defined and given several useful equivalent mathematical representations. In Section 2, linear feedback is introduced, and the relations between the open- and the closed-loop characteristic are established. In the final section, nonlinearities with several inputs and several outputs are considered.

1 Sector conditions

1.1 Single-input case

The simplest memoryless nonlinearity has a single input and a single output related by a characteristic ϕ. The output at time t, $y(t)$, is given by

$$y(t) = \phi[u(t)] \qquad \text{for all } t$$

In general, ϕ is a relation between real numbers, not necessarily a function. Throughout the discussion we could allow the characteristic to be time varying, thus $y(t) = \phi[u(t), t]$, the only change needed would be to require that all the inequalities hold for all t.

1 **Definition** Let $\phi\colon \mathbb{R} \to \mathbb{R}$ with $\phi(0) = 0$. We say that $\phi \in$ **sector** (k_1, k_2) iff $k_1 e^2 < e\phi(e) < k_2 e^2$, $\forall e \in \mathbb{R}$ with $e \neq 0$. Similarly, we say that $\phi \in$ **sector** $[k_1, k_2)$ iff $k_1 e^2 \leq e\phi(e) < k_2 e^2$, $\forall e \in \mathbb{R}$ with $e \neq 0$. There are several equivalent ways of expressing these sector conditions. We state them as an equivalence theorem.

2 **Equivalence Theorem** Let $k_1, k_2 \in \mathbb{R}$ with $k_1 \leq k_2$. Let $\phi\colon \mathbb{R} \to \mathbb{R}$ with $\phi(0) = 0$. U.t.c. the following four statements are equivalent:

(i) $k_1 \leq \phi(e)/e \leq k_2, \qquad \forall e \neq 0$

(ii) $k_1 e^2 \leq e\phi(e) \leq k_2 e^2, \qquad \forall e \in \mathbb{R}$

(iii) $[\phi(e) - k_1 e][\phi(e) - k_2 e] \leq 0, \qquad \forall e \in \mathbb{R}$

(iv) $|\phi(e) - ce|^2 \leq r^2 |e|^2, \qquad \forall e \in \mathbb{R}$

where

$$c \triangleq \tfrac{1}{2}(k_1 + k_2), \qquad r \triangleq \tfrac{1}{2}(k_2 - k_1), \qquad k_1 k_2 = c^2 - r^2$$

3 **Corollary** With, in addition, $k_1 > 0$, statement (i) implies

(v) $(1/k_2)\phi(e)^2 \leq e\phi(e) \leq (1/k_1)\phi(e)^2, \qquad \forall e \in \mathbb{R}$

Proof (i) $\Leftrightarrow$ (ii) [Since (ii) holds obviously when $e = 0$, we need only consider $e \neq 0$.]

Multiplying (i) by e^2, we obtain (ii).
Multiplying (ii) by e^{-2}, we obtain (i).
(iii) $\Leftrightarrow$ (iv) Follows by calculation:

$$(\phi - k_1 e)(\phi - k_2 e) = \phi^2 - 2\frac{k_1 + k_2}{2}\phi e + k_1 k_2 e^2 = (\phi - ce)^2 - r^2 e^2$$

once we note that $k_1 k_2 = c^2 - r^2$. Hence (iii) $\Leftrightarrow$ (iv).

(ii) $\Rightarrow$ (iii)

$$0 \geq (e\phi - k_1 e^2)(e\phi - k_2 e^2) = e^2(\phi - k_1 e)(\phi - k_2 e)$$

Hence (iii) follows since $e^2 \geq 0$.

(iii) $\Rightarrow$ (ii) Multiply (iii) by e^2 and note that (for $e \neq 0$) $k_2 e^2 \geq k_1 e^2$; hence $e\phi(e)$ is intermediate between these two numbers.

(i) $\Rightarrow$ (v) With $k_1 > 0$, (i) implies that $\phi(e)/e > 0$, $\forall e \neq 0$. Invert (i) and multiply by $\phi^2(e)$ to get (v).

(v) $\not\Rightarrow$ (i) Might still have $\phi(e) = 0$, $\forall e$. ∎

1.2 Multiple-input case

In this case, nothing is gained by assuming a finite number of inputs. Since the inequalities depend only on scalar products, we work with a Hilbert space $\mathscr{H}$. In most applications $\mathscr{H} = \mathbb{R}^n$.

4 **Equivalent Conditions** Let $\mathscr{H}$ be a Hilbert space with *real* scalar product $\langle \cdot | \cdot \rangle$ and associated norm $\|\cdot\|$. Let $\phi: \mathscr{H} \to \mathscr{H}$, and $\phi(\theta) = \theta$, where θ is the zero vector in $\mathscr{H}$. Let k_1 and k_2 be two real constants with $k_2 \geq k_1$.

U.t.c., statements (iii′) and (iv′) are equivalent:

(iii′) $\langle \phi(e) - k_1 e | \phi(e) - k_2 e \rangle \leq 0, \qquad \forall e \in \mathscr{H}$

(iv′) $\|\phi(e) - ce\|^2 \leq r^2 \|e\|^2 \qquad \forall e \in \mathscr{H}$

with

$$\begin{cases} c = \frac{1}{2}(k_1 + k_2) \\ r = \frac{1}{2}(k_2 - k_1) \end{cases} \Leftrightarrow \begin{cases} k_1 + k_2 = 2c \\ k_1 k_2 \quad = c^2 - r^2 \end{cases}$$

Proof Immediate by completing the square.

$$\begin{aligned} 0 \geq \langle \phi(e) - k_1 e | \phi(e) - k_2 e \rangle &= \langle \phi(e) | \phi(e) \rangle - 2\frac{k_1 + k_2}{2} \langle \phi(e) | e \rangle \\ &\quad + (c^2 - r^2)\langle e, e \rangle \\ &= \|\phi(e) - ce\|^2 - r^2\|e\|^2 \end{aligned}$$ ∎

Exercise 1 Give a geometrical interpretation of Definition (1) in terms of the graph of ϕ.

Exercise 2 For $k = 1$, 2, and n, give a geometrical interpretation in $\mathbb{R}^k$ of (iii′) and (iv′). [For $\mathbb{R}^2$, $\phi(e)$ must lie in the disk of center ce and of radius $r\|e\|$.]

Exercise 3 Give interpretations in R^2 of the following inequalities. Assume $k_2 \geq k_1 > 0$.

$$k_1\|e\|^2 \leq \langle\phi(e)|e\rangle \leq k_2\|e\|^2 \qquad \forall e \in \mathbb{R}^2$$
$$(1/k_2)\|\phi(e)\|^2 \leq \langle\phi(e)|e\rangle \leq (1/k_1)\|\phi(e)\|^2 \qquad \forall e \in \mathbb{R}^2$$

Exercise 4 Let $\phi\colon \mathscr{H} \to \mathscr{H}$, $\phi(\theta) = \theta$, and $0 < k_1 < k_2$. Show that (all conditions hold for all $e \in \mathscr{H}$)

(a) $\langle e|\phi(e)\rangle \geq k_1\|e\|^2 \Rightarrow \|e\|\ \|\phi(e)\| \leq (1/k_1)\|\phi(e)\|^2$
(b) $\langle e|\phi(e)\rangle \geq (1/k_2)\|\phi(e)\|^2 \Rightarrow \|e\|\ \|\phi(e)\| \leq k_2\|e\|^2$

2 Linear feedback around a nonlinearity (memoryless case)

The simplest case of a nonlinear feedback system is that of a memoryless nonlinearity with a memoryless linear feedback around it. We consider first the single-input–single-output case.

2.1 Formulation and geometric interpretation

Let $\phi\colon \mathbb{R} \to \mathbb{R}$ and $\phi(0) = 0$. Let $1/k$ be the gain of the feedback path, with $k \neq 0$. The equations of the feedback system shown in Fig. I.1 are

$$y = \phi(e) \triangleq \phi_c(u) \tag{1}$$
$$u = e + (1/k)\phi(e) \tag{2}$$

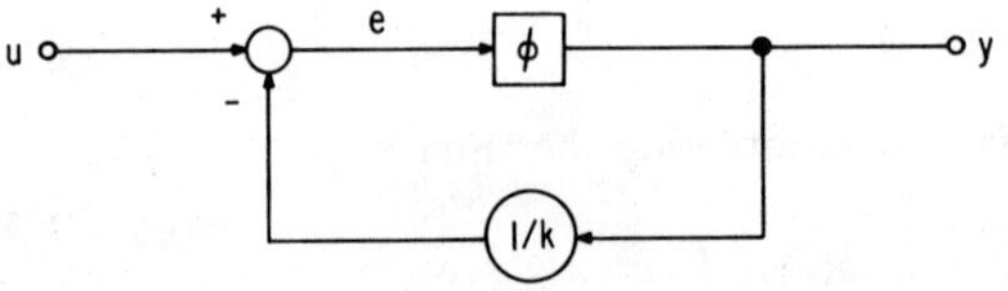

Figure I.1

Given any $u \in \mathbb{R}$, if we can solve (2) for e, then (1) will give **the closed-loop characteristic** $\phi_c\colon u \mapsto y$.

Equation (2) is given a geometric interpretation in Fig. I.2; think of the solutions $(e, \phi(e))$ of (2) as being the intersections of the graphs

$$\{(e, y) \mid y = \phi(e),\ e \in \mathbb{R}\} \tag{3}$$
$$\{(e, y) \mid y = ku - ke,\ e \in \mathbb{R};\ u, k \text{ fixed constants}\} \tag{4}$$

Thus (e, y) is a solution of (1) and (2) if and only if it is an intersection of the graphs of (3) and (4).

Figure I.2

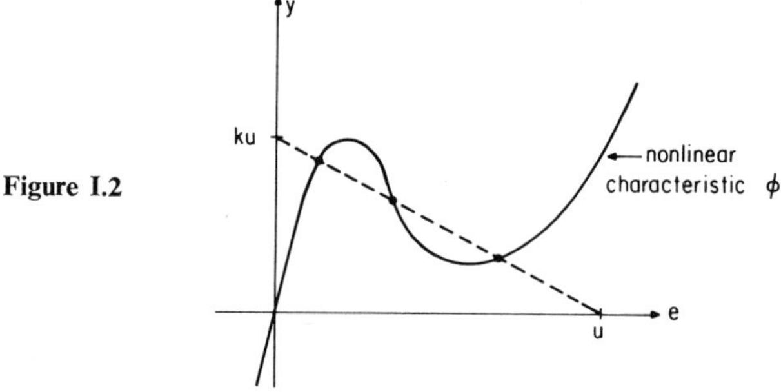

5 **Remark** The closed-loop characteristic ϕ_c is not necessarily a function; if it is a function, its domain does not necessarily include all $\mathbb{R}$.

6 **Remark** This extremely simple example exhibits the fact that in nonlinear feedback systems, one must distinguish the questions of *existence of solutions, uniqueness, continuous dependence* (on the input), and the *finite-gain property.*

Exercise 1 For each of the following, choose a $\phi(\cdot)$ and a k such that

(a) for some u, (2) has no solution;
(b) for some u, (2) has many solutions;
(c) for some u, (2) has infinitely many solutions;
(d) for some u, the solution e does not depend continuously on u;
(e) as $u \to u_0$ (a finite constant), $e \to \infty$.

Exercise 2 Give an example of a characteristic ϕ: $\mathbb{R} \to \mathbb{R}$ such that

(a) $\forall u \in \mathbb{R}$, Eq. (2) has a *unique* solution e, and
(b) there is no *finite* b such that $u \in [-1, 1] \Rightarrow e \in [-b, b]$

(i.e., to a "bounded input" there does not necessarily correspond a "bounded output").

2.2 Sector conditions

In the following, ϕ_c may be either a function from a subset of $\mathbb{R}$ to $\mathbb{R}$ or a relation in $\mathbb{R}^2$ [i.e., a set of ordered pairs $(u, \phi_c(u))$ in $\mathbb{R} \times \mathbb{R}$]. In both cases, "$\phi_c \in$ sector $[a, b]$" means the graph of $\phi_c \in$ sector $[a, b] \triangleq \{(u, y) \mid au \leq y \leq bu\}$.

7 **Theorem** For the system defined by (1) and (2):

$$\phi \in \text{sector } [0, \infty) \Leftrightarrow \phi_c \in \text{sector } [0, k] \tag{8}$$

$$\phi \in \text{sector } (-k, \infty) \Leftrightarrow \phi_c \in \text{sector } (-\infty, k) \tag{9}$$

Proof Note that for $e \neq 0$,

$$\frac{\phi_c(u)}{u} = \frac{\phi(e)}{e + \dfrac{1}{k}\phi(e)} = \frac{\left(\dfrac{\phi(e)}{e}\right)}{1 + \dfrac{1}{k}\left(\dfrac{\phi(e)}{e}\right)}$$

Thus

10 $$\frac{\phi_c(u)}{u} = \frac{\dfrac{\phi(e)}{e}}{1 + \dfrac{1}{k}\dfrac{\phi(e)}{e}}$$

The graph of $\phi_c(u)/u$ versus $\phi(e)/e$ is shown in Fig. I.3. The equivalences (8) and (9) follow immediately from that graph. ∎

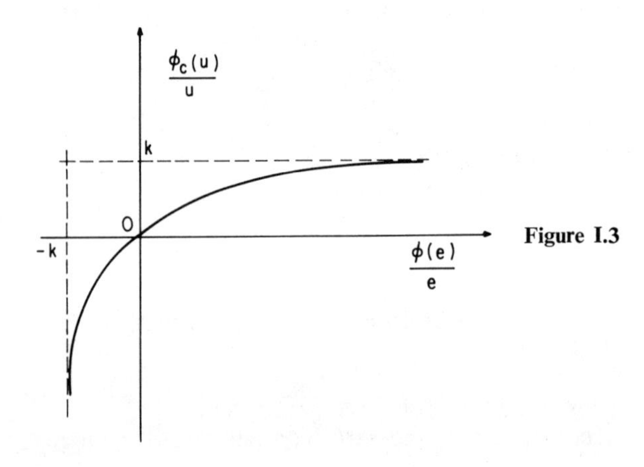

Figure I.3

11 **Remark** Theorem (7) does not assert that, for each $u \in \mathbb{R}$, $\phi_c(u)$ is defined, or that it is unique, or that it depends continuously on u. It simply states a relation between the graph of the *function* ϕ and that of the *relation* ϕ_c. For example, Theorem (7) says that if $u \neq 0$ and if one or more $\phi_c(u)$ are defined, then $\phi \in$ sector $[0, \infty)$ implies that $0 \leq \phi_c(u)/u < k$; loosely, this means that if $\phi \in$ sector $[0, \infty)$, then the "dc gain" of the nonlinear feedback system lies in $[0, k)$. Thus a bounded input u produces (whenever one or more output is defined) a bounded output $\phi_c(u)$. This is the first of many cases that we shall encounter later where the finite-gain question can be settled apart from the questions of existence, uniqueness, and continuity.

2.3 Slope relations

As before, $\phi\colon \mathbb{R} \to \mathbb{R}$ and $\phi(0) = 0$. Suppose that ϕ is differentiable on $\mathbb{R}$ and $-k < \phi'(e) < \infty$ for all $e \in \mathbb{R}$. Then the map $e \mapsto u$ defined by (2), namely,

12
$$u = e + (1/k)\phi(e)$$

is differentiable and has a positive derivative on $\mathbb{R}$. Hence the corresponding inverse map $u \mapsto e$ is differentiable and has a positive derivative. Composing the differentiable map $u \mapsto e$ with the differentiable map $e \mapsto \phi(e) = \phi_c(u)$, we conclude that $u \mapsto \phi_c(u)$ is differentiable. Now, by (1),

$$\frac{d\phi_c(u)}{du} = \frac{d\phi(e)}{du} = \frac{d\phi(e)}{de}\frac{de}{du}$$

and, by (2),

$$\frac{d\phi_c(u)}{du} = \frac{\dfrac{d\phi(e)}{de}}{1 + \dfrac{1}{k}\dfrac{d\phi(e)}{de}}$$

or

13
$$\boxed{\phi_c' = \frac{\phi'}{1 + \dfrac{1}{k}\phi'}}$$

where it is understood that ϕ' is evaluated at e and ϕ_c' is evaluated at the *corresponding* u, i.e., at $u = e + (1/k)\phi(e)$.

With these preliminaries in mind, we can state the following.

14 **Theorem** Let $\phi\colon \mathbb{R} \to \mathbb{R}$, $\phi(0) = 0$, and ϕ be differentiable on $\mathbb{R}$. Let $k > 0$. Let ϕ_c be defined in terms of ϕ by (1) and (2). U.t.c.

(a) $\phi'\colon \mathbb{R} \to (-k, \infty) \Rightarrow$
  - (i) $\phi_c\colon u \mapsto y$ is a differentiable map and $-\infty < \phi_c'(u) < k$;
  - (ii) $u \mapsto e$ is differentiable, one to one, and strictly increasing;
  - (iii) $u = 0 \Rightarrow \phi_c(u) = 0$;

(b) $\phi'\colon \mathbb{R} \to [0, \infty) \Leftrightarrow \phi_c'\colon \mathbb{R} \to [0, k)$;

Proof (ai) follows from the considerations above and from (10).

(aii) follows from the derivative of (2) with respect to e.

(aiii) holds because $\phi_c(0) = 0$ by (1) and (2).

(b) follows directly from (13). ∎

Exercise 3 Assume that (a) holds, what can be said about the domain of the map $u \mapsto e$? Show that as u increases, the corresponding e increases, but that it is possible for $y = \phi_c(u)$ to be decreasing over some intervals.

Exercise 4 To illustrate the separation between questions of existence and uniqueness, consider the equation $y = \phi(x)$, where $\phi: \mathbb{R} \to \mathbb{R}$ and $\phi'(x) > 0$, $\forall x \in \mathbb{R}$. (a) Show that if for some given y there is a solution x_0, then it is the *unique* solution. (b) Give an example where for some ϕ and some y, the equation $y = \phi(x)$ has *no* solution.

3 Multiple nonlinearities

We shall merely state the results for the case where u, e, and y take values in $\mathbb{R}^n$. As a preparation, we propose an exercise.

Exercise 1 Let $\langle \cdot | \cdot \rangle$ be a real scalar product in a linear space $\mathscr{L}$. Let $x, y \in \mathscr{L}$ and

1 $$\bar{x} \triangleq (x + y)/2, \qquad \tilde{x} \triangleq (x - y)/2$$

Then

2 $$\langle x | y \rangle = \|\bar{x}\|^2 - \|\tilde{x}\|^2$$

The following result generalizes Theorem (2.7).

3 **Proposition** Let $\phi: \mathbb{R}^n \to \mathbb{R}^n$, $\phi(\theta) = \theta$. Let the $n \times n$ matrix K be the gain in the feedback path (see Fig. I.4); then the equations of the feedback system are

4 $$u = e + K\phi(e)$$

5 $$y = \phi(e) = \phi_c(u)$$

Let $A_1, A_2 \in \mathbb{R}^{n \times n}$ and

6 $$\bar{A} \triangleq (A_1 + A_2)/2, \qquad \tilde{A} \triangleq (A_1 - A_2)/2$$

U.t.c.

(a) $\langle \phi(e) - A_1 e | \phi(e) - A_2 e \rangle = \|\phi(e) - \bar{A}e\|^2 - \|\tilde{A}e\|^2$;

(b) the following four inequalities are equivalent:

(i) $\langle \phi(e) - A_1 e | \phi(e) - A_2 e \rangle \le 0$ \
(ii) $\|\phi(e) - \bar{A}e\|^2 \le \|\tilde{A}e\|^2$ } $\forall e \in \mathbb{R}^n$

(iii) $\langle (A_1 K + I)\phi_c(u) - A_1 u | (A_2 K + I)\phi_c(u) - A_2 u \rangle \le 0$ \
(iv) $\|(I + \bar{A}K)\phi_c(u) - \bar{A}u\|^2 \le \|\tilde{A}K\phi_c(u) - \tilde{A}u\|^2$ } $\forall u \in \mathbb{R}^n$.

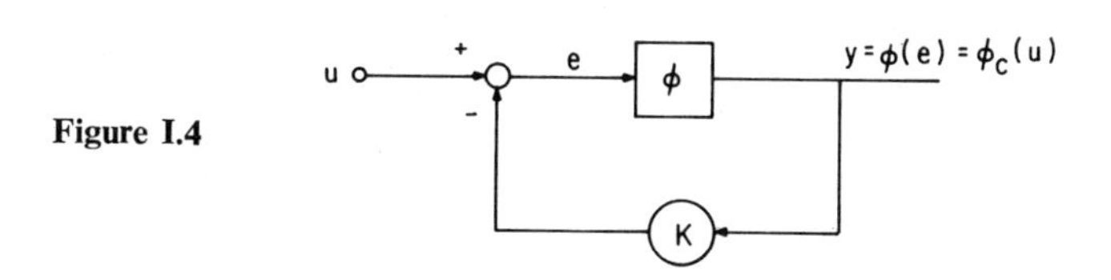

Figure I.4

Proof Statement (a) and the equivalences (i) ⇔ (ii) and (iii) ⇔ (iv) follow immediately from Exercise (1). The equivalence (i) ⇔ (iii) follows from (4) and (5); indeed, substitute $u - K\phi_c(u)$ for e, and $\phi_c(u)$ for $\phi(e)$. ∎

It is apparent that before we are able to tackle systems with dynamics, we must develop techniques for describing classes of inputs. To do so, we study norms in the next chapter.

Notes and references

The material in this chapter is well known to specialists. For similar approaches, see, for example, Johnson [Joh.1] and Thathachar *et al.* [Tha.1].

II NORMS

The purpose of this chapter is to supply us with a number of tools that we shall use repeatedly in the sequel. It is important for us to think of norms as a yardstick with which we measure the size of vectors in $\mathbb{R}^n$, or of real-valued function, or of vector-valued functions. Also we use norms to measure the "gain" of linear operators. In Section 1, we introduce the general definition of norm together with many examples that we shall repeatedly use in later chapters. In Section 2, we define equivalent norms and prove that all norms in finite-dimensional spaces are equivalent.

Section 3 establishes some inclusion relations between some normed spaces that will be frequently encountered later. A geometric interpretation of norms is given in Section 4; it gives an intuitive insight into the concept of norm and the way of visualizing the difference between norms. Section 5 defines the concept of induced norms of linear maps, and two examples of convolution maps are worked out in Section 6. In Section 7, the relation between norms and spectral radius is developed in detail. Finally, in Section 8, the concept of measure of a matrix, which is closely related to the concept of norm, is developed. It is used to obtain lower and upper bounds on solution of differential equations and to obtain an existence and uniqueness result for equilibrium points.

1 Norms: definitions and examples

1 Let E be a *linear space* over the *field* $\mathbb{K}$. (Typically, $\mathbb{K}$ is $\mathbb{R}$ or $\mathbb{C}$). The zero vector in E is denoted by θ. We say that the function $\rho: E \to \mathbb{R}_+$ is a **norm on** E iff

(i) $x \in E$ and $x \neq \theta \Rightarrow \rho(x) > 0$
(ii) $\rho(\alpha x) = |\alpha| \rho(x), \ \forall \alpha \in \mathbb{K}, \ \forall x \in E$
(iii) $\rho(x + y) \leq \rho(x) + \rho(y), \ \forall x, y \in E$ (triangle inequality)

Remark Given a linear space E, there may be many possible norms on E. However, given the linear space E and a norm ρ on E, the pair (E, ρ) is called a **normed space**.

Example 1 Let the linear space E be $\mathbb{C}^n$. More precisely, $x \in \mathbb{C}^n$ means that $x = (x_1, x_2, \ldots, x_n)$ with $x_i = \mathbb{C}, \forall i$. We shall repeatedly use the following norms on E:

$$\|x\|_1 \triangleq \sum_{i=1}^{n} |x_i| \tag{2}$$

$$\|x\|_p \triangleq \left(\sum_{i=1}^{n} |x_i|^p \right)^{1/p}, \qquad \text{where } 1 \leq p < \infty \tag{3}$$

$$\|x\|_\infty \triangleq \max_i |x_i| \tag{4}$$

$\|x\|_2$ is called the **Euclidean** norm of x.

Exercise 1 Consider $\mathbb{R}^n$ and define norms as above. For $\mathbb{R}^2$ draw the sets $\{x \mid \|x\|_p = 1\}$ for $p = 1, 2, 4, \infty$.

Example 2 Let E be the space of infinite sequences of complex numbers: $x = (\xi_1, \xi_2, \ldots)$ with $\xi_i \in \mathbb{C}$ for $i = 1, 2, \ldots$. Frequently used norms on appropriate proper subsets of E are given as follows:

$$\|x\|_1 \triangleq \sum_{i=1}^{\infty} |\xi_i| \tag{5}$$

$$\|x\|_p \triangleq \left(\sum_{i=1}^{\infty} |\xi_i|^p \right)^{1/p}, \qquad 1 \leq p < \infty \tag{6}$$

$$\|x\|_\infty \triangleq \sup_{i \geq 1} |\xi_i| \tag{7}$$

The corresponding normed spaces are called, respectively, l^1, l^p, l^∞.

We used above the expression "on appropriate subsets of E" because the norms defined by (5), (6), and (7) have the property that (calling $\rho(x)$ any such norm)

$$M \triangleq \{x \in E \mid \rho(x) < \infty\} \text{ is a linear subspace of } E$$

Indeed, it follows directly from Minkowski's inequality that if $x_1, x_2 \in M$, then $x_1 + x_2 \in M$ because $\rho(x_1) + \rho(x_2) \geq \rho(x_1 + x_2)$.

Example 3 Let $E = \{f: \mathbb{R} \to \mathbb{R} \mid f \text{ locally (Lebesgue) integrable}\}$. Frequently used norms on appropriate proper subsets of E are as follows:

$$\|x\|_1 \triangleq \int |x(t)|\, dt \tag{8}$$

$$\|x\|_p \triangleq \left(\int |x(t)|^p\, dt\right)^{1/p}, \qquad 1 \leq p < \infty \tag{9}$$

$$\|x\|_\infty \triangleq \operatorname*{ess\,sup}_{t \in \mathbb{R}} |x(t)| = \inf\{a \in \mathbb{R} \mid \mu[\{t \mid |x(t)| > a\}] = 0\} \tag{10}$$

where $\mu[A]$ denotes the Lebesgue measure of the set A.† The corresponding normed spaces are called, respectively, L^1, L^p, L^∞.

More generally, for a given $w: \mathbb{R} \to \mathbb{R}$ positive, continuous, and bounded on $\mathbb{R}$, we can define a norm as follows:

$$\|x\|_p \triangleq \left(\int w(t)\,|x(t)|^p\, dt\right)^{1/p}, \qquad 1 \leq p < \infty \tag{11}$$

and the corresponding expression for $\|x\|_\infty$.

Example 4 Let $E = \{f: \mathbb{R} \to \mathbb{R}^n, f = (f_1, f_2, \ldots, f_n) \mid \text{all } f_i\text{'s locally (Lebesgue) integrable}\}$. Let $|\cdot|$ denote *any norm on* $\mathbb{R}^n$, then we define

$$\|f\|_p \triangleq \left(\int |f(t)|^p\, dt\right)^{1/p}, \qquad 1 \leq p < \infty \tag{12}$$

$$\|f\|_\infty \triangleq \operatorname*{ess\,sup}_{t \in \mathbb{R}} |f(t)| \tag{13}$$

Exercise 2 For the linear space E defined in Example 2, give an example of some $x \in E$ for which $\|x\|_1 = \infty$ but $\|x\|_\infty = 1$. Give some $x \in E$ for which $\|x\|_\infty = \infty$. (These examples justify the locution "*on appropriate proper subsets of E*".)

Note: It is a standard, though messy, exercise in functional analysis to verify that each of the functions (2) to (13) satisfy the axioms of the norm.

---

† In our later work we shall abuse notation and write $\sup|x(t)|$ instead of $\operatorname{ess\,sup}|x(t)|$.

Example 5 Let $E = \mathbb{C}^{n\times n}$, the set of all $n \times n$ matrices with elements in $\mathbb{C}$. E is a linear space. The following are norms on $\mathbb{C}^{n\times n}$.

14 $$\|A\|_a \triangleq \max_{i,j} |a_{ij}|$$

15 $$\|A\|_b \triangleq \sum_{i,j=1}^{n} |a_{ij}|$$

16 $$\|A\|_s \triangleq \left(\sum_{i,j=1}^{n} |a_{ij}|^2\right)^{1/2}$$

17 $$\|A\|_1 \triangleq \max_j \sum_{i=1}^{n} |a_{ij}| \qquad \text{(column sums)}$$

18 $$\|A\|_2 \triangleq \max_i [\lambda_i(A^*A)]^{1/2} \qquad \text{(where } \lambda_i(M) \text{ denotes the } i\text{th eigenvalue of } M)$$

19 $$\|A\|_\infty \triangleq \max_i \sum_{j=1}^{n} |a_{ij}| \qquad \text{(row sums)}$$

In this example we consider matrices as elements of a linear space. In a later section, we shall consider matrices as representations of linear maps and shall relate the matrix norms to the vector norms of the domain and range spaces.

Exercise 3 Let $\|\cdot\|$ denote a norm on R^n. Let $\phi(\cdot)$ be continuous and map $[0, T]$ into $\mathbb{R}^n$. By examining the Riemann sums, show that

20 $$\left\|\int_0^T \phi(t)\, dt\right\|_\infty \le \int_0^T \|\phi(t)\|_\infty\, dt$$

In fact, as we shall see later, inequality (20) holds for *any* norm in $\mathbb{R}^n$. Furthermore, it also holds for any ϕ: $[0, T]$ into $\mathbb{R}^n$, which is Lebesgue integrable.

2 Equivalent norms

1 Let E be a linear space. Let $\|\cdot\|_a$ and $\|\cdot\|_b$ be two norms on E. The norms $\|\cdot\|_a$ and $\|\cdot\|_b$ are said to be **equivalent** iff there exist two positive numbers m_l and m_u such that

2 $$m_l\|x\|_a \le \|x\|_b \le m_u\|x\|_a, \qquad \forall x \in E$$

It is crucial to note that the *same* m_l and m_u must work for *all* $x \in E$ in (2). The relation expressed by (2) between the two norms is an *equivalence* relation (check reflexivity, symmetry, transitivity).

If two norms are equivalent, then sequences that converge in terms of one norm converge in terms of the other. The same holds for continuity and boundedness. In short, equivalent norms define identical topologies. In applications, some norms are preferable because they give sharper results as we shall see below.

Exercise 1 Let

$$A = \begin{bmatrix} 0.9 & 10^4 \\ 0 & 0.9 \end{bmatrix}$$

Calculate the norm of A using the six norms of Example 5 of Section 1. Prove that $A^k \to \theta$ as $k \to \infty$. (Any comment on your results?)

3 **Theorem** All norms on $\mathbb{C}^n$ are equivalent.

Proof (a) First we show that *any* norm $\|\cdot\|$ in $\mathbb{C}^n$ is a continuous function in the sense that whenever $x \in \mathbb{C}^n$ tends to $\bar{x} \in \mathbb{C}^n$, then the real number $\|x\|$ tends to the real number $\|\bar{x}\|$. Call x_i, $(\bar{x}_i)$, the ith component of x, $(\bar{x})$, with respect to some basis $\{e_1, e_2, \ldots, e_n\}$. From advanced calculus, if $x \to \bar{x}$, then $x_i \to \bar{x}_i$ for $i = 1, 2, \ldots, n$. Now for any x, $\bar{x} \in \mathbb{C}^n$, using the axioms of the norm

$$0 \le \big|\|x\| - \|\bar{x}\|\big| \le \|x - \bar{x}\| = \left\| \sum_{i=1}^{n} (x_i - \bar{x}_i)e_i \right\| \le \sum_{i=1}^{n} |x_i - \bar{x}_i| \, \|e_i\|$$

Hence $x \to \bar{x}$ implies that $\|x\| \to \|\bar{x}\|$.

(b) Let

$$S_\infty = \{x \in \mathbb{C}^n \mid \|x\|_\infty = 1\}$$

Clearly S_∞ is a bounded set. Furthermore, it is closed, since it is the inverse image of the closed set $\{1\}$ under the continuous map $\|\cdot\|_\infty$. Let $\|\cdot\|$ be an arbitrary norm on $\mathbb{C}^n$. Now the continuous function $z \mapsto \|z\|$, restricted to the closed and bounded set S_∞, reaches its minimum and maximum at, say, z_m and z_M, respectively. Thus,

$$0 < \|z_m\| \le \|z\| \le \|z_M\|, \qquad \forall z \in S_\infty$$

Let x be any point in $\mathbb{C}^n$ with $x \ne \theta$, then $x/\|x\|_\infty \in S_\infty$. Therefore,

$$\|z_m\| \le \left\| \frac{x}{\|x\|_\infty} \right\| \le \|z_M\|, \qquad \forall x \in \mathbb{C}^n, \quad x \ne \theta$$

Consequently,

$$\|z_m\| \, \|x\|_\infty \le \|x\| \le \|z_M\| \, \|x\|_\infty, \qquad \forall x \in \mathbb{C}^n$$

Hence the norms $\|\cdot\|$ and $\|\cdot\|_\infty$ are equivalent. The same holds for any other pair of norms, say, $\|\cdot\|$ and $\|\cdot\|'$, by transitivity. ∎

4 **Notation** From now on we shall encounter norms on $\mathbb{R}^n$ or $\mathbb{C}^n$, norms on function spaces, and induced norms of linear operators. Some authors use $\|\cdot\|$ to denote the first and $|\|\cdot\||$ to denote the last two. From now on we shall use $|\cdot|$ for norms on $\mathbb{R}^n$ or $\mathbb{C}^n$ and $\|\cdot\|$ for norms on function spaces or for induced norms of linear operators. We shall also use $|\cdot|$ to denote the absolute value of a number in $\mathbb{R}$ or $\mathbb{C}$.

5 **Remark** In infinite-dimensional spaces, norms are not necessarily equivalent. For example, in the space of infinite sequences (Section 1, Example 2) if

$$x_1 = (1, 0, 0, \dots), x_2 = (1, 2^{-1}, 0, \dots), x_3 = (1, 2^{-1}, 3^{-1}, \dots), \dots$$

then

$$\|x_k\|_\infty = 1, \qquad \forall k \in \mathbb{Z}_+$$

and the sequence $(x_k)_1^\infty$ converges. However,

$$\|x_k\|_1 \to \infty, \qquad \text{as} \quad k \to \infty$$

6 **Example** Let E be the space of sequences in $\mathbb{C}^n$; i.e., $x \in E$ iff $x = (\xi_1, \xi_2, \dots)$ with $\xi_i \in \mathbb{C}^n$ for $i = 1, 2, \dots$. Let $|\cdot|$ denote *any* norm on $\mathbb{C}^n$. Thus, $|\xi_i|$ denotes the nonnegative number equal to the norm of the $\mathbb{C}^n$ *vector* ξ_i. Then on some proper subsets of E, we can define norms

$$\|x\|_1 \triangleq \sum_{i=1}^{\infty} |\xi_i| \tag{7}$$

$$\|x\|_p \triangleq \left(\sum_{i=1}^{\infty} |\xi_i|^p\right)^{1/p}, \qquad 1 \le p < \infty \tag{8}$$

$$\|x\|_\infty \triangleq \sup_{i \ge 1} |\xi_i| \tag{9}$$

The corresponding normed spaces are denoted, respectively, by l_n^1, l_n^p, l_n^∞. Verify that if we set up the definition of l_n^p using two different norms on $\mathbb{C}^n$, we end up with the same proper subsets of E.

3 Relations between normed spaces

In discrete-time systems, the input is completely specified by the corresponding sequence of values. Thus, we consider the space of sequences with values in $\mathbb{R}$ (or $\mathbb{C}$). Associated with the norms defined in (1.5) to (1.7), we have the normed spaces l^1, l^p, and l^∞.

1 **Theorem** We have the strict inclusions $l^1 \subset l^p \subset l^\infty$, for any integer $p \in (1, \infty)$.

Proof Let $x = (\xi_1, \xi_2, \ldots)$, where $\xi_i \in \mathbb{C}$, $\forall i \in \mathbb{Z}_+$. Consider any integer $p \in [1, \infty)$. If $x \in l^p$, then $\sum_{i=1}^{\infty} |\xi_i|^p < \infty$. Therefore, for any integer k, $|\xi_k|^p \leq \sum_{i=1}^{\infty} |\xi_i|^p < \infty$, hence $x \in l^\infty$. Thus, $l^p \subset l^\infty$ for $p \in [1, \infty)$.

Now for any integer $N \geq 0$ and any integer $p \geq 1$,

$$\sum_{i=1}^{N} |\xi_i|^p \leq \left(\sum_{i=1}^{N} |\xi_i| \right)^p \leq (\|x\|_1)^p$$

Hence, as $N \to \infty$, if $x \in l^1$, we have $\|x\|_p \leq \|x\|_1 < \infty$. Thus, $l^1 \subset l^p$. ■

2 **Exercise 1** Use Example (2.6) to verify that

3 $$l_n^1 \subset l_n^p \subset l_n^\infty, \qquad \text{for integers} \quad p \in (1, \infty)$$

and show that these inclusion relations are strict.

In continuous-time systems, the inputs and outputs are functions of time t, and t is usually restricted to $t \geq 0$. For simplicity, we shall use Lebesgue integration results. (Any reader uncomfortable with Lebesgue theory may take all the functions to be piecewise continuous; see Appendix A.) We say that f: $\mathbb{R}_+ \to \mathbb{R}$ is *locally integrable* iff f is integrable over any bounded interval (i.e., intervals such as $[a, b]$ with $0 \leq a \leq b < \infty$).

For any fixed $p \in [1, \infty)$, we say that f: $\mathbb{R}_+ \to \mathbb{R}$ **belongs to** L^p iff f is locally integrable and $\int_0^\infty |f(t)|^p \, dt < \infty$. We write

4 $$\|f\|_p = \left(\int_0^\infty |f(t)|^p \, dt \right)^{1/p}$$

We say that f: $\mathbb{R}_+ \to \mathbb{R}$ **belongs to** L^∞ iff $\text{ess sup}_{t \geq 0} |f(t)| < \infty$. We write

5 $$\|f\|_\infty = \operatorname*{ess\,sup}_{t \geq 0} |f(t)|$$

By essential supremum we mean

$$\operatorname*{ess\,sup}_{t \geq 0} |f(t)| = \inf\{a \,|\, |f(t)| \leq a \text{ almost everywhere}\}$$

that is, $|f(t)| \leq a$ except for a set of measure zero, and the ess sup is the smallest number which has that property. From now on we shall write sup for ess sup.

It is understood once and for all that elements of L^p are equivalence classes in the sense that if f and $g \in L^p$ but

$$\|f - g\|_p = 0$$

the functions f and g (which may be different as functions) are considered to be the same element of L^p. In the same spirit, we write $\sup |x(t)|$ instead of ess $\sup |x(t)|$.

6 **Exercise 2** Let $f(t) = \sin t$ for $t \geq 0$. Let $g(t) = 1$ for $t > 0$ and $g(0) = 2$. Show that

$$\sup_{t\geq 0}|f(t)| = 1, \qquad \sup_{t\geq 0}|g(t)| = 2, \qquad \text{and} \quad \|f\|_\infty = \|g\|_\infty$$

Let p be fixed but $p \in [1, \infty]$. It is well known that the linear space L^p together with the norm $\|\cdot\|_p$ is complete (i.e., every Cauchy sequence in L^p converges to an element in L^p; furthermore, this element is unique). Complete normed spaces are called **Banach spaces.**

7 **Fact** If $f\colon \mathbb{R}_+ \to \mathbb{R}$ and $f \in L^1 \cap L^\infty$, then $f \in L^p$ for $p \in [1, \infty]$.

Proof Since $f \in L^1$, the Lebesgue measure of the set I, where $I \triangleq \{t \,|\, |f(t)| \geq 1\}$, is finite. This fact together with $f \in L^\infty \Rightarrow \int_I |f|^p\, dt < \infty$. Now if I^c denotes the complement of I,

$$\infty > \int_{I^c} |f|\, dt \geq \int_{I^c} |f|^p\, dt, \qquad \text{for all} \quad p \in [1, \infty)$$

The conclusion follows from these two observations. ∎

The relation among L^1, L^2, and L^∞ is shown in the Venn diagram of Fig. II.1. The diagram illustrates that $f \in L^1 \cap L^\infty \Rightarrow f \in L^2$.

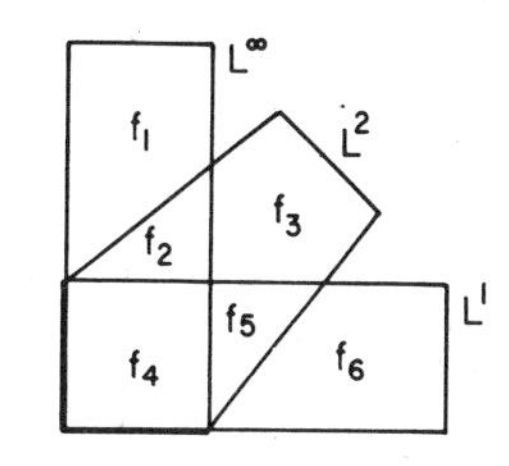

Figure II.1

8 **Exercise 3** Consider functions mapping $\mathbb{R}_+$ into R and defined by

$$f_1\colon t \mapsto 1; \qquad f_2\colon t \mapsto \frac{1}{1+t}; \qquad f_3\colon t \mapsto \frac{1}{1+t}\,\frac{1+t^{1/4}}{t^{1/4}};$$

$$f_4\colon t \mapsto \varepsilon^{-t}; \qquad f_5\colon t \mapsto \frac{1}{1+t^2}\,\frac{1+t^{1/4}}{t^{1/4}}; \qquad f_6\colon t \mapsto \frac{1}{1+t^2}\,\frac{1+t^{1/2}}{t^{1/2}}$$

Show that these functions satisfy the inclusion relations shown on the Venn diagram in Fig. II.1.

9 **Exercise 4** Let $[a, b]$ be a bounded interval (i.e., a and b are finite). Show that $L^1[a, b] \supset L^2[a, b] \supset L^\infty[a, b]$, where

$$L^p[a, b] = \left\{ f\colon [a, b] \to \mathbb{R} \,\middle|\, \int_a^b |f(t)|^p\, dt < \infty \right\}$$

10 **Exercise 5** Let $1 \leq p \leq \infty$ and f_p: $\mathbb{R}_+ \to \mathbb{R}$ be defined by

$$f_p\colon t \mapsto \left[\frac{1}{(t)^{1/2}[1 + \log(t)]}\right]^{2/p}$$

Show that if $p' \in [1, \infty)$ and if $p' \neq p$, then $f_p \notin L^{p'}$, but $f_p \in L^p$.

11 **Remark** In later applications, we shall consider functions from $\mathbb{R}_+$ into $\mathbb{R}^n$. In this case, *all* above definitions hold, except that $|f(t)|$ is interpreted as the chosen norm of the *vector* $f(t) \in \mathbb{R}^n$; one norm in $\mathbb{R}^n$ is chosen once and for all for the whole development. Since all norms in $\mathbb{R}^n$ are equivalent, norms in $\mathbb{R}^n$ are selected for numerical convenience and for obtaining best bounds.

12 **Notation** Sometimes we consider functions on $\mathbb{R}$ (or $\mathbb{R}_+$) to $\mathbb{R}$ (or $\mathbb{R}^n$). To keep track of these cases we use the symbol

$$L_n{}^p(\mathbb{R}_+) \triangleq \left\{f\colon \mathbb{R}_+ \to \mathbb{R}^n \,\middle|\, \int_0^\infty |f(t)|^p \, dt < \infty\right\}$$

and a similar definition for $L_n{}^p(\mathbb{R})$. In case $n = 1$, we drop the subscript n. Once it is understood that we consider $\mathbb{R}$ (or $\mathbb{R}_+$) exclusively, we then use the abbreviation $L_n{}^p$.

4 Geometric interpretation of norms

In order to obtain a more intuitive interpretation of norms, we show below that to every norm is associated a certain type of convex set. Conversely, to any such convex set is associated a norm. We start by defining some concepts.

1 Let E be a linear space, over $\mathbb{R}$ or $\mathbb{C}$. A set K in E is said to be **convex** iff $x, y \in K \Rightarrow \lambda x + (1 - \lambda)y \in K$, $\forall \lambda \in [0, 1]$. A set K in E is said to be **balanced** (équilibré) iff $x \in K \Rightarrow \alpha x \in K$, $\forall |\alpha| \leq 1$. A set K in E is said to be **absorbing** iff $x \in E \Rightarrow \exists \lambda(x) \geq 0$ such that $x \in \lambda(x)K$. The set $\{y \mid y = \lambda x,\ \lambda \in \mathbb{R}_+\}$ is called the **ray** Ox.

2 **Theorem** Let E be a linear space.

(A) If $N\colon E \to \mathbb{R}_+$ is a norm on E, then the unit ball associated with $N(\cdot)$, namely, the set

$$B = \{x \in E \mid N(x) \leq 1\}$$

is *convex*, *balanced*, *absorbing* and B intersects every ray Ox on *a finite interval* (i.e., $\forall x \in E$, $\exists \lambda_N < \infty$ such that $Ox \cap B = \{y \mid y = \lambda x,\ 0 \leq \lambda \leq \lambda_N\}$).

(B) If the set $K \subset E$ is convex, balanced, absorbing and if K intersects every ray Ox on a finite interval, then the function $p_K: E \to \mathbb{R}_+$ defined by

3 $$p_K(x) \triangleq \inf\{\lambda \mid \lambda > 0 \text{ and } x \in \lambda K\}$$

is a norm on E.

4 **Remark** The ray condition is indispensable; to wit, let $K \subset \mathbb{R}^2$ and $K = \{(x, y) \mid x \in \mathbb{R}, |y| \leq 1\}$. Clearly K is convex, balanced, and absorbing, but p_K is not a norm $[p_K(x_0) = 0$ for $x_0 = (1, 0)]$.

Proof (A) By assumption N is a norm.

(i) B is convex because $x, y \in B$ imply $N(x) \leq 1$, $N(y) \leq 1$. Now $\forall \lambda \in [0, 1]$.

$$N[\lambda x + (1 - \lambda)y] \leq N(\lambda x) + N[(1 - \lambda)y] = \lambda N(x) + (1 - \lambda)N(y) \leq 1$$

Hence $\lambda x + (1 - \lambda)y$ is in B, for all $\lambda \in [0, 1]$.

(ii) B is balanced because $x \in B \Rightarrow N(x) \leq 1$. Hence $\forall |\alpha| \leq 1$, $N(\alpha x) = |\alpha| N(x) \leq |\alpha| \leq 1$; i.e., $\alpha x \in B$ for all $|\alpha| \leq 1$.

(iii) B is absorbing because for any $x \in E$, $N(x) < \infty$ and $x/N(x) \in B$; i.e., $x \in N(x)B$.

(iv) $Ox \cap B = \{\lambda x \mid \lambda \geq 0$ and $N(\lambda x) \leq 1\}$. Now $N(\lambda x) \leq 1 \Leftrightarrow |\lambda| \leq 1/N(x)$; hence $\lambda x \in Ox \cap B$ iff $0 \leq \lambda \leq 1/N(x)$.

(B) By assumption K has the four properties; we have to show that the function p_K satisfies the axioms of a norm.

(i) Obviously by (3), $p_K(\theta) = 0$. Next we show that $x \neq \theta \Rightarrow p_K(x) > 0$ by contradiction. Suppose $x_0 \neq \theta$ and $p_K(x_0) = 0 = \inf\{\lambda \mid \lambda > 0, x_0 \in \lambda K\}$. Hence $\forall \lambda > 0$, $x_0 \in \lambda K$; i.e., $(1/\lambda)x_0 \in K$. Hence the whole ray Ox_0 is contained in K.

(ii) Since K is absorbing, $p_K(x) < \infty$ for any $x \in E$.

(iii) $p_K(\alpha x) = |\alpha| p_K(x)$ because K is balanced. Indeed, $\alpha x \in \lambda K$ for some λ implies $|\alpha| x \in \lambda K$ or $x \in (\lambda/|\alpha|)K$. Hence

$$p_K(x) = (1/|\alpha|)p_K(\alpha x)$$

(iv) $p_K(x + y) \leq p_K(x) + p_K(y)$ follows from the convexity of K and the definition of p_K. By definition of p_K, for any $\varepsilon > 0$,

$$\frac{x}{p_K(x) + \varepsilon} \quad \text{and} \quad \frac{y}{p_K(y) + \varepsilon} \in K$$

Since K is convex (we drop the subscript K for simplicity),

$$\left[\frac{p(x) + \varepsilon}{p(x) + p(y) + 2\varepsilon}\right] \frac{x}{p(x) + \varepsilon} + \left[\frac{p(y) + \varepsilon}{p(x) + p(y) + 2\varepsilon}\right] \frac{y}{p(y) + \varepsilon} \in K$$

So, $\forall \varepsilon > 0$, $x + y \subset [p(x) + p(y) + 2\varepsilon]K$; hence $p(x + y) \leq p(x) + p(y)$. ∎

5 Induced norms of linear maps

5.1 The space of linear maps

Let E be a linear space over the field $\mathbb{K}$, which is $\mathbb{R}$ or $\mathbb{C}$. Let $\mathscr{L}(E, E)$ be the class of all *linear* maps from E into E. $\mathscr{L}(E, E)$ is a linear space if the **addition** of A and B is defined by

1 $$(A + B)x = Ax + Bx, \qquad \forall x \in E, \quad \forall A, B \in \mathscr{L}(E, E)$$

and the **scalar product** of α and A is defined by

2 $$(\alpha A)(x) = \alpha(Ax), \qquad \forall \alpha \in \mathbb{K}, \quad \forall x \in E, \quad \forall A \in \mathscr{L}(E, E)$$

In addition, the **product** AB can be defined as the composition of the maps A and B:

3 $$(AB)(x) = A(Bx), \qquad \forall x \in E, \quad \forall A, B \in \mathscr{L}(E, E)$$

Note that the *product is not commutative*. It is easy to check that

(i) multiplication defined by (3) is associative;
(ii) addition and multiplication are distributive;
(iii) multiplication and scalar multiplication commute;
(iv) I, the identity map from E into E, is the unit of the multiplication.

Thus with the three operations defined by (1), (2), and (3), *$\mathscr{L}(E, E)$ is a (noncommutative) algebra with a unit.* (Refer to Appendix D for a discussion of algebras.)

4 **Remark** With obvious but simple modifications, the considerations of this chapter apply to linear maps from a linear space E to a linear space F. In Section 5.2, where we introduce induced norms, it becomes then crucial to distinguish between the norms on the domain and the norms on the range. To avoid cluttering the notation, we restrict ourselves to $\mathscr{L}(E, E)$, i.e., to the case where the domain and the range are the same spaces.

5.2 Induced norms

Let $|\cdot|$ be a norm on E and $A \in \mathscr{L}(E, E)$. Define the function $\|\cdot\|$ from a subset of $\mathscr{L}(E, E)$ into $\mathbb{R}_+$ by

5 $$\|A\| \triangleq \sup_{x \neq \theta} |Ax|/|x|$$

6 **Fact** Definition (5) is equivalent to

7 $$\|A\| = \sup_{|z|=1} |Az|$$

8 $\|A\|$ is called the **induced norm** of the linear map A or *the operator norm induced by the vector norm* $|\cdot|$.

To show that (5) and (7) are equivalent, let $z = x/|x|$, then

$$|Az| = \left|A\left(\frac{x}{|x|}\right)\right| = \left|\frac{1}{|x|} Ax\right| = \frac{1}{|x|}|Ax| \qquad \blacksquare$$

To interpret (7) geometrically, let K be the convex, balanced, absorbing set corresponding to the vector norm $|\cdot|$; i.e., the unit ball

$$K \triangleq \{x \in E \,|\, |x| \leq 1\}$$

Let AK denote the image of K under the map A. Then (7) is equivalent to

9
$$\|A\| = \inf\{\lambda \,|\, AK \subset \lambda K\}$$

Roughly speaking, $\|A\|$ is the smallest magnification factor λ for which λK includes AK.

10 **Theorem** Let $|\cdot|$ be any norm on $\mathbb{C}^n$. Let A be a nonsingular linear map from $\mathbb{C}^n$ to $\mathbb{C}^n$. Let $\|\cdot\|$ denote the induced norm on $n \times n$ matrices with elements in $\mathbb{C}$. U.t.c.

(a) There is a constant β which depends only on n and $|\cdot|$ such that

11
$$\|A^{-1}\| \leq \beta \frac{\|A\|^{n-1}}{|\det A|}$$

(b) If Euclidean norms are used, then $\beta \leq 1$.

Proof (a) From the equivalence of norms and (2.3), there are constants α_l and α_u such that

$$\alpha_l \max_{i,j} |a_{ij}| \leq \|A\| \leq \alpha_u \max_{i,j} |a_{ij}|$$

Then (11) follows from Cramer's formula.

(b) By polar decomposition

$$A = UH$$

where U is unitary (i.e., $UU^* = I$) and H is Hermitian. Note that

$$|\det A| = |\det U|\,|\det H| = |\det H|$$

Since A is nonsingular and $H^2 = A^*A$, H is positive definite. Call $h_1, h_2, \ldots, h_n$ its eigenvalues and order them so that $0 < h_1 \leq h_2 \leq \cdots \leq h_n$. By the properties of the (operator) norm induced by the Euclidean norm [see (1.18)],

12
$$\|A\| = \|H\| = h_n \qquad \text{and} \qquad \|A^{-1}\| = \|H^{-1}\| = 1/h_1$$

So

$$\|A^{-1}\| = \frac{1}{h_1} \le \frac{(h_n)^{n-1}}{h_1 h_2 \cdots h_n} = \frac{\|A\|^{n-1}}{\det H} = \frac{\|A\|^{n-1}}{|\det A|} \tag{13}$$ ∎

Note that the inequality (13) holds with equal sign if $h_2 = h_n$. In fact, the right-hand side of (13) is equal to the left-hand side times $\prod_{k=2}^{n} (h_n/h_k)$.

5.3 Continuous linear maps

Let $(E, |\cdot|)$ be a normed space over the field $\mathbb{K}$, and let $\|\cdot\|$ be the induced norm on some subspace of $\tilde{\mathscr{L}}(E, E)$. We define

$$\mathscr{L}(E, E) \triangleq \{A \in \tilde{\mathscr{L}}(E, E) \,|\, \|A\| < \infty\} \tag{14}$$

Theorem U.t.c. $\forall A, B \in \mathscr{L}(E, E), \forall \alpha \in \mathbb{K}, \forall x \in E$

$$|Ax| \le \|A\| \; |x| \tag{15}$$

$$\|\alpha A\| = |\alpha| \; \|A\| \tag{16}$$

$$\|A + B\| \le \|A\| + \|B\| \tag{17}$$

$$\|AB\| \le \|A\| \; \|B\| \tag{18}$$

Proof All these inequalities follow directly from Definition (7). For example,

$$\|AB\| = \sup_{|z|=1} |ABz| \le \|A\| \sup_{|z|=1} |Bz| = \|A\| \; \|B\|$$ ∎

The inequalities above show that $\mathscr{L}(E, E)$ is a normed algebra. It can be shown that if $(E, |\cdot|)$ is complete (i.e., if E is a Banach space), then $\mathscr{L}(E, E)$ is also a *Banach algebra* with the norm (7). It is, in fact, a noncommutative Banach algebra with a unit.

Exercise 1 Let $A \in \tilde{\mathscr{L}}(E, E)$. Show that the following three statements are equivalent:

(i) The linear function A is continuous at $\theta \in E$.
(ii) The linear function A is continuous on E.
(iii) The induced norm of A, $\|A\|$, is finite.

This exercise justifies our saying that $\mathscr{L}(E, E)$ is the **class of all continuous linear maps from the normed space E into E.**

Some authors call the elements of $\mathscr{L}(E, E)$ "bounded" linear maps. This terminology conflicts with the general definition of a bounded map from a normed space into another normed space. What they mean is that $A \in \mathscr{L}(E, E)$, iff $A \in \tilde{\mathscr{L}}(E, E)$, and the restriction of A to the unit ball is a bounded map.

Remark Suppose that on $\tilde{\mathscr{L}}(E, E)$ we define a norm $N(\cdot)$ which, *in addition to the axioms of the norm*, satisfies

19 $$N(AB) \leq N(A)N(B)$$

and suppose that we have a vector norm $|\cdot|$ such that

20 $$|Ax| \leq N(A)|x|, \qquad \forall x \in E, \quad \forall A \in \tilde{\mathscr{L}}(E, E)$$

Then we say that $N(\cdot)$ is an (operator) norm on $\tilde{\mathscr{L}}(E, E)$ **compatible** with the (vector) norm $|\cdot|$ on E.

Exercise 2 (i) If $\|\cdot\|$ is the norm induced by $|\cdot|$ and if $N(\cdot)$ is any norm compatible with $|\cdot|$, show that

21 $$\|A\| \leq N(A), \qquad \forall A \in \mathscr{L}(E, E)$$

(ii) In the matrix case, show that $A \mapsto \max_{i,j} |a_{ij}|$ obeys the axioms of a norm on the space of matrices but not (19).

(iii) Show that $A \mapsto (\sum_{ij}, |a_{ij}|^2)^{1/2}$ is compatible with the Euclidean norm.

(iv) Refer to the examples of Section 1 and show that, for $p = 1, 2, \infty$, $\|A\|_p$ [defined by (1.17) to (1.19)] is induced by $|x|_p$.

6 Two examples

The two examples that follow are designed to illustrate the fact that the induced norm depends on the vector norm. The results of these examples will be useful later.

Example 1 Let $(E, |\cdot|_\infty) = L^\infty(\mathbb{R}_+) = \{f\colon \mathbb{R}_+ \to \mathbb{R} \,|\, \|f\|_\infty < \infty\}$. Let H be a linear map defined on E in terms of an integrable function $h\colon \mathbb{R} \to \mathbb{R}$;

1 $$H\colon u \mapsto Hu \triangleq h * u, \qquad \forall u \in L^\infty$$

i.e.,

2 $$(Hu)(t) = \int_0^t h(t - \tau)u(\tau)\, d\tau, \qquad \forall t \in \mathbb{R}_+$$

We assume that $\|h\|_1 = \int_0^\infty |h(t)|\, dt < \infty$.

3 **Theorem** U.t.c.

(a) $H\colon L^\infty \to L^\infty$

(b) $\|H\|$, the induced norm of the linear map H, is given by

$$\|H\|_\infty = \|h\|_1; \qquad \text{i.e.,} \quad \|h * u\|_\infty \leq \|h\|_1 \|u\|_\infty, \qquad \forall u \in L^\infty$$

and $\|h * u\|_\infty$ can be made arbitrarily close to $\|h\|_1 \|u\|_\infty$ by appropriate choice of u.

Proof We start by calculating the induced norm of H. We drop the subscript ∞ throughout; e.g., $\|u\|$ denotes the L^∞ norm of $u: \mathbb{R}_+ \to \mathbb{R}$. We have three norms in this proof: the absolute value of real numbers, e.g., $|u(t)|$; the norm on L^∞, e.g., $\|u\|$; the induced norm on $\mathscr{L}(E, E)$, namely, $\|H\|$.

4
$$\begin{aligned}\|H\| &= \sup_{\|u\|=1} \|h * u\| = \sup_{\|u\|=1} \sup_{t \geq 0} |(h * u)(t)| \\ &= \sup_{\|u\|=1} \left[\sup_{t \geq 0} \left| \int_0^t h(t-\tau) u(\tau)\, d\tau \right| \right] \\ &\leq \sup_{\|u\|=1} \left[\sup_{t \geq 0} \int_0^t |h(t-\tau)|\, |u(\tau)|\, d\tau \right]\end{aligned}$$

Since $\|u\| = 1$,

$$\|H\| \leq \sup_{t \geq 0} \int_0^t |h(t-\tau)|\, d\tau \leq \int_0^\infty |h(t')|\, dt'$$

Hence

5
$$\|H\| \leq \int_0^\infty |h(t')|\, dt' = \|h\|_1$$

This inequality shows that H is a *continuous* linear map from L^∞ into L^∞. Inequality (5) shows also that $\|h\|_1$ is an upper bound on the induced norm of the map $H: L^\infty \to L^\infty$. Let us show that $\|h\|_1$ is the induced norm. Consider a sequence of inputs $u_1, u_2, \ldots,$ with $\|u_i\| = 1$, where for $t = 1, 2, 3, \ldots,$ we define

$$u_t: \tau \mapsto u_t(\tau) = \operatorname{sgn}[h(t-\tau)], \qquad \tau \in \mathbb{R}_+, \quad t \in \mathbb{Z}_+$$

and we take $h(t) = 0$ for $t < 0$. Consider now the value at time t of the output due to $u_t(\cdot)$

$$(h * u_t)(t) = \int_0^t |h(t-\tau)|\, d\tau \leq \|h * u_t\|_\infty, \qquad t = 1, 2, \ldots$$

where $\|\cdot\|_\infty$ denotes the norm on E. Hence for $t = 1, 2, 3, \ldots,$ we have by (5)

$$\int_0^t |h(\tau)|\, d\tau \leq \|h * u_t\|_\infty \leq \|H\| \leq \int_0^\infty |h(\tau)|\, d\tau = \|h\|_1$$

Letting $t \to \infty$, these inequalities imply that $\|H\| = \|h\|_1$. ∎

Example 2 Let $E = L^2(\mathbb{R}) = \{f: \mathbb{R} \to \mathbb{R} \mid \|f\|_2 < \infty\}$. Let H be a linear map defined on L^2 by $H: u \mapsto Hu$, where

6
$$(Hu)(t) = \int_{-\infty}^\infty h(t-\tau) u(\tau)\, d\tau, \qquad \forall t \in \mathbb{R}$$

7 **Theorem** If the linear map H is defined by (6), where $h \in L^1$, then

(a) $H: L^2 \to L^2$,

(b) $\|H\|_2$, the induced norm of the linear map $H \in \mathscr{L}(L^2, L^2)$, is given by

$$\|H\|_2 = \max_{\omega \in \mathbb{R}} |\hat{h}(j\omega)| \tag{8}$$

Proof Since $h \in L^1$, its Fourier transform $\mathscr{F}(h) = \hat{h}(j\omega)$ is uniformly continuous on $\mathbb{R}$ and $\to 0$ as $|\omega| \to \infty$. (See Appendix B.1.1.) Now, with all integrals below being over $\mathbb{R}$, we have

$$\begin{aligned}\|Hu\|_2{}^2 = \|h * u\|_2{}^2 &= \int (h * u)(t)(h * u)(t)\, dt \\ &= \frac{1}{2\pi} \int \widehat{(h * u)}(j\omega)\widehat{(h * u)}(j\omega)^*\, d\omega \qquad \text{(Parseval)} \\ &= \frac{1}{2\pi} \int |\hat{h}(j\omega)|^2 |\hat{u}(j\omega)|^2\, d\omega \qquad \text{(convolution theorem)}\end{aligned}$$

By Parseval,

$$\|u\|_2 = 1 \Leftrightarrow \|\hat{u}\|_2 = (2\pi)^{1/2} \Leftrightarrow (2\pi)^{-1} \int |\hat{u}(j\omega)|^2\, d\omega = 1$$

Hence, $\forall u$ such that $\|u\|_2 = 1$,

$$\|Hu\|_2{}^2 \leq \max_{\omega \in \mathbb{R}} [|\hat{h}(j\omega)|^2]$$

Thus, the induced norm satisfies

$$\|H\|_2 \leq \max_{\omega \in \mathbb{R}} |\hat{h}(j\omega)| \tag{9}$$

Note that since $\omega \mapsto |\hat{h}(j\omega)|$ is continuous on $\mathbb{R}$ and $\to 0$ as $|\omega| \to \infty$, the maximum exists. We are going to show that $\|H\|_2$ is actually equal to the right-hand side of (9). Observe that for $\lambda > 0$,

$$\mathscr{F}(e^{-\lambda t^2}) = (\pi/\lambda)^{1/2} \exp[-\omega^2/4\lambda]$$

and

$$\begin{aligned}&\mathscr{F}[\exp(-\lambda t^2) \cos \omega_0 t] \\ &\quad = \tfrac{1}{2}(\pi/\lambda)^{1/2}\{\exp[-(\omega - \omega_0)^2/4\lambda] + \exp -[(\omega + \omega_0)^2/4\lambda]\}\end{aligned}$$

As $\lambda \to 0$, this expression tends to $\pi[\delta(\omega - \omega_0) + \delta(\omega + \omega_0)]$, where $\delta(\cdot)$ denotes the Dirac delta (generalized) function. Pick ω_0 to be the abscissa of the maximum of $\omega \mapsto |\hat{h}(j\omega)|$; for each λ pick a normalization $n(\lambda)$ such that

$$u_\lambda(t) = n(\lambda)[\exp(-\lambda t^2)] \cos \omega_0 t$$

has unit norm. Since $|\hat{h}(j\omega)|$ is continuous, we see that

$$\|h * u_\lambda\|_2 \to \max_\omega |\hat{h}(j\omega)| \qquad \text{as} \quad \lambda \to 0$$

Consequently, we have shown that

$$\|H\|_2 = \max_\omega |\hat{h}(j\omega)|$$

10 **Remark** These results can be generalized to the case where u and $h * u$ are vector valued; i.e., map $\mathbb{R}_+$ into $\mathbb{R}^n$. We state the result as an exercise.

Exercise 1 Let $u: \mathbb{R}_+ \to \mathbb{R}^n$ and let u be locally integrable. Let H be the matrix impulse response; so $H: \mathbb{R}_+ \to \mathbb{R}^{n \times n}$. Assume throughout that the elements of H, namely, the $h_{ij}(\cdot)$'s, are in L^1, for $i, j = 1, 2, \ldots, n$. Denote by $\overline{H}$ the linear operator defined by

$$\overline{H}: u \mapsto \overline{H}u \triangleq H * u$$

where

$$(H * u)(t) = \int_0^\infty H(t - \tau)u(\tau)\, d\tau$$

Establish the following induced norms:

(a) $u \in L_n^\infty(\mathbb{R}_+)$: $\|u\|_\infty = \max_i \sup_{t \geq 0} |u_i(t)|$; show that the induced norm of $\overline{H}$ is

$$\|\overline{H}\|_\infty = \max_i \int_0^\infty \sum_{j=1}^n |h_{ij}(\tau)|\, d\tau \qquad \text{(row sum)} \tag{11}$$

(b) $u \in L_n^2(\mathbb{R}_+)$: $\|u\|_2^2 = \int_0^\infty \sum_{i=1}^n |u_i(t)|^2\, dt$; show that the induced norm of $\overline{H}$ is

$$\|\overline{H}\|_2 = (\lambda_{\max})^{1/2} \tag{12}$$

where

$$\lambda_{\max} = \max_\omega \max_i \lambda_i[\hat{H}(j\omega)^* \hat{H}(j\omega)] \tag{13}$$

where $\lambda_i(M)$ denotes the (necessarily real) ith eigenvalue of the Hermitian matrix M.

(c) $u \in L_n^1(\mathbb{R}_+)$: $\|u\|_1 = \int_0^\infty \sum_{i=1}^n |u_i(t)|\, dt$; show that the induced norm of $\overline{H}$ is

$$\|\overline{H}\|_1 = \max_j \int_0^\infty \sum_{i=1}^n |h_{ij}(t)|\, dt \qquad \text{(column sum)} \tag{14}$$

7 Norms and spectral radius

Let $A \in \mathbb{C}^{n \times n}$ and

1 $$r(A) \triangleq \max_i |\lambda_i(A)|$$

where $r(A)$ is called the **spectral radius** *of* A.

2 **Exercise 1** Show that for *any* induced norm, $r(A) \leq \|A\|$.

For the given matrix A, we may try to find a norm on $\mathbb{C}^n$ that gives the "minimum" induced norm for A. In fact, we shall prove the following theorem.

3 **Theorem** Let $\mathcal{N}$ denote the set of all norms on $\mathbb{C}^n$; then for any $A \in \mathbb{C}^{n \times n}$,

4 $$\inf_{|\cdot| \in \mathcal{N}} \left[\sup_{x \in \mathbb{C}^n} (|Ax|/|x|) \right] = r(A)$$

By the definition of the infimum, (4) is equivalent to inequality (2) and the statement that for any $\varepsilon > 0$ and any $A \in \mathbb{C}^{n \times n}$, there is a (vector) norm on $\mathbb{C}^n$ such that the corresponding induced norm satisfies

5 $$\|A\| \leq r(A) + \varepsilon$$

Proof Let J be the Jordan form of A; then there is a *nonsingular* matrix P s.t.

$$J = PAP^{-1} = \Lambda + U$$

where Λ is diagonal and all the elements of U are either 0 or 1 with all nonzero elements located on the diagonal *above* the main diagonal. For some small $\delta > 0$, define the nonsingular matrix D by

$$D \triangleq \operatorname{diag}[1, \delta^{-1}, \delta^{-2}, \ldots, \delta^{-(n-1)}]$$

Then

$$DJD^{-1} = \Lambda + \delta U$$

Define a norm $|\cdot|$ on $\mathbb{C}^n$ by

$$x \mapsto |DPx|_2$$

where $|\cdot|_2$ is the Euclidean norm on $\mathbb{C}^n$. The corresponding induced norm is

$$\|A\| = \max_{|x|=1} |Ax| = \max_{|DPx|_2=1} |DPAx|_2$$

With $z \triangleq DPx$, we have $DPAx = DPAP^{-1}D^{-1}z = (\Lambda + \delta U)z$; consequently,

$$\begin{aligned}\|A\|^2 &= \max_{|z|_2=1} \langle(\Lambda + \delta U)z | (\Lambda + \delta U)z\rangle \\ &\leq \max_{|z|_2=1} \{|\Lambda z|_2{}^2 + 2\delta|\langle Uz|\Lambda z\rangle| + \delta^2|Uz|_2{}^2\} \\ &\leq r(A)^2 + 2\delta r(A) + \delta^2\end{aligned}$$

or

$$\|A\| \leq r(A) + \delta$$

Therefore, by choosing $\delta \leq \varepsilon$, we achieve (5). ∎

The trouble with this result is that the vector norm must be specially tailored for the matrix A. It is, however, useful in applications where the problem involves only one matrix; for in that case the norm can be tailored to that matrix.

Exercise 2 Let N be a norm on $\mathbb{C}^n$. Show that $x \mapsto N(Px)$ is a norm on C^n if and only if P is a *nonsingular* matrix $\in \mathbb{C}^{n \times n}$. Show that if P is singular, then ρ: $x \mapsto N(Px)$ satisfies axioms (ii) and (iii) of the norms [see (II.1.1)], but (i) is replaced by

(i′) $\rho(x) \geq 0, \qquad \forall x \in \mathbb{C}^n$.

(In such a case, ρ is called a seminorm.)

Exercise 3 (contraction mapping theorem) The following is a statement of the contraction mapping theorem in a form particularly useful for applications. The proof is essentially the same as the usual textbook case.

Let (P, d) be a metric space and $(\mathscr{B}, \|\cdot\|)$ be a Banach space. Let $p_0 \in P$ and $x_0 \in \mathscr{B}$. Consider the closed balls:

$$B_P = \{p \in P \,|\, d(p - p_0) \leq r_P\}$$
$$B_{\mathscr{B}} = \{x \in \mathscr{B} \,|\, \|x - x_0\| \leq r_{\mathscr{B}}\}$$

If

(i) $f: B_P \times B_{\mathscr{B}} \to \mathscr{B}$ and f is continuous in $B_P \times B_{\mathscr{B}}$;

(ii) there is some $k < 1$ such that

$$\|f(p, x) - f(p, x')\| \leq k\|x - x'\|, \qquad \forall p \in B_P, \quad \forall x, x' \in B_{\mathscr{B}}$$

(iii) $\|f(p, x_0) - x_0\| \leq (1 - k)r_{\mathscr{B}}, \qquad \forall p \in B_P$

then

(a) $\forall p \in B_P$, the iteration scheme

$$x_{n+1}(p) = f[p, x_n(p)], \qquad \text{with} \quad x_0(p) = x_0$$

converges to a *unique continuous* function $\bar{x}: B_P \to B_{\mathscr{B}}$ such that

$$\bar{x}(p) = f[p, \bar{x}(p)], \qquad \forall p \in B_P$$

(b) the convergence is uniform in p over B_P; i.e., for the given k and the given B_P,

$$\|\bar{x}(p) - x_n(p)\| \leq k^n r_{\mathscr{B}}, \qquad \forall p \in B_P, \quad \forall n \in \mathbb{Z}_+$$

(*Hint*: Be sure to verify that $x_n(p) \in B_{\mathscr{B}}$ for all $n \geq 1$, and all $p \in B_P$.)

In general, any function such as $f(p, \cdot)$, which maps a set $B_{\mathscr{B}}$ into a Banach space $\mathscr{B}$ and which satisfies an inequality like (ii) above, is called a **contraction** over $B_{\mathscr{B}}$.

Exercise 4 Let A be a continuous linear map from a Banach space E into itself. We say that $\lambda \in \mathbb{C}$ is a spectral value of A iff $A - \lambda I$ does not have a continuous inverse on E. Call the spectrum of A, $\mathrm{Sp}(A)$, the set of all spectral values of A, and the spectral radius of A, the positive number

$$\mathscr{r}(A) \triangleq \sup_{\lambda \in \mathrm{Sp}(A)} |\lambda|$$

(a) Show that

$$(A - \lambda I)^{-1} = -\sum_{k=0}^{\infty} \lambda^{-(k+1)} A^k$$

and that the series converges absolutely [in $\mathscr{L}(E; E)$] for $|\lambda| > \|A\|$.

(b) Show that $(A - \lambda I)^{-1} \in \mathscr{L}(E; E)$ for $|\lambda| > \mathrm{Sp}(A)$.

Exercise 5 Let A, $B \in \mathscr{L}(E; E)$, E a Banach space. Show that it is *not* generally true that

$$\mathscr{r}(AB) \leq \|A\| \mathscr{r}(B), \qquad \mathscr{r}(AB) \leq \mathscr{r}(A)\mathscr{r}(B)$$

(*Hint*: Consider 2×2 matrices, one of which is nil potent.)

8 The measure of a matrix

Let $|\cdot|$ be some norm on $\mathbb{C}^n$. Let $\|\cdot\|$ denote the corresponding induced norm on the $n \times n$ matrices in $\mathbb{C}^{n \times n}$. The function $\|\cdot\|: \mathbb{C}^{n \times n} \to \mathbb{R}_+$ is a convex function; therefore, at every point $X \in \mathbb{C}^{n \times n}$, $\|\cdot\|$ has a *one-sided directional* derivative in any direction $A \in \mathbb{C}^{n \times n}$; i.e., the limit

$$\lim_{\theta \searrow 0} (\|X + \theta A\| - \|X\|)/\theta$$

exists for all X and all A.

The one-sided directional derivative of $\|\cdot\|$ at $I \in \mathbb{C}^{n\times n}$ in the direction A is called the **measure of the matrix** A and is denoted by $\mu(A)$. Thus,

1
$$\mu(A) \triangleq \lim_{\theta \searrow 0}(\|I + \theta A\| - 1)/\theta$$

We shall prove the existence of this limit in Lemma (4) below.

The concept of the measure of a matrix appears naturally in the study of differential equations. Consider $\dot{x}(t) = A(t)x(t)$, where $A(\cdot)$ is continuous. Let us bound the one-sided derivative in the positive direction of $t \mapsto |\phi(t)|$, where $\phi(\cdot)$ is a solution of the differential equation:

2
$$\begin{aligned} D^+|\phi(t)| &\triangleq \lim_{\theta \searrow 0}[|\phi(t+\theta)| - |\phi(t)|]/\theta \\ &= \lim_{\theta \searrow 0}[|\phi(t) + \theta A(t)\phi(t)| - |\phi(t)|]/\theta \\ &\le \lim_{\theta \searrow 0}[\|I + \theta A(t)\| \, |\phi(t)| - |\phi(t)|]/\theta \end{aligned}$$

Hence by (1)

3
$$D^+|\phi(t)| \le \mu(A(t))|\phi(t)|$$

Inequality (3) is sharper than the standard one

$$D^+|\phi(t)| \le \|A(t)\| \, |\phi(t)|$$

Indeed, $\mu(A(t))$ may be negative, whereas $\|A(t)\|$ is always nonnegative.

4 **Lemma** For any $A \in \mathbb{C}^{n\times n}$, $\mu(A)$ is well defined.

Proof Call $f(\theta)$ the ratio in (1); we show that $f(\theta)$ decreases as $\theta \searrow 0$ and that it is bounded below. Hence as θ decreases to $0, f(\theta)$ tends to a well-defined limit. Let $k \in (0, 1)$.

$$\begin{aligned} k\theta f(k\theta) &= \|I + k\theta A\| - 1 = \|k(I + \theta A) + (1-k)I\| - 1 \\ &\le k\|I + \theta A\| + 1 - k - 1 = k(\|I + \theta A\| - 1) \\ &= k\theta f(\theta) \end{aligned}$$

So for $k \in (0, 1)$, $f(k\theta) \le f(\theta)$; i.e., f is decreasing as θ decreases. Now $f(\theta) \ge -\|A\|$ because, for $\theta > 0$,

$$\theta f(\theta) = \|I + \theta A\| - 1 \ge 1 - \theta\|A\| - 1 = -\theta\|A\|$$

Hence the conclusion follows. ∎

Properties of μ

For convenience, we list a number of properties of μ in the following theorem.

5 **Theorem** Let $A, B \in \mathbb{C}^{n\times n}$, and μ be given by (1). Then

6 (a) $$\mu(I) = 1, \qquad \mu(-I) = -1, \qquad \mu(0) = 0$$

(*Note*: $\mu(A) = 0$ *does not imply* that $A = 0$.)

7 (b) $$-\|A\| \le -\mu(-A) \le \mu(A) \le \|A\|$$

8 (c) $$\mu(cA) = c\mu(A), \qquad \forall c \ge 0$$

9 (d) $$\mu(A + cI) = \mu(A) + c, \qquad \forall c \in \mathbb{R}$$

10 (e) $$\max[\mu(A) - \mu(-B), -\mu(-A) + \mu(B)] \le \mu(A + B) \le \mu(A) + \mu(B)$$

(f) $$\mu\colon \mathbb{C}^{n\times n} \to \mathbb{R} \qquad \text{is convex on} \quad C^{n\times n}$$

11 $$\mu[\lambda A + (1-\lambda)B] \le \lambda\mu(A) + (1-\lambda)\mu(B), \qquad \forall \lambda \in [0, 1]$$

12 (g) $$|\mu(A) - \mu(B)| \le |\mu(A - B)| \le \|A - B\|$$
$$|\mu(A) - \mu(B)| \le |\mu(B - A)| \le \|A - B\|$$

13 (h) $$-\mu(-A) \le \operatorname{Re} \lambda_i(A) \le \mu(A), \qquad \forall i \in \{1, 2, \ldots, n\}$$

14 (i) $$-\mu(-A)|x| \le |Ax| \qquad \text{and} \qquad -\mu(A)|x| \le |Ax|, \quad \forall x \in C^n$$

(*Note*: $|Ax|$ *is not bounded above* by $\mu(A)|x|$.)

(j) Let $|\cdot|$ be a norm on $\mathbb{C}^n$ and $P \in \mathbb{C}^{n\times n}$ be nonsingular. Call μ_P the measure defined in terms of the induced norm corresponding to the vector norm $|\cdot|_P$ defined by $x \mapsto |x|_P = |Px|$. Then

15 $$\mu_P(A) = \mu(PAP^{-1})$$

(k) If A is nonsingular,

16 $$-\mu(-A) \le (\|A^{-1}\|)^{-1} \le \|A\|$$

Proof (a) Immediate from Definition (1).

(b) The triangle inequality and $\theta > 0$ give

$$-\|A\| = \frac{1 - \theta\|A\| - 1}{\theta} \le \frac{\|I + \theta A\| - 1}{\theta} \le \frac{1 + \theta\|A\| - 1}{\theta} = \|A\|$$

and

$$-\|A\| = \frac{1 - \theta\|A\| - 1}{\theta} = \frac{1 - \theta\|-A\| - 1}{\theta} \le -\frac{\|I + \theta(-A)\| - 1}{\theta}$$

Finally, the relation between $\mu(A)$ and $-\mu(-A)$ follows from

$$0 = \|I + \theta(A - A)\| - 1 \le (\|I + 2\theta A\| - 1 + \|I - 2\theta A\| - 1)/2$$

(c) (8) is true for $c = 0$ in view of (6). For $c > 0$, observe that

$$(\|I + \theta cA\| - 1)/\theta = c(\|I + c\theta A\| - 1)/c\theta$$

Since $c > 0$, as $\theta \searrow 0$, so does $c\theta$.

(d) Consider

$$\frac{\|I + \theta(A + cI)\| - 1}{\theta} = \frac{(1 + c\theta)\|I + [\theta/(1 + c\theta)]A\| - 1}{\theta}$$

$$= \frac{\|I + [\theta/(1 + c\theta)]A\| - 1}{\theta/(1 + c\theta)} + c$$

Finally, $\forall c \in \mathbb{R}$, as $\theta \searrow 0$, $\theta/(1 + c\theta) \searrow 0$.

(e) For the second inequality

$$\|I + \theta(A + B)\| - 1 = \tfrac{1}{2}(\|I + 2\theta A + I + 2\theta B\| - 2)$$
$$\leq \tfrac{1}{2}(\|I + 2\theta A\| - 1) + \tfrac{1}{2}(\|I + 2\theta B\| - 1)$$

With $\theta \searrow 0$, we conclude $\mu(A + B) \leq \mu(A) + \mu(B)$.

The other inequality in (10) follows from the one just proved:

$$\mu(A) = \mu(A + B - B) \leq \mu(-B) + \mu(A + B) \tag{18}$$

$$\mu(B) = \mu(A + B - A) \leq \mu(-A) + \mu(A + B) \tag{19}$$

(f) Convexity is immediate from (8) and the second inequality (10).

(g) The second inequality (12) follows from (7). To obtain the first, replace B by $-B$ in (18) and obtain

$$\mu(A) - \mu(B) \leq \mu(A - B)$$

Replacing $-A$ by A in (19), we obtain

$$\mu(B) - \mu(A) \leq \mu(B - A)$$

and (12) follows.

(h) Let $e \in \mathbb{C}^n$ be a normalized eigenvector of A associated with the eigenvalue λ_i; so $Ae = \lambda_i e$ and $\|I + \theta(-A)\| \geq |e - \theta\lambda_i e|$. Therefore,

$$-\frac{\|I + \theta(-A)\| - 1}{\theta} \leq -\frac{|e - \theta\lambda_i e| - 1}{\theta} = -\frac{|1 - \theta\lambda_i| - 1}{\theta}$$

As $\theta \searrow 0$, the right-hand side tends to $\operatorname{Re} \lambda_i$ and the left to $-\mu(-A)$. To obtain the second inequality, consider

$$\frac{\|I + \theta A\| - 1}{\theta} \geq \frac{|e + \theta\lambda_i e| - 1}{\theta} = \frac{|1 + \theta\lambda_i| - 1}{\theta}$$

Again as $\theta \searrow 0$, we obtain the second inequality.

(i) For $\theta > 0$

$$|Ax| = |x - (x - \theta Ax)|/\theta = |x - (I - \theta A)x|/\theta \leq (|x| - \|I - \theta A\|\ |x|)/\theta$$
$$= -[(\|I + \theta(-A)\| - 1)|x|]/\theta \underset{\theta \searrow 0}{\rightarrow} -\mu(-A)|x|$$

where in the last step we noted that the left-hand side is independent of θ. The second inequality (i) follows from the derivation above by changing A into $-A$ and noting that $|Ax| = |-Ax|$.

(j) $$\|I + \theta A\|_P \triangleq \sup_{|x|_P=1} |x + \theta Ax|_P \neq$$
$$= \sup_{|Px|=1} |Px + \theta PAP^{-1}Px| \triangleq \|I + \theta PAP^{-1}\|$$

(k) By (14)
$$-\mu(-A)|x| \leq |Ax| \qquad \text{and} \qquad \inf_{|x|=1} |Ax| = (\|A^{-1}\|)^{-1}$$
the first inequality follows. For the second, take the norm of $AA^{-1} = I$. ∎

24 **Theorem** Let $x = (x_1, x_2, \ldots, x_n) \in \mathbb{C}^n$ and $A = (a_{ij}) \in \mathbb{C}^{n\times n}$; then

$\|x\|_1 = \sum_1^n \|x_i\|$	$\\|A\\|_1 = \max_j \sum_i \|a_{ij}\|$ (column sum)	$\mu_1(A) = \max_j \left[\mathrm{Re}(a_{jj}) + \sum_{i \neq j} \|a_{ij}\|\right]$
$\|x\|_2 = \left((\sum_1^n \|x_i\|^2\right)^{1/2}$	$\\|A\\|_2 = \left(\max_i \lambda_i(A^*A)\right)^{1/2}$	$\mu_2(A) = \max_i [\lambda_i(A + A^*)/2]$
$\|x\|_\infty = \max_i \|x_i\|$	$\\|A\\|_\infty = \max_i \sum_j \|a_{ij}\|$ (row sum)	$\mu_\infty(A) = \max_i \left[\mathrm{Re}(a_{ii}) + \sum_{j=1, j \neq i} \|a_{ij}\|\right]$

Proof The calculation of $\mu_i(A)$ $(i = 1, 2, \infty)$ is a simple exercise using the definition. (A^* denotes, as usual, the complex conjugate of A.) ∎

Exercise 1 Show that if $A \neq 0$ and if A is skew Hermitian, or skew symmetric, then $\mu_2(A) = 0$.

Exercise 2 Let $A \in \mathbb{R}^{n\times n}$ be a singular, positive semidefinite, symmetric matrix. Show that $\mu_2(-A) = 0$.

26 **Comments** The formulas of Theorem (24) show that $\mu(A)$ is easy to calculate for $p = 1, \infty$ or to estimate for $p = 2$. Also $\mu(A)$ may actually be smaller than the corresponding $\|A\|$. Also, $\mu(A)$ may be negative.

As applications of the notion of measure we give two facts. The first one gives *upper* and *lower* bounds on solutions of linear differential equations, and the second gives a sufficient condition for the existence and uniqueness of operating points in circuit theory.

27 **Theorem** Let $t \mapsto A(t)$ be a regulated function from $\mathbb{R}_+$ to $\mathbb{C}^{n\times n}$. Then the solution of

$$\dot{x}(t) = A(t)x(t) \tag{28}$$

satisfies the inequalities

$$|x(t_0)|\exp\left\{-\int_{t_0}^{t} \mu[-A(t')]\,dt'\right\} \le |x(t)| \le |x(t_0)| \exp\int_{t_0}^{t} \mu[A(t')]\,dt' \tag{29}$$

Proof Let $x(t)$ denote any nonzero solution of (28), let $n(t) = |x(t)|$ and $D^+n(t)$ denote the right-hand derivative of $n(\cdot)$ at t; then by definition, for all $t \notin D$, where D is the at most countable set of points at which $A(\cdot)$ is discontinuous,

$$D^+n(t) = \lim_{\theta\searrow 0}[n(t+\theta) - n(t)]/\theta = \lim_{\theta\searrow 0}[|x(t) + \theta A(t)x(t)| - |x(t)|]/\theta \tag{30}$$

But

$$|x(t) + \theta A(t)x(t)| \le \|I + \theta A(t)\|\,|x(t)|$$

Inserting this inequality in (30) and using the definition of μ, we obtain

$$D^+n(t) \le \mu[A(t)]n(t) \tag{31}$$

Since $n(t) > 0$ for all t, (31) becomes

$$D^+n(t)/n(t) \le \mu[A(t)]$$

and the second inequality (29) follows by integration. The first inequality is proved in a similar manner. ∎

In many applications one has to find the operating point (or equilibrium point) for a system described by

$$\dot{x} = f(x) + u \tag{32}$$

where u, $x \in \mathbb{R}^n$ and f: $\mathbb{R}^n \to \mathbb{R}^n$. The problem is to find an $x \in \mathbb{R}^n$ such that $f(x) = u$. It is important to know whether this equation has solutions for any $u \in \mathbb{R}^n$ and whether such solutions are unique. The theorem below gives sufficient conditions for this to be the case. $Df(x)$ denotes the derivative of f at x (equivalently, the Jacobian matrix of f at x).

33 **Theorem** Let f: $\mathbb{R}^n \to \mathbb{R}^n$ be continuously differentiable. U.t.c., if there exists a function m: $\mathbb{R}_+ \to \mathbb{R}_+$ such that

$$\mu[Df(x)] \le -m(|x|) < 0, \qquad \forall x \in \mathbb{R}^n \tag{34}$$

where $m(\alpha) > 0$ for all $\alpha > 0$ and

$$\int_0^\infty m(\alpha)\,dx = \infty \tag{35}$$

then $x \mapsto f(x)$ is a C^1 diffeomorphism of $\mathbb{R}^n$ onto itself [equivalently, f is a continuously differentiable bijection of $\mathbb{R}^n$ *onto* $\mathbb{R}^n$ with a continuously differentiable inverse]; thus, for any $u \in \mathbb{R}^n$, (32) has a solution x which depends in a C^1 fashion on x.

Proof By Palais' theorem our claim will be established if we show that $\det[Df(x)] \neq 0$, $\forall x \in \mathbb{R}^n$ and that $|x| \to \infty$ implies that $|f(x)| \to \infty$. The first condition follows from the observation that $\forall y \in \mathbb{R}^n$ with $y \neq 0$,

$$|Df(x)y| = |-Df(x)y| \geq -\mu[Df(x)]|y| \geq m(|x|)|y| > 0$$

where we used (14) and assumption (34).

The second requirement holds true because by using Taylor's theorem about 0, the origin of $\mathbb{C}^n$, we obtain

$$f(x) = f(0) + \left[\int_0^1 Df(\lambda x)\, d\lambda\right] x$$

So

$$\begin{aligned}
|f(x)| &\geq \left|\left[\int_0^1 Df(\lambda x)\, d\lambda\right] x\right| - |f(0)| \\
&\geq -\mu\left\{\int_0^1 Df(\lambda x)\, d\lambda\right\}|x| - |f(0)| && \text{by (14)} \\
&\geq -\int_0^1 \mu[Df(\lambda x)]\, d\lambda\, |x| - |f(0)| && \text{by (11)} \\
&\geq \int_0^1 m(\lambda|x|)\, d\lambda\, |x| - |f(0)| && \text{by (34)} \\
&= \int_0^{|x|} m(\alpha)\, d\alpha - |f(0)|
\end{aligned}$$

and the second requirement holds as a consequence of (35). ∎

36 **Remark** The theorem still holds if (34) is replaced by

37 $$\mu[-Df(x)] \leq -m(|x|) < 0, \qquad \forall x \in \mathbb{R}^n$$

Notes and references

The discussion of norms and equivalent norms is standard [Yos.2, Die.1, Edw.1, Hou.1]. The examples may be illuminating. The calculations of induced norms were introduced in the engineering literature by Sandberg, in his many papers starting in 1963, and by Zames at about the same time. (See reference list.) The notion of measure of a matrix is due to Dahlquist [Dah.1]. Inequality (8.29) can be found in Coppel's book [Cop.1]. For Theorem (8.32) see the paper by Desoer and Haneda [Des.11].

III GENERAL THEOREMS

This chapter is abstract because abstraction saves time. Indeed, suppose that we solve a dozen specific problems and that we detect a common pattern in their solution. It would obviously be useful to abstract from these solutions the essence of those characteristics that lead to the solution; then when encountering a new problem, we would know what to look for. This is, of course, very beneficial, but what is the cost? The cost is that this process of abstraction requires care. Indeed, in a specific concrete problem, certain features of the problem are well known and well understood; so one takes advantage of them without comment. (In other words, familiarity makes you believe that it is simpler than it actually is.) In an abstract setup, all required properties must be precisely stated, and every step of the reasoning must be carefully scrutinized. On the other hand, it often happens that some extremely simple abstract reasonings lead to very general and useful theorems. A number of such theorems are collected in this chapter.

In the first section, we set up the general framework which will underlie our future work. Next we state, prove, and discuss the small gain theorem in its general and in its incremental form. In Section 4, we prove another boundedness result, which has an interesting converse. In the next section, we prove a very general existence and uniqueness result with which we can prove that most of the feedback systems that we shall encounter are determinate in the sense that to a specific input they have a *unique* response. Section 6 is devoted to the loop transformation theorem, which can be thought of as a "stability equivalence" result. The chapter ends by the general definition of $\mathscr{L}$ stability and a general feedback property.

1 Setting of the problem

A large number of feedback systems can be put in the form shown in Fig. III.1. The symbols u_1, u_2, denote the *inputs*, y_1, y_2 the *outputs*, and e_1, e_2 the *errors*. The u_i's, y_i's, and e_i's ($i = 1, 2$) are functions of time; usually they

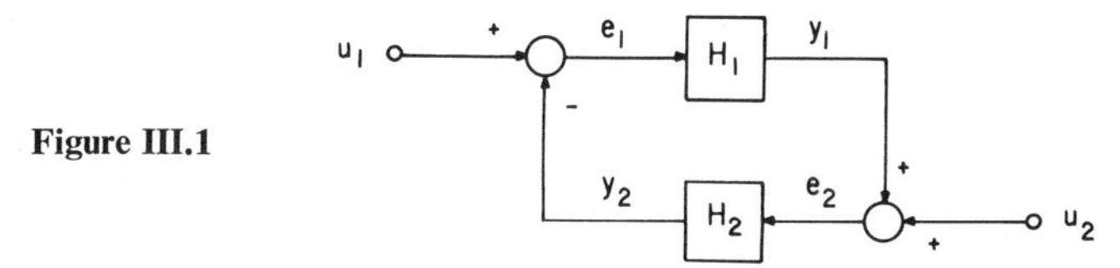

Figure III.1

are defined for $t \geq 0$ or for $t \in \mathbb{Z}_+$; usually they take values in $\mathbb{R}$, $\mathbb{R}^n$ (sometimes, $\mathbb{C}^n$), or in a normed space or a Hilbert space. The general problem under investigation is: Given some assumptions on H_1, H_2, show that if u_1, u_2 belong to some class, then e_1, e_2 and y_1, y_2 also belong to the same class. The equations of the feedback system are

$$u_1 = e_1 + H_2 e_2 \quad (1)$$
$$u_2 = e_2 - H_1 e_1 \quad (2)$$

H_1 (H_2) is an operator which acts on its input e_1 (e_2, resp.) to produce the output y_1 (y_2, resp.). Equations (1) and (2) have an obvious control interpretation shown in Fig. III.1. It is worthwhile to point out that they have also an n-port interpretation (Fig. III.2 shows the case of two-ports). Let the u_i take values in $\mathbb{R}^2$ with components $(u_i)_1$, $(u_i)_2$. The operator H_1 is an "impedance" type operator; it operates on currents and gives out voltages.

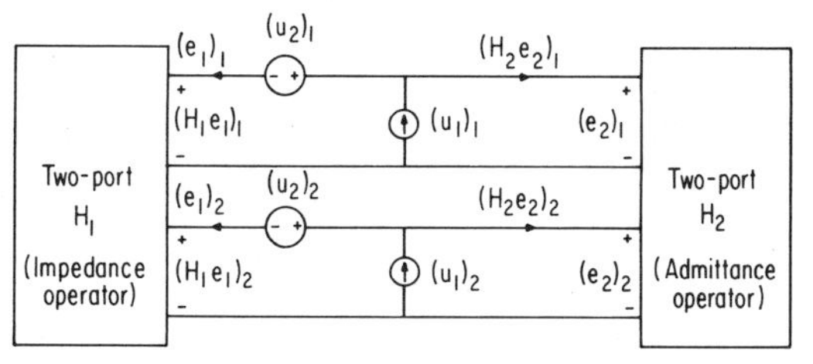

Figure III.2

The operator H_2 is an "admittance"-type operator; it operates on voltages and gives out currents. Equation (1) expresses the Kirchhoff current law, and Eq. (2) expresses the Kirchhoff voltage law.

General framework

Since we wish to cover continuous-time and discrete-time systems and also systems in which the u_i's, e_i's, and y_i's are either real valued or take values in $\mathbb{R}^n$ or even in normed spaces (for distributed systems), we set up the following general framework.

Let

$\mathscr{T}$: subset of $\mathbb{R}_+$ (typically, $\mathscr{T} = \mathbb{R}_+$ or $\mathbb{Z}_+$)
$\mathscr{V}$: normed space with norm $\|\cdot\|$ (typically, $\mathscr{V} = \mathbb{R}, \mathbb{R}^n, \mathbb{C}, \mathbb{C}^n$)
$\mathscr{F}$: $\{f: \mathscr{T} \to \mathscr{V}\}$ = set of all functions mapping $\mathscr{T}$ into $\mathscr{V}$

The function space $\mathscr{F}$ is a natural linear space over $\mathbb{C}$ (or $\mathbb{R}$) under pointwise addition and scalar multiplication, which are defined as follows:

$$(f+g)(t) = f(t) + g(t), \qquad \forall f, g \in \mathscr{F}; \quad \forall t \in \mathscr{T}$$
$$(\alpha f)(t) = \alpha f(t), \qquad \forall f \in \mathscr{F}; \quad \forall t \in \mathscr{T}; \quad \forall \alpha \in \mathbb{C} \text{ (or } \mathbb{R})$$

For each $T \in \mathscr{T}$, let P_T be the *linear* map of $\mathscr{F}$ into $\mathscr{F}$ such that with $f_T \triangleq P_T f$ we have

4
$$f_T(t) = \begin{cases} f(t), & t \leq T \quad (t, T \in \mathscr{T}) \\ \theta_{\mathscr{V}}, & t > T \end{cases}$$

where $\theta_{\mathscr{V}}$ is the zero vector in $\mathscr{V}$. The linearity of P_T is obvious from its definition. P_T is a projection on $\mathscr{F}$ since $P_T^2 = P_T$. We say that f_T is obtained by **truncating** f at T.

5 Introduce a norm $\|\cdot\|$ on $\mathscr{F}$; this defines a **normed linear subspace** $\mathscr{L}$ of the linear space $\mathscr{F}$:

$$\mathscr{L} \triangleq \{f: \mathscr{T} \to \mathscr{V} \,|\, \|f\| < \infty\}$$

(Typically, $\|f\| = \int_0^\infty \|f(t)\|\, dt$ or $\|f\| = \sum |\, \|f(k)\|$.) Associated with the normed space $\mathscr{L}$ is the **extended space** $\mathscr{L}_e$ defined by

6
$$\mathscr{L}_e \triangleq \{f: \mathscr{T} \to \mathscr{V} \,|\, \forall T \in \mathscr{T}, \|f_T\| < \infty\}$$

We shall impose *throughout* the following requirements on the norm $\|\cdot\|$ that is used to define $\mathscr{L}$ and $\mathscr{L}_e$ [see (5) and (6) above]:

7 (i) $\forall f \in \mathscr{L}_e$, the map $T \mapsto \|f_T\|$ is monotonically increasing;
8 (ii) $\forall f \in \mathscr{L}$,

$$\|f_T\| \to \|f\|, \qquad \text{as} \quad T \to \infty$$

The following notation will turn out to be useful:

$$P_T \mathscr{L}_e = \{f \in \mathscr{L}_e | f = f_T\}$$

With these two assumptions, we may reinterpret Definitions (5) and (6) of $\mathscr{L}$ and $\mathscr{L}_e$ as follows: f belongs to $\mathscr{L}$ iff the real-valued function $T \mapsto \|f_T\|$ is bounded on $\mathscr{T}$, and $f \in \mathscr{L}_e$ iff $T \mapsto \|f_T\|$ maps $\mathscr{T}$ into $\mathbb{R}$ (i.e., there are no growth constraints!). If $\mathscr{V}$ is either $\mathbb{R}$ or $\mathbb{R}^n$, and if $\|\cdot\|$ is an L^p norm, we denote $\mathscr{L}$ by L^p or $L_n^{\,p}$; similarly, $\mathscr{L}_e$ is denoted by $L_e^{\,p}$ or L_{ne}^p. For the discrete case, we write l^p, $l_n^{\,p}$, $l_e^{\,p}$, and l_{ne}^p.

Exercise 1 (a) Take $\mathscr{L}$ to be L^∞. Let f: $t \mapsto \exp(t^2)$. Does $f \in L^\infty$? Does $f \in L_e^{\,\infty}$?

(b) Give examples of sequences in $l_e^{\,1}$ but not in l^1, in $l_e^{\,\infty}$ but not in l^∞.

Exercise 2 Consider the restriction of P_T to $\mathscr{L}$ and call it still P_T. Show that in terms of induced norms, $\|P_T\| \leq 1$. Thus, P_T is a *continuous linear operator* on $\mathscr{L}$, and its operator norm is at most 1.

Most models used in system theory are nonanticipative; so we define nonanticipative maps.

Let H: $\mathscr{L}_e \to \mathscr{L}_e$; H is said to be **causal** (*nonanticipative*) iff

$$P_T H P_T = P_T H, \qquad \forall T \in \mathscr{T} \tag{9}$$

Exercise 3 Let H_1, H_2: $\mathscr{L}_e \to \mathscr{L}_e$ and be nonanticipative. Show that $H_1 H_2$ is also nonanticipative. (*Hint*: Use the fact that the composition of two functions is associative.)

Exercise 4 Let $h \in L^1(\mathbb{R})$ and $u \in L^2(\mathbb{R})$. Show that the map H: $L^2(\mathbb{R}) \to L^2(\mathbb{R})$ defined by

$$H: u \mapsto Hu = h * u$$

i.e.,

$$(Hu)(t) = \int_{-\infty}^{\infty} h(t-\tau)u(\tau)\, d\tau, \qquad t \in \mathbb{R}$$

is nonanticipative if and only if $h(t) = 0$, almost everywhere on $(-\infty, 0)$.

Exercise 5 Assumption (7) on the norms $\|\cdot\|$ in $\mathscr{F}$ is not necessarily fulfilled by any norm. Construct an example. [*Hint*: Consider the space of measures μ on $\mathbb{R}_+$; define the norm as in Appendix (C.3.3); show that for some μ, $\|\mu_T\| > \|\mu\|$.]

Exercise 6 Within the general framework above, assumption (7) need not always hold. Let $\mathscr{L}$ be the class of functions having well-defined Fourier transforms [by Appendix B, $\mathscr{L} \supset L^1$, $\mathscr{L} \supset L^2$, $\mathscr{L} \ni \delta(t)$, ...]. Let $f \in \mathscr{L}_e$ and let $f_T = P_T f \in \mathscr{L}$; define the norm of f_T by

$$\|f_T\| \triangleq \sup_{\omega \in \mathbb{R}} |\hat{f}_T(j\omega)|, \qquad \forall f \in \mathscr{L}, \quad \forall T \in \mathbb{R}$$

where $\hat{f}_T$ is the Fourier transform of f_T.

(a) Show that for $f \in L^2(\mathbb{R})$, the relation above defines a norm.

(b) Let $f(t) = e^t 1(-t) - 0.2\delta(t - 10^{-3})$, where $1(t)$ denotes the unit step. Show that $\|P_0 f\| = \|f_0\| > \|f\|$.

Exercise 7 Some interconnections of nonanticipative subsystems are not nonanticipative. Give an example. [*Hint*: Consider a discrete system with unity feedback; $u_1, e_1, y_1 \colon \mathbb{Z}_+ \to \mathbb{R}$, $u_2 \equiv 0$, H_2 = identity map, $(H_1 e_1)(n) = -e_1(n) + e_1(n-1)$, for all $n \in \mathbb{Z}_+$.] Discuss what happens if H_1 is perturbed a little so that $(\tilde{H}_1 e_1)(n) = -(1+\varepsilon)e_1(n) + e_1(n-1)$, with $\varepsilon \ll 1$.

Exercise 8 Let $H_1, H_2 : \mathscr{L}_e \to \mathscr{L}_e$. If H_1 is a *linear* map and if $(I + H_1 H_2)^{-1}$ and $(I + H_2 H_1)^{-1}$ are well-defined maps from $\mathscr{L}_e$ into $\mathscr{L}_e$, show that

$$H_1(I + H_2 H_1)^{-1} = (I + H_1 H_2)^{-1} H_1$$

Give a system theoretic interpretation in terms of block diagrams. Give an example to show that this relation is false if H_1 is not a linear map.

Exercise 9 In the general framework above, suppose that u_2 is identically zero. Suppose that $(I + H_2 H_1)^{-1}$ is a well-defined map from $\mathscr{L}_e$ into $\mathscr{L}_e$, then show that, for the feedback system shown in Fig. III.1 and described by (1) and (2), we have

$$y_1 = H_1(I + H_2 H_1)^{-1} u_1, \qquad \forall u_1 \in \mathscr{L}_e$$

Exercise 10 Consider an alternate definition of nonanticipative map. Again let $H \colon \mathscr{L}_e \to \mathscr{L}_e$; then H is said to be nonanticipative iff $\forall T \in \mathscr{T}$ and $\forall x, y \in \mathscr{L}_e$.

$$P_T x = P_T y \Rightarrow P_T H x = P_T H y \tag{10}$$

Show that definitions (9) and (10) are equivalent.

2 Small gain theorem

The small gain theorem is a very general theorem, which gives sufficient conditions under which a "bounded input" produces a "bounded output." Its formulation is chosen so that the question of boundedness is completely disconnected from the questions of existence, uniqueness, etc.

1 **Theorem** Consider the system shown in Fig. III.1. Let $H_1, H_2 : \mathscr{L}_e \to \mathscr{L}_e$. Let $e_1, e_2 \in \mathscr{L}_e$ and *define* u_1 and u_2 by

2 $$u_1 = e_1 + H_2 e_2$$

3 $$u_2 = e_2 - H_1 e_1$$

Suppose that there are *constants* $\beta_1, \beta_2, \gamma_1 \geq 0, \gamma_2 \geq 0$ s.t.

4, 5 $$\left.\begin{aligned} \|(H_1 e_1)_T\| &\leq \gamma_1 \|e_{1T}\| + \beta_1 \\ \|(H_2 e_2)_T\| &\leq \gamma_2 \|e_{2T}\| + \beta_2 \end{aligned}\right\}, \qquad \forall T \in \mathscr{T}$$

U.t.c., if $\gamma_1 \gamma_2 < 1$, then

6, 7 (i) $$\left.\begin{aligned} \|e_{1T}\| &\leq (1 - \gamma_1\gamma_2)^{-1}(\|u_{1T}\| + \gamma_2 \|u_{2T}\| + \beta_2 + \gamma_2 \beta_1) \\ \|e_{2T}\| &\leq (1 - \gamma_1\gamma_2)^{-1}(\|u_{2T}\| + \gamma_1 \|u_{1T}\| + \beta_1 + \gamma_1 \beta_2) \end{aligned}\right\}, \qquad \forall T \in \mathscr{T}$$

(ii) if, in addition

$$\|u_1\|, \|u_2\| < \infty$$

then e_1, e_2, y_1, y_2 have *finite* norms, and the norms of the errors, namely, $\|e_1\|$ and $\|e_2\|$, are bounded by the right-hand sides of (6) and (7), provided all subscripts T are dropped.

8 Given an operator $H_1 : \mathscr{L}_e \to \mathscr{L}_e$, suppose that there are real numbers $\bar{\beta}_1$ and $\bar{\gamma}_1$ such that

8a $$\|(H_1 x)_T\| \leq \bar{\gamma}_1 \|x_T\| + \bar{\beta}_1, \qquad \forall x \in \mathscr{L}_e, \quad \forall T \in \mathscr{T}$$

Clearly $\bar{\gamma}_1$ is not uniquely defined by the above inequality. Intuitively, it is clear that we are interested in the smallest $\bar{\gamma}_1$ that "works." More precisely, we call **gain of** H_1 the number $\gamma(H_1)$ defined by

8b $$\gamma(H_1) = \inf \{\bar{\gamma}_1 \in \mathbb{R}_+ \mid \exists \bar{\beta}_1 \text{ s.t. inequality (8a) holds}\}$$

This infimum will often be denoted by $\gamma(H_1)$ or γ_1. With this terminology, Theorem (1) can be interpreted to state that if $\gamma(H_1)$, the gain of H_1, and $\gamma(H_2)$, the gain of H_2, have a product smaller than 1, then, provided a solution exists, any bounded input pair (u_1, u_2) produces a bounded output pair, and the map $(u_1, u_2) \to (y_1, y_2)$ has also finite gain.

Exercise Show that if H_1 is causal, then condition (8a) can be replaced by

8c $$\|H_1 x\| \leq \bar{\gamma}_1 \|x\| + \bar{\beta}_1, \qquad \forall x \in \mathscr{L} \quad (\text{not } \mathscr{L}_e!)$$

Note that, in (8c), since x ranges only on $\mathscr{L}$, T drops out from the picture.

9 **Comments** (a) *Generality* Theorem (1) applies to continuous-time or discrete-time systems. The system may be single-input–single-output (i.e.,

$\mathscr{V} = \mathbb{R}$) or multiple-input multiple-output (i.e., $\mathscr{V} = \mathbb{R}^n$) or any *normed* space (distributed systems).

(b) *Statement* The theorem assumes the bare minimum; it assumes $e_1, e_2 \in \mathscr{L}_e$ and defines u_1 and u_2 accordingly. In practice, u_1, u_2 are given and e_1, e_2 are calculated. Thus, the formulation above avoids the question of existence of solutions of (2) and (3). In practice, the constants β_i and γ_i are obtained by bounding

$$\|(H_i e_i)_T\|$$

by $\gamma_i\|e_{iT}\| + \beta_i$ for *all* $e_i \in \mathscr{L}_e$, *all* $T \in \mathscr{T}$. For this purpose, inequality (II.8.29) and the Bellman-Gronwall lemma Appendix (E.1) are very useful.

(c) The form of the assumptions are improved versions of results of Sandberg [San. 6, 7, 8, 9, 10, 11], Zames [Zam. 3], Lee-Desoer [Lee. 1]. The usual formulation sets $\bar{\beta}_1 = 0$ and therefore does not apply to the memoryless nonlinearity $\phi\colon \mathbb{R} \to \mathbb{R}$, where

$$\phi(e_1) = e_1 + [|e_1|^{1/2}/(1 + |e_1|^{1/2})]$$

Nor does it apply to some cases of relays with hysteresis, and to saturating nonlinearities, whereas the present one does.

(d) The results extend to the case where H_1 and H_2 are *relations* (i.e., "multivalued functions"). In that case, (4) and (5) must hold for all the "images" $H_i e_i$ of each $e_i \in \mathscr{L}_e$ ($i = 1, 2$). This fact is very useful in the case of feedback systems with hysteresis.

(e) Theorems (II.6.3), (II.6.8), and Exercise 1 of Section II.6 give very useful evaluations of gains for convolution maps.

Exercise 1 With Theorem (1) in mind, construct an example (say, of the type studied in Chapter I) for which existence and/or uniqueness and/or continuous dependence fails even though the product of the *gains* $\gamma(H_1)\gamma(H_2) < 1$.

Proof of Theorem (1) From (2), we see that $\forall T \in \mathscr{T}$,

$$e_{1T} = u_{1T} - (H_2 e_2)_T \tag{10}$$

Since all vectors $\in \mathscr{L}_e$,

$$\|e_{1T}\| \leq \|u_{1T}\| + \|(H_2 e_2)_T\| \leq \|u_{1T}\| + \gamma_2\|e_{2T}\| + \beta_2, \qquad \forall T \in \mathscr{T} \tag{11}$$

We have a similar calculation from (3)

$$\|e_{2T}\| \leq \|u_{2T}\| + \gamma_1\|e_{1T}\| + \beta_1, \qquad \forall T \in \mathscr{T} \tag{12}$$

Hence, using the fact that $\gamma_2 \geq 0$,

$$\|e_{1T}\| \leq \gamma_1\gamma_2\|e_{1T}\| + (\|u_{1T}\| + \gamma_2\|u_{2T}\| + \beta_2 + \gamma_2\beta_1) \tag{13}$$

Since $\gamma_1\gamma_2 < 1$,

14 $$\|e_{1T}\| \le (\|u_{1T}\| + \gamma_2\|u_{2T}\| + \beta_2 + \gamma_2\beta_1)(1 - \gamma_1\gamma_2)^{-1}$$

The remainder follows immediately. ∎

Exercise 2 Consider a feedback system where $u_1, e_1, y_1, e_2, y_2 : \mathbb{R}_+ \to \mathbb{R}$; H_1 and H_2 map $L^\infty(\mathbb{R}_+)$ into itself; the input u_2 is identically zero. More precisely, $H_1 e_1 = g * e_1$, where g is a given function in $L^1(\mathbb{R}_+)$; $(H_2 e_2)(t) = \phi[e_2(t), t]$, where ϕ: $\mathbb{R} \times \mathbb{R}_+ \to \mathbb{R}$ is continuous and belongs to the sector $[0, k)$. Assume that for all $u_1 \in L^\infty(\mathbb{R}_+)$, there is a unique solution $e_1, y_1 \in L^\infty(\mathbb{R}_+)$. Obtain conditions on the constant k and the function $g(\cdot)$ such that $u_1 \in L^\infty(\mathbb{R}_+)$ implies $y_1 \in L^\infty(\mathbb{R}_+)$. Under the conditions found, exhibit a number m such that

$$\|y_1\|_\infty \le m\,\|u_1\|_\infty, \qquad \forall u_1 \in L^\infty(\mathbb{R}_+)$$

Exercise 3 Repeat Exercise 2 for discrete systems, i.e., $u_1, e_1, y_1 : \mathbb{Z}_+ \to \mathbb{R}$; H_1 and H_2 map l^∞ into itself;...

Exercise 4 Consider a feedback system where $u_2 \equiv \theta$ and $H_2 = I$, the identity; thus $(I + H_1)e_1 = u_1$. Suppose that H_1: $\mathscr{L} \to \mathscr{L}$ and that $(I + H_1)^{-1}$: $\mathscr{L} \to \mathscr{L}$. Show that under these conditions, $\gamma[(I + H_1)^{-1}] < \infty$ if and only if $\exists$ constants ε, and β_1' with $\varepsilon > 0$ such that

$$\|(\mathrm{I} + H_1)e\| \ge \varepsilon\,\|e\| + \beta_1', \qquad \forall e \in \mathscr{L}$$

If $u_2 \equiv 0$, there is no longer need to separate the gain of H_1 and the gain of H_2; one can consider the "loop gain" $H_2 H_1$. The following corollary illustrates the idea.

15 **Corollary** Consider the system shown in Fig. III.1, where $u_2 \equiv 0$. Let $H_1, H_2 : \mathscr{L}_e \to \mathscr{L}_e$. Let $e_1 \in \mathscr{L}_e$ and define u_1 by

16 $$u_1 = e_1 + H_2 e_2$$

17 $$e_2 = H_1 e_1$$

Suppose that there are constants γ_{21}, γ_1, β_{21}, and β_1, with $\gamma_{21} \ge 0$, $\gamma_1 \ge 0$, s.t.

$$\left.\begin{aligned} \|(H_2 H_1 e_1)_T\| &\le \gamma_{21}\|e_{1T}\| + \beta_{21} \\ \|(H_1 e_1)_T\| &\le \gamma_1\|e_{1T}\| + \beta_1 \end{aligned}\right\}, \qquad \forall T \in \mathscr{T}$$

U.t.c., if $\gamma_{21} < 1$, then

$$\|e_{1T}\| \le [1/(1 - \gamma_{21})](\|u_{1T}\| + \beta_{21})$$

$$\|y_{1T}\| \le [\gamma_1/(1 - \gamma_{21})](\|u_{1T}\| + \beta_{21}) + \beta_1$$

Note that Comments (9) above apply also to the corollary. What the corollary shows is that once the "loop gain" is smaller than 1, the closed-loop system has finite gain. Compare the corollary with Theorem (I.2.7).

Proof Exercise for the reader. ∎

3 Small gain theorem: incremental form

We now consider a theorem that guarantees existence, uniqueness, boundedness, and continuity.

1 **Theorem** Consider the feedback system shown in Fig. III.1 and described by Eqs. (1.1) and (1.2). Assume that for each T, $P_T \mathscr{L}_e$ is a *complete* normed linear space (i.e., a Banach space). Let $H_1, H_2 : \mathscr{L}_e \to \mathscr{L}_e$. Suppose there are constants $\tilde{\gamma}_1$ and $\tilde{\gamma}_2$ such that $\forall T \in \mathscr{T}$ and $\forall \xi, \xi' \in \mathscr{L}_e$

$$\|(H_1 \xi)_T - (H_1 \xi')_T\| \leq \tilde{\gamma}_1 \|\xi_T - \xi_T'\| \tag{2}$$

$$\|(H_2 \xi)_T - (H_2 \xi')_T\| \leq \tilde{\gamma}_2 \|\xi_T - \xi_T'\| \tag{3}$$

U.t.c., if $\tilde{\gamma}_1 \tilde{\gamma}_2 < 1$, then

(i) $\forall u_1, u_2 \in \mathscr{L}_e$ $\exists$ a *unique* solution $e_1, e_2, y_1, y_2 \in \mathscr{L}_e$, which can be obtained by iteration;

(ii) the map $(u_1, u_2) \mapsto (e_1, e_2)$ is uniformly continuous on $P_T \mathscr{L}_e \times P_T \mathscr{L}_e$ and on $\mathscr{L} \times \mathscr{L}$;

(iii) If, in addition, the solution corresponding to $u_1 = u_2 = \theta$ is in $\mathscr{L}$, then $u_1, u_2 \in \mathscr{L} \Rightarrow e_1, e_2 \in \mathscr{L}$.

4 **Comments** (a) If H_1 is linear, assumption (2) is very closely related to assumption (2.4). More precisely, if H_1 is a *linear* map and if for some γ_1

$$\|(H_1 \xi)_T\| \leq \gamma_1 \|\xi_T\|, \qquad \forall \xi \in \mathscr{L}_e, \quad \forall T \in \mathscr{T}$$

then

$$\|(H_1(\xi - \xi')]_T\| \leq \gamma_1 \|\xi_T - \xi_T'\|, \qquad \forall \xi, \xi' \in \mathscr{L}_e, \quad \forall T \in \mathscr{T}$$

(b) The incremental small gain theorem answers all four questions: existence, uniqueness, boundedness, and continuous dependence.

(c) It is a simple exercise to prove that (2) and (3) imply that H_1 and H_2 are nonanticipative.

5 Given a nonanticipative operator $H_1 : \mathscr{L}_e \to \mathscr{L}_e$ which satisfies (2), the infinium of all real numbers $\tilde{\gamma}_1$ which satisfy (2) is called the **incremental gain of** H_1. It is often denoted by $\tilde{\gamma}(H_1)$, or for simplicity, $\tilde{\gamma}_1$.

Proof (i) From the feedback Equations (1.1) and (1.2), we obtain

$$e_2 = u_2 + H_1(u_1 - H_2 e_2)$$

and by truncation

$$e_{2T} = u_{2T} + [H_1(u_1 - H_2 e_2)]_T, \qquad \forall T \in \mathscr{T}$$

Using nonanticipativeness of H_1 and H_2,

$$e_{2T} = u_{2T} + \{H_1[u_{1T} - (H_2 e_{2T})_T]\}_T$$

This equation is of the form $e_{2T} = f(e_{2T})$. We claim that f is a contraction on $P_T \mathscr{L}_e$; indeed, $\forall T \in \mathscr{T}$ and $\forall e_{2T}, e'_{2T} \in P_T \mathscr{L}_e$,

$$\begin{aligned}\|\{H_1[u_{1T} - (H_2 e_{2T})_T]\}_T - \{H_1[u_{1T} - (H_2 e'_{2T})]\}_T\| &\leq \tilde{\gamma}_1 \|(H_2 e_{2T})_T - (H_2 e'_{2T})\| \\ &\leq \tilde{\gamma}_1 \tilde{\gamma}_2 \|e_{2T} - e'_{2T}\|\end{aligned}$$

where we used successively assumptions (2) and (3). By assumption $\tilde{\gamma}_1\tilde{\gamma}_2 < 1$, consequently f is a contraction. Therefore, $\forall T \in \mathscr{T}$, $\forall u_1, u_2 \in \mathscr{L}_e$, the resulting e_{2T} is uniquely defined element of $P_T \mathscr{L}_e$. The same holds for e_{1T} since by (1.1) and nonanticipativeness of H_2, we have

$$e_{1T} = u_{1T} - (H_2 e_{2T})_T$$

(ii) For any $T \in \mathscr{T}$, for any (u_1, u_2), $(u_1', u_2') \in \mathscr{L}_e \times \mathscr{L}_e$, there is a unique solution (e_1, e_2), $(e_1', e_2') \in \mathscr{L}_e \times \mathscr{L}_e$. Also

$$e_{1T} = u_{1T} - (H_2 e_{2T})_T, \qquad e'_{1T} = u'_{1T} - (H_2 e'_{2T})_T$$

Subtracting, taking norms, and using the triangle inequality, we obtain

$$\|e_{1T} - e'_{1T}\| \leq \|u_{1T} - u'_{1T}\| + \tilde{\gamma}_2 \|e_{2T} - e'_{2T}\|$$

Similarly,

$$\|e_{2T} - e'_{2T}\| \leq \|u_{2T} - u'_{2T}\| + \tilde{\gamma}_1 \|e_{1T} - e'_{1T}\|$$

$$\|e_{1T} - e'_{1T}\| \leq (\|u_{1T} - u'_{1T}\| + \tilde{\gamma}_2 \|u_{2T} - u'_{2T}\|)(1 - \tilde{\gamma}_1\tilde{\gamma}_2)^{-1}, \qquad \forall T \in \mathscr{T} \tag{6}$$

Hence (ii) follows.

(iii) follows from (6) and the corresponding inequality for e_2 when $u_1' = u_2' = \theta$ is inserted. ∎

Exercise 1 Formulate and prove a corollary to Theorem (1) which is the analogue of Corollary (2.15) to Theorem (2.1).

Exercise 2 Consider a system that satisfies all the conditions of Theorem (1). Suppose that $u_1, \tilde{u}_1, u_2, \tilde{u}_2, \in \mathscr{L}_e$ but that $u_1 - \tilde{u}_1$ and $u_2 - \tilde{u}_2 \in \mathscr{L}$. Show that $e_1 - e_2 \in \mathscr{L}$ and

$$\|e_1 - \tilde{e}_1\| \leq (\|u_1 - \tilde{u}_1\| + \tilde{\gamma}_2 \|u_2 - \tilde{u}_2\|)(1 - \tilde{\gamma}_1\tilde{\gamma}_2)^{-1}.$$

4 A boundedness result

We may think of the small gain theorem and its incremental form as two extreme forms of boundedness results. The former assumes the least—the finiteness of the gains [see (2.4) and (2.5)]; the latter assumes the most—finite incremental gains for H_1 and H_2 [see (3.2) and (3.3)]. We now state and prove a theorem that uses somewhat intermediate assumptions. It emphasizes assumptions on the composite function $H_2 H_1$, which, in a very rough way, can be thought of as the loop gain.

1 **Theorem** Consider the system shown in Fig. III.1 and described by (1.1) and (1.2). Assume that H_1 and H_2 are nonanticipative, that the gain $\gamma(H_1) < \infty$ and the incremental gain $\tilde{\gamma}(H_2) < \infty$. U.t.c.

(a) if $\exists\ \varepsilon > 0$ s.t.†

$$\|(I + H_2 H_1)e\|_T \geq \varepsilon \|e\|_T, \qquad \forall e \in \mathscr{L}_e, \quad \forall T \in \mathscr{T} \tag{2}$$

then $(u_1, u_2) \in \mathscr{L} \times \mathscr{L}$ implies that any solution (e_1, e_2) that is in $\mathscr{L}_e \times \mathscr{L}_e$ is also in $\mathscr{L} \times \mathscr{L}$ and for some $k < \infty$

$$\|e_i\| \leq k[\|u_1\| + \|u_2\|], \qquad i = 1, 2, \quad \forall u_1, u_2 \in \mathscr{L} \tag{3}$$

(b) If the relation between (u_1, u_2) and (e_1, e_2) is a nonanticipative map from $\mathscr{L} \times \mathscr{L}$ into $\mathscr{L} \times \mathscr{L}$ which has finite gain, then (3) implies (2).

Proof (a) Consider fixed $u_1, u_2 \in \mathscr{L}$ and a corresponding solution (e_1, e_2) of Eqs. (1.1) and (1.2) with $e_1, e_2 \in \mathscr{L}_e$. Then

$$e_1 + H_2 H_1 e_1 = u_1 - [H_2(H_1 e_1 + u_2) - H_2 H_1 e_1]$$

Upon truncation, since P_T is linear

$$P_T(I + H_2 H_1)e_1 = P_T u_1 - P_T[H_2(H_1 e_1 + u_2) - H_2 H_1 e_1]$$

Using the fact that the incremental gain $\tilde{\gamma}(H_2) < \infty$,

$$\|(I + H_2 H_1)e_1\|_T \leq \|u_1\|_T + \tilde{\gamma}(H_2)\|u_2\|_T$$

Now using the assumption (2) and letting $T \to \infty$ in the right-hand side, we obtain with the help of (1.8)

$$\varepsilon \|e_1\|_T \leq \|u_1\| + \tilde{\gamma}(H_2)\|u_2\|$$

Thus,

$$\|e_1\| \leq \varepsilon^{-1}\|u_1\| + \varepsilon^{-1}\tilde{\gamma}(H_2)\|u_2\| \tag{5}$$

† To lighten the notation, we write $\|u_2\|_T$ instead of $\|u_{2T}\|$.

i.e., $e_1 \in \mathscr{L}$. Now from $e_2 = u_2 + H_1 e_1$, we obtain

6 $$\|e_2\| \leq \|u_2\| + \gamma(H_1)[\varepsilon^{-1}\|u_1\| + \varepsilon^{-1}\tilde{\gamma}(H_2)\|u_2\|]$$

Therefore, (3) is established, and k may be taken to be

$$\max[\varepsilon^{-1}, \tilde{\gamma}(H_2)\varepsilon^{-1}, \gamma(H_1)\varepsilon^{-1}, 1 + \gamma(H_1)\tilde{\gamma}(H_2)\varepsilon^{-1}]$$

(b) Let $u_2 \equiv 0$; then to $u_1 \in \mathscr{L}$, there is a unique $e_1 \in \mathscr{L}$ such that

$$(I + H_2 H_1)e_1 = u_1$$

From (3) it follows that $\gamma[(I + H_2 H_1)^{-1}] < \infty$; therefore, $\forall T \in \mathscr{T}$

$$\begin{aligned}\|P_T e_1\| &= \|P_T(I + H_2 H_1)^{-1}(I + H_2 H_1)e_1\| \\ &\leq \gamma[(I + H_2 H_1)^{-1}] \ \|P_T(I + H_2 H_1)e_1\|\end{aligned}$$

from which (2) follows. ∎

Exercise 1 Consider the following special case to show that condition (2) is closely related to the Nyquist criterion. Let u_1, e_1, y_1 map $\mathbb{R}_+ \to \mathbb{R}$; let $u_2 \equiv 0$ and H_2 be the identity map. Let $H_1 e_1 = g * e_1$, where $g \in L^1(\mathbb{R}_+)$ and its Laplace transform $\hat{g}(s)$ is a rational function which is analytic in $\operatorname{Re} s \geq 0$ and which tends to zero as $|s| \to \infty$. Show that if the Nyquist diagram of $\hat{g}$ [i.e., the map $\omega \mapsto \hat{g}(j\omega)$, $\omega \in \mathbb{R}$] encircles one or more times the critical point $(-1, 0)$, then (2) does not hold. [*Hint*: Use a state representation for H_1; choose appropriate initial conditions and an appropriate exponential form for $e_1(\cdot)$.]

5 An existence and uniqueness theorem

In this section, we restrict ourselves to $\mathscr{T} = \mathbb{R}_+$. Indeed, for the discrete-time case, the problem of existence and uniqueness is completely different. Instead of solving for a function from $\mathbb{R}_+$ to $\mathscr{V}$, we have to solve, at each sampling time, for one point in $\mathscr{V}$. An example of result required for the discrete-time case, where

$$x(n) = f[x(n)] + u(n)$$

$x(n), u(n) \in \mathbb{R}^n$, $f\colon \mathbb{R}^n \to \mathbb{R}^n$, is given by Theorem (II.8.33).

We wish to show that the existence and uniqueness of the solution (e_1, e_2) of Eqs. (1.1) and (1.2) in the space $\mathscr{L}_e \times \mathscr{L}_e$ can be guaranteed on the basis of some quite reasonable assumptions, which are usually far less restrictive than those required for guaranteeing finite gain.

To simplify the notation, it is convenient to think of the pairs (u_1, u_2) and (e_1, e_2) as single elements of $\mathscr{L}_e \times \mathscr{L}_e$, denoted, respectively, by u and e. Similarly, instead of the maps H_1 and H_2, let us think in terms of the map

$$H: \mathscr{L}_e \times \mathscr{L}_e \to \mathscr{L}_e \times \mathscr{L}_e$$

defined by

$$H: (e_1, e_2) \mapsto (H_2 e_2, -H_1 e_1)$$

Then Eqs. (1.1) and (1.2) become

1 $$u = e + He$$

Furthermore, no confusion will arise if we abbreviate $\mathscr{L}_e \times \mathscr{L}_e$ by $\mathscr{L}_e^2$.

The following theorem will require a Lipschitz-type condition on H and will guarantee that for any $u \in \mathscr{L}_e^2$, there is one and only one solution $e \in \mathscr{L}_e^2$ of (1).

2 **Theorem** Let H: $\mathscr{L}_e^2 \to \mathscr{L}_e^2$ and be *nonanticipative*. Let $\mathscr{T} = \mathbb{R}_+$. Let P_t be the projection defined on $\mathscr{L}_e^2$ as in (1.4). Define a new projection by

3 $$\tilde{P}_{t,\Delta} = P_{t+\Delta} - P_t, \qquad t, \Delta, t + \Delta \in \mathbb{R}_+$$

U.t.c., if for all compact intervals $I \subset \mathbb{R}_+$, there are numbers $\tilde{\gamma}(I) < 1$ and $\Delta(I) > 0$ such that $\forall t \in I$ and $\forall e, e' \in \mathscr{L}_e^2$ subject to $P_t e = P_t e'$,

$$\|\tilde{P}_{t,\Delta}(He - He')\| \le \gamma \|\tilde{P}_{t,\Delta}(e - e')\|$$

(where for simplicity we have suppressed the dependence of Δ and γ on I) and if $\forall t$ and Δ, $\tilde{P}_{t,\Delta}\, \mathscr{L}_e^2$ is complete, then for any $u \in \mathscr{L}_e^2$, the equation $u = e + He$ has one and only one solution.

Proof Suppose we have computed a solution up to some $t \ge 0$, let us show that the solution *can* be extended *uniquely* on all $\mathbb{R}_+$. Let I be a compact interval including t and such that $I \cap (t, \infty)$ is nonempty. Now for the Δ and γ corresponding to the chosen I, let

5 $$\tilde{e}_\Delta \triangleq \tilde{P}_{t,\Delta} e = P_{t+\Delta} e - P_t e$$

and $\tilde{u}_\Delta$ be similarly defined. Now apply $\tilde{P}_{t,\Delta}$ to $u = e + He$,

6 $$\tilde{e}_\Delta = \tilde{u}_\Delta - \tilde{P}_{t,\Delta} H(P_t e + \tilde{e}_\Delta)$$

where we used the nonanticipativeness of H. Equation (6) is of the form $\tilde{e}_\Delta = f(\tilde{e}_\Delta)$, since $\tilde{u}_\Delta$ is given and $P_t e$ is known. Thus, f: $\tilde{P}_{t,\Delta}\, \mathscr{L}_e^2 \to \tilde{P}_{t,\Delta}\, \mathscr{L}_e^2$. We claim that f is a contraction on $\tilde{P}_{t,\Delta} \mathscr{L}_e^2$. Indeed, for all $\tilde{e}_\Delta, \tilde{e}_\Delta' \in \tilde{P}_{t,\Delta} \mathscr{L}_e^2$,

7 $$\begin{aligned} \|f(\tilde{e}_\Delta) - f(\tilde{e}_\Delta')\| &= \|\tilde{P}_{t,\Delta}[H(P_t e + \tilde{e}_\Delta) - H(P_t e + \tilde{e}_\Delta')]\| \\ &\le \tilde{\gamma}(I) \|\tilde{P}_{t,\Delta}(\tilde{e}_\Delta - \tilde{e}_\Delta')\| \\ &\le \tilde{\gamma}(I) \|\tilde{e}_\Delta - \tilde{e}_\Delta'\| \end{aligned}$$

where we used successively the linearity of $\tilde{P}_{t,\Delta}$, (5), (6), and inequality (4). From (7), we conclude that f is a contraction on the (complete) normed space $\tilde{P}_{t,\Delta}\mathscr{L}_e^2$ since $\tilde{\gamma}(I) < 1$ by assumption. Therefore, the iteration scheme

$$\tilde{e}_\Delta^{(n+1)} = f(\tilde{e}_\Delta^{(n)}), \qquad n = 0, 1, 2, \ldots$$

starting from *any* initial guess, $\tilde{e}_\Delta^{(0)}$, will converge to the unique solution on $(t, t + \Delta]$. Thus, by starting at $t = 0$ and by repeating this process, we can construct piece by piece the unique solution of Eq. (1) on $(0, \infty)$. ∎

8 **Corollary** Suppose that, in addition to the assumption of the theorem, we assume that H is linear; then using the notation of (5) to (7), the condition (4) becomes: For any compact interval I, there exist $\tilde{\gamma}(I) < 1$ and $\Delta(I) > 0$ such that

8a
$$\|\tilde{P}_{t,\Delta} H\tilde{e}_\Delta\| \le \tilde{\gamma}\|\tilde{e}_\Delta\|$$

for all $t \in I$, and for all $\tilde{e}_\Delta \in \tilde{P}_{t,\Delta}\mathscr{L}_e^2$.

Proof Follows directly from (7). ∎

9 **Comments** (a) The most important example of an engineering system that does not fulfill such condition is the chattering phenomenon in servos [Flu. 1]. The simplest example is where H_1 is an integrator (i.e., H_1 is defined by its transfer function $1/s$) and H_2 is a memoryless nonlinearity with characteristic $\phi(e_2) = 1$ for $e_2 \ge 0$ and $\phi(e_2) = -1$ for $e_2 < 0$.

(b) In the assumptions of the theorem above, the order of the quantifiers is very important. For any chosen compact interval I, the same $\gamma(I)$ and $\Delta(I)$ must "work" for all $t \in I$. The solution is constructed over successive intervals of length $\Delta(I) > 0$; so, eventually, the process moves out of the compact interval I. Then a new compact interval is chosen, say, I', for which there is a $\Delta(I')$ and $\gamma(I')$.... Clearly, the process will never stop because, by assumption, for any compact interval I, there is a $\Delta(I) > 0$ which "works" for all $t \in I$.

(c) If H is time invariant, successive compact intervals can be chosen to be translates of the first one, and the same Δ and γ can be used throughout. For some time-varying problems, as the solution is continued further to the right, $\Delta(I)$ must be chosen smaller and smaller in order to achieve $\gamma(I) < 1$ in (4). Then there is no unique Δ that works for all $t \in \mathbb{R}_+$.

Exercise 1 Consider the special case where

(a) the feedback loop is open (i.e., H_2 maps everything into the zero vector);

(b) $u_1(t) = e_1(t)$, $y_1(t) \in \mathbb{R}^n$, $u(\cdot)$ is regulated (Appendix A.1.2);

(c) $y_1 = H_1 e_1$ is defined in terms of a differential equation $\dot{y}_1 = f(y_1, e_1, t)$ where f is continuous on $\mathbb{R}^n \times \mathbb{R}^n \times \mathbb{R}_+$.

Display assumptions on f such that the input output map $u_1 \mapsto y_1$ satisfies (4).

Exercise 2 Let u_1, e_1, e_2 map $\mathbb{R}_+$ into $\mathbb{R}$. Take $u_2 \equiv 0$. Suppose that $(H_1 e_1)(t) = \phi(e_1, t)$, where $\phi(\cdot, \cdot)$ is continuous and the conditions for some $\tilde{\gamma} < \infty$, satisfies,

$$|\phi(\sigma, t) - \phi(\sigma', t)| \leq \tilde{\gamma}|\sigma - \sigma'|, \quad \forall \sigma, \sigma' \in \mathbb{R}, \quad \forall t \in \mathbb{R}_+, \quad t \mapsto \phi(0, t) \in L_e^1$$

Suppose that $(H_2 e_2)(t) = (g * e_2)(t)$, where $g \in L_e^1(\mathbb{R}_+)$. Show that for any $u_1 \in L_e^\infty$, there is one and only one solution e_1 and $e_2 \in L_e^\infty$. [*Hint*: Consider the equation $e_1(t) = u_1(t) - (g * e_2)(t)$, where $e_2(t) = \phi[e_1(t), t]\ldots$ Note that $f\colon t \mapsto \int_0^t |g(\tau)|\, d\tau$ is continuous with $f(0) = 0$.]

Exercise 3 Consider the equation

$$e(t) = u(t) + \int_0^t G(t - \tau) e(\tau)\, d\tau \tag{10}$$

where $u\colon \mathbb{R}_+ \to \mathbb{R}^n$, $u \in L_{ne}^p$, for some $p \in [1, \infty]$; also $G\colon \mathbb{R}_+ \to \mathbb{R}^{n \times n}$ and all elements of $G \in L_e^1$. Show that Eq. (10) has one and only one solution $e(\cdot) \in L_{ne}^p$ for each $u \in L_{ne}^p$. (*Hint*: $t \mapsto |G(t)|$ is in L_e^1; $t \mapsto \int_0^t |G(\tau)|\, d\tau$ is continuous, monotonically increasing, and equal to zero at $t = 0, \ldots$.)

Exercise 4 Consider the equation

$$e(t) = u(t) + \int_0^t f[\tau, e(\tau), u(\tau)]\, d\tau, \qquad t \geq 0 \tag{11}$$

where $u\colon \mathbb{R}_+ \to \mathbb{R}^n$, $u \in L_{ne}^\infty$; also $f\colon \mathbb{R}_+ \times \mathbb{R}^n \times \mathbb{R}^n$ is continuous and satisfies a *global Lipschitz condition*, namely, there is a $k \in \mathbb{R}_+$ such that

$$|f(t, \xi, \eta) - f(t, \xi', \eta)| \leq k|\xi - \xi'|, \qquad \forall t \in \mathbb{R}_+, \quad \forall \xi, \xi', \eta \in \mathbb{R}^n$$

Show that Eq. (11) has, for each $u \in L_{ne}^\infty$, one and only one solution $e \in L_{ne}^\infty$.

6 Loop transformation theorem

First, let us make the following observation.

Exercise 1 Let H_1 and K be maps from $\mathcal{L}_e$ into $\mathcal{L}_e$. (Note that neither H_1 nor K need be linear.) U.t.c., $(I + KH_1)^{-1}\colon \mathcal{L}_e \to \mathcal{L}_e \Leftrightarrow H_1(I + KH_1)^{-1}\colon \mathcal{L}_e \to \mathcal{L}_e$. [$\Rightarrow$ is immediate. For $\Leftarrow$, consider the identity

$$I - KH_1(I + KH_1)^{-1} = (I + KH_1)^{-1}]$$

Exercise 2 Let E, F, and G be linear spaces. Let $g\colon G \to E$; let f_1 and f_2 map E into F. Show that

$$(f_1 + f_2) \circ g = f_1 \circ g + f_2 \circ g$$

[*Hint*: By definition $(f_1 + f_2)(x) = f_1(x) + f_2(x)$.] Show that if $E = F = G$, in order to have

$$g \circ (f_1 + f_2) = g \circ f_1 + g \circ f_2$$

g must, except for trivial cases, be a *linear* map from E into E.

Consider the feedback system S shown in Fig. III.1 and described by

1 $$u_1 = e_1 + H_2 e_2$$

2 $$u_2 = e_2 - H_1 e_1$$

We shall derive from the given feedback system S another feedback system S_K such that S is "stable" if and only if S_K is "stable." It will turn out that some straightforward theorems, such as (2.1) and (3.1) above, applied to S_K lead to very interesting stability conditions for S. The system S_K is shown in Fig. III.3 and will be derived in the proof of the theorem in the following.

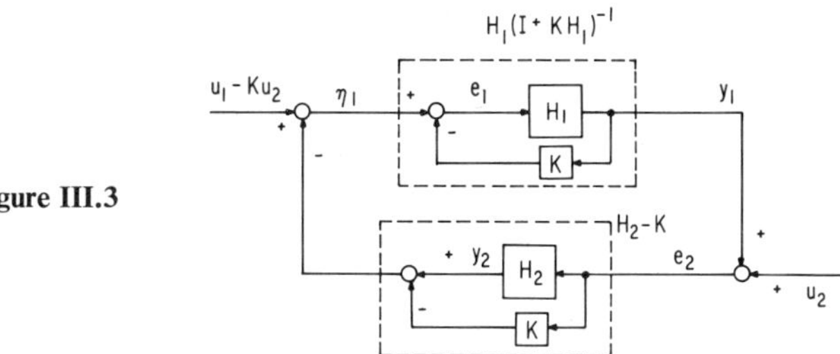

Figure III.3

3 **Theorem** Let H_1, H_2, K, and $(I + KH_1)^{-1}$ map $\mathscr{L}_e$ into $\mathscr{L}_e$. Let K be *linear*, U.t.c.,

(a) if u_1, u_2, e_1, e_2 are in $\mathscr{L}_e$ and are solutions of S [i.e., of Eqs. (1) and (2)], then $u_1 - Ku_2$, u_2, $\eta_1 \triangleq (I + KH_1)e_1$, and e_2 are in $\mathscr{L}_e$ and are solutions of S_K [i.e., of Eqs. (5) and (7), in the following];

(b) conversely, if $u_1 - Ku_2$, u_2, η_1, and e_2 are in $\mathscr{L}_e$ and are solutions of S_K, then u_1, u_2, $e_1 \triangleq (I + KH_1)^{-1}\eta_1$, and e_2 are in $\mathscr{L}_e$ and satisfy S;

(c) assertions (a) and (b) still hold if $\mathscr{L}_e$ is *everywhere* replaced by $\mathscr{L}$;

(d) if $u_2 \equiv 0$, then (a), (b), and (c) still hold even when K is nonlinear.

Proof Since K is linear, we obtain from (2)

4 $$Ke_2 = K(u_2 + H_1 e_1) = Ku_2 + KH_1 e_1$$

Using this result in (1), we obtain successively

$$e_1 = u_1 - (H_2 - K)e_2 - Ku_2 - KH_1e_1$$

and

5 $$\eta_1 \triangleq (I + KH_1)e_1 = (u_1 - Ku_2) - (H_2 - K)e_2$$

Writing e_1 in terms of η_1,

6 $$e_1 = (I + KH_1)^{-1}\eta_1$$

we obtain from (2)

7 $$e_2 = u_2 + H_1(I + KH_1)^{-1}\eta_1$$

Equations (5) and (7) represent the system S_K shown in Fig. III.3; indeed, by inspection, e_1 is related to η_1 by the first equality of (5). (a) follows from the derivation of (5) and (7) from (1) and (2). (b) is obtained by tracing this derivation in the reverse direction and by invoking Exercise 1. (c) is immediate. Finally, (d) follows, once it is recognized that the linearity of K was used only once, namely, in obtaining (4).

8 **Comment** Strictly speaking, it is not necessary to assume that $(I + KH_1)^{-1}$ is defined on $\mathscr{L}_e$. An examination of the proof will show that we need only that the feedback system of Fig. III.3 be such that $\eta_1, e_2, y_1 \in \mathscr{L}_e$ for any input pair $(u_1, u_2) \in \mathscr{L}_e^2$, equivalently, that the equations

$$\eta_1 = (u_1 - Ku_2) - (H_2 - K)e_2, \qquad e_2 = u_2 + y_1, \qquad y_1 = H_1(\eta_1 - Ky_1)$$

have a unique solution $(\eta_1, e_2, y_1) \in \mathscr{L}_e \times \mathscr{L}_e \times \mathscr{L}_e$.

Exercise 3 Give a circuit theoretic interpretation of the loop transformation shown in Fig. III.3 in terms of the n-port model of Fig. III.2.

7 $\mathscr{L}$ Stability

Throughout the remainder of the book, we shall consider systems of the form shown in Fig. III.1 and described by (1.1) and (1.2). Let us note that the stability theorems above such as Theorem (2.1); Theorem (3.1); Exercise 1, Section 3; and Theorem (4.1) not only guarantee that whenever u_1 and u_2 belong to $\mathscr{L}$ then e_1, e_2, y_1, y_2 also belong to $\mathscr{L}$, but more than that they guarantee that there is a constant k such that

1 $$\|e_i\| \leq k(\|u_1\| + \|u_2\|), \qquad i = 1, 2$$

2 $$\|y_i\| \leq k(\|u_1\| + \|u_2\|), \qquad i = 1, 2 \qquad \forall u_1, u_2 \in \mathscr{L}$$

The important point is that k is *independent* of u_1 and u_2.

3 Therefore, from now on we shall say that a system described by (1.1) and (1.2) is $\mathscr{L}$ **stable** whenever there is a constant $k < \infty$ such that (1) and (2) hold. For example, the loop transformation theorem (6.3) essentially gives conditions under which the system S is $\mathscr{L}$ stable if and only if the system S_K is $\mathscr{L}$ stable; it is an $\mathscr{L}$ stability equivalence theorem.

Relation between stability and instability

Provided the term "instability" is suitably narrowly defined, the observation in the following exhibits when "instability" occurs.

4 **Observation** Let H be nonanticipative and map $\mathscr{L}_e^2$ into $\mathscr{L}_e^2$. Let $(I + H)^{-1}$ be nonanticipative and map $\mathscr{L}_e^2$ into $\mathscr{L}_e^2$. U.t.c. the feedback system $(I + H)e = u$ is "stable" in the sense that it has the properties:

(a) e is given in terms of u by nonanticipative map from $\mathscr{L}^2$ into $\mathscr{L}^2$;
(b) $\exists \gamma < \infty$ s.t. $\|e\| \leq \gamma\|u\|$, for all $u \in \mathscr{L}^2$, if and only if

$(I + H)$ has a nonanticipative inverse which maps $\mathscr{L}^2$ into $\mathscr{L}^2$, and $(I + H)^{-1}$ has finite gain.

Proof $\Leftarrow$ Immediate from $(I + H)^{-1}u = e$.
$\Rightarrow$ the map $u \mapsto e$ is, by assumption, nonanticipative and sends $u \in \mathscr{L}^2$ into an $e \in \mathscr{L}^2$. ∎

The relationship between stability and instability can be clarified by the following tree of dichotomies; to emphasize these dichotomies, we label the cases by sequences of zeros and ones as in Boolean algebra.

0: $(I + H)^{-1}$ cannot be defined on all of $\mathscr{L}^2$.

Then the problem is not well formulated because for some $u \in \mathscr{L}^2$, one cannot define e, i.e., the equations have no solution for some inputs $\in \mathscr{L}^2$.

1: $(I + H)^{-1}$ is defined on all of $\mathscr{L}^2$.
- 1.0: $(I + H)^{-1}[\mathscr{L}^2]$ is a strict superset of $\mathscr{L}^2$.
  Thus, for some $u \in \mathscr{L}^2$, $e \triangleq (I + H)^{-1}u \notin \mathscr{L}^2$.
- 1.1: $(I + H)^{-1}[\mathscr{L}^2] \subset \mathscr{L}^2$.
  - 1.1.0: $\gamma[(I + H)^{-1}] = \infty$.
    Then there is a sequence $(u_i) \subset \mathscr{L}^2$ with the corresponding $e_i \in \mathscr{L}^2$, for all i, but $\|e_i\|/\|u_i\| \to \infty$.
  - 1.1.1: $\gamma[(I + H)^{-1}] < \infty$.
    - 1.1.1.0: $(I + H)^{-1}$ is noncausal.
    - 1.1.1.1: $(I + H)^{-1}$ is causal.

Only for the case 1.1.1.1 do we have $\mathscr{L}$ stability. In Chapter V, some classes of unstable feedback systems will be demonstrated by showing that either 1.0 is the case or that 1.1.1.0 is the case.

8 General feedback formula

If H_1 is *linear*, there are two ways of writing the relation between u_1 and y_1; H_2, however, may be nonlinear, This flexibility is very useful in many computations.

1 **Theorem** Consider the system shown in Fig. III.1. Let $H_1, H_2, (I + H_1 H_2)^{-1}$, and $(I + H_2 H_1)^{-1}$ map $\mathscr{L}_e$ into $\mathscr{L}_e$. U.t.c., if $u_2 = 0$ and if H_1 is *linear*, then

$$y_1 = H_1(I + H_2 H_1)^{-1} u_1 = (I + H_1 H_2)^{-1} H_2 u_1 \tag{2}$$

Proof

$$H_1 + H_1 H_2 H_1 = I \cdot H_1 + (H_1 H_2) H_1 = (I + H_1 H_2) H_1 \tag{3}$$

where we used the fact that the composition of two functions is associative and then the definition of the sum of the two functions. Furthermore, since H_1 is *linear*,

$$H_1 + H_1 H_2 H_1 = H_1(I + H_2 H_1) \tag{4}$$

Combining (3) and (4) and, composing it on the left with $(I + H_1 H_2)^{-1}$ and on the right with $(I + H_2 H_1)^{-1}$, we obtain (2). ∎

Exercise Consider a feedback system as shown in Fig. III.1 when $u_1, e_1, y_1 : \mathbb{R}_+ \to \mathbb{R}^n$; $u_2(t) = \theta, \quad \forall t$. Suppose that H_1 consists of a given "plant" P *preceded* by a "compensator" G. Thus $H_1 = PG$. We assume throughout that P and G are *linear*. Since

$$y_1 = PG[I + H_2 PG]^{-1} u_1 \tag{5}$$

consider a "comparison system" consisting of the same "plant" P preceded by a compensator G_0; call y_0 the output of this open-loop system:

$$y_0 = PG_0 u \tag{6}$$

If we choose

$$G_0 = G(I + H_2 P_n G)^{-1} \tag{7}$$

Then, when $P = P_n$, $y_0 = y_1$ *for all* u. Consider now an *arbitrary* change in P; more precisely, let P change from P_n to $\tilde{P} = P_n + \Delta P$. Then, by (6),

$$\Delta y_0 = \Delta P G_0 u$$

(a) Show that

8 $$\Delta y_1 = (I + \tilde{P}GH_2)^{-1} \Delta y_0$$

(b) Prove (8) directly, for ΔP small, by taking derivatives in function spaces. [*Hint*: Note that $PG(I + H_2 PG)^{-1} = (I + PGH_2)^{-1} PG$.]

9 **Comment** This formula is important because it shows that if the "loop gain" PGH_2 is large, then a given change ΔP in the plant will cause a much smaller change in the closed-loop system (5) than in the open-loop system (6). This fact is fundamental in the engineering usefulness of feedback systems.

Notes and references

The general setting of the problem is due to Sandberg [San.3, 4, 5, 6, 9] and Zames [Zam.1, 2, 3]. A detailed discussion of causality can be found in Saeks [Sae.1, 2]. The small gain theorem has been used in many ways by many people with varying degrees of generality. In its two general forms, it appears in Sandberg [San.9] and Zames [Zam.3]. The existence and uniqueness result is a formalization of the conventional argument for Volterra integral equations of the second kind (see, for example, Zames [Zam.1]). The loop shifting theorem has a long history. It was known to and used by Sandberg [San.2, 9] and Zames [Zam.3]; the fact that linearity is no longer required if $u_2 \equiv 0$ is due to Sandberg [San.10]. Equation (8.8) is a well-known result of sensitivity theory [Per.1]. The boundedness result of Section 2 is due to Willems [Wil. 5].

IV LINEAR SYSTEMS

0 Introduction

Most of the results concerning nonlinear feedback systems are based, in some manner or other, on properties of liner feedback systems. Therefore, it is important to develop the best possible results for linear feedback systems and to have them in a form that makes them readily applicable to the nonlinear case. This is the main purpose of this chapter.

In the development that follows, the input $u(\cdot)$ and the output $y(\cdot)$ of the feedback systems under consideration take values in $\mathbb{R}^n$. If $n = 1$, we refer to these systems as single-loop feedback systems or as scalar systems, or, more precisely, as single-input–single-output systems. If $n > 1$, we refer to them as multivariable systems or as multiple-loop feedback systems, or, more precisely, as n-input–n-output systems. Wherever possible, all results are stated for multivariable systems, and results that are specifically applicable to scalar systems are stated only to the extent that the main contrasts with the multivariable case can be exhibited.

Sections 1, 2, and 3 consider exclusively time-invariant *lumped* systems, i.e., systems with rational transfer functions. The thrust of Section 1 is to contrast the properties of scalar systems versus those of multivariable systems [see Theorem (1.12)]. Section 2 develops, for the same class of systems, the factorization method for obtaining necessary and sufficient conditions for the stability of multivariable systems and provides much of the insight that is later needed to study multivariable distributed systems. Section 3 considers the case where the feedback path contains dynamics and investigates the problem of "pole" and "zero" cancellation.

Section 4 turns to distributed systems and develops the basic necessary and sufficient conditions for stability that are used throughout the rest of the book. Important notions such as pseudo-right-coprime factorizations are introduced and comprehensive results are obtained for the practically significant case of a multivariable system whose transfer function has a finite number of poles in the closed right-half-plane, but is otherwise stable. The graphical test for the stability of distributed systems is given in Section 5. Three cases of increasing generality are considered in succession, and the most general results are given without proof; the proof would require too long an excursion into the theory of almost periodic functions. Section 6 develops the main results concerning discrete-time systems, and the parallels as well as the contrasts with the continuous-time case are indicated. In Section 7 we present the basic results concerning linear time-varying systems, including necessary and sufficient conditions for "open-loop" stability, and a perturbational result for both continuous-time and discrete-time systems.

Section 8 uses Liapunov theory to give bounds on the rate of variation of a nonlinear differential system that insure overall exponential stability when the "frozen" system is exponentially stable. This formulation has the advantage that it reduces to well-known conditions in case the system is linear. Finally, Section 9 studies the problem of linearization: Under what conditions is it true that the linearized version of a nonlinear differential system gives good results on all of $\mathbb{R}_+$? Among other things, the results obtained justify the use of small-signal equivalent circuits in analysis and design and the use of variational equations in control and optimization problems.

1 Linear feedback systems with rational transfer functions

Notation

$\mathbb{R}[s] \triangleq$ commutative ring of *polynomials* in the (complex) variable s with coefficients in $\mathbb{R}$. It can be shown that $\mathbb{R}[s]$ is a principal ideal domain.

$\mathbb{R}(s) \triangleq$ (commutative) field of *rational functions* in s with coefficients in $\mathbb{R}$.

$\mathbb{R}[s]^{m \times q}$, $(\mathbb{R}(s)^{m \times q})$ $\triangleq$ class of all $m \times q$ matrices whose elements are in $\mathbb{R}[s]$ ($\mathbb{R}(s)$, resp.). If $N(s) \in \mathbb{R}[s]^{m \times q}$, then $N(s)$ is called a **polynomial matrix.**

$\overline{\mathbb{C}}$ denotes the *extended* complex plane (i.e., the complex plane *including the point at infinity*.)

It is understood, once and for all, that the ratios of polynomials

$$\frac{s+1}{s(s+2)} \quad \text{and} \quad \frac{(s+1)(s-1)}{s(s+2)(s-1)}$$

represent the *same* rational function f and that f has, in $\overline{\mathbb{C}}$, -1 and ∞ as zeros and 0 and -2 as poles. The two expressions above represent the *same* rational function precisely in the same way as the expressions 0.5 and $\frac{1}{2}$ represent the same real number.

We consider two cases: first, the single-input–single-output, linear, time-invariant feedback system whose feedback is f and whose open-loop transfer function is $\hat{g}(s) \in \mathbb{R}(s)$; second, the n-input–n-output, linear, time-invariant feedback systems whose feedback is the matrix $F \in \mathbb{R}^{n \times n}$ and whose open-loop transfer function is $\hat{G}(s) \in \mathbb{R}^{n \times n}(s)$. As shown in Fig. IV.1, u is the input, y is the output, and e is the error; the basic equations are

1 $$y = G*e$$

2 $$e = u - Fy$$

3 $$\hat{y}(s) = \hat{G}(s)[I + F\hat{G}(s)]^{-1}\hat{u}(s), \qquad \hat{y}(s) = \frac{\hat{g}(s)}{1 + f\hat{g}(s)}\hat{u}(s)$$

4 $$\hat{H}(s) = \hat{G}(s)[I + F\hat{G}(s)]^{-1}, \qquad \hat{h}(s) = \frac{\hat{g}(s)}{1 + f\hat{g}(s)}$$

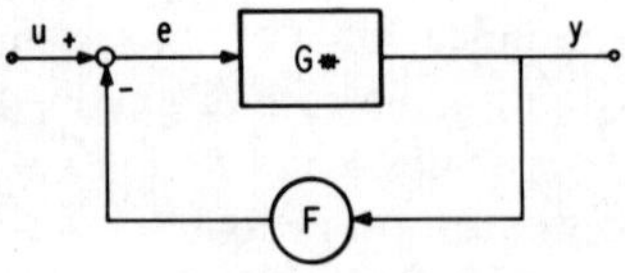

Figure IV.1

We say that $\hat{G}(s) \in \mathbb{R}^{n \times n}(s)$ $[\hat{g}(s) \in \mathbb{R}(s)]$ is **proper (strictly proper)** iff all elements of $\hat{G}(s)$ $[\hat{g}(s)$ itself$]$ are bounded at ∞ (tend to zero at ∞, resp.).

5 A *rational* transfer function $\hat{H}(s)$ is said to be **exponentially stable** iff (i) it is proper, and (ii) all its poles have negative real parts.

6 **Fact** If $\hat{H}(s) \in \mathbb{R}(s)^{n \times n}$ is exponentially stable and strictly proper, then the corresponding impulse response $H(t)$ and its derivative $\dot{H}(t)$ have the following properties:

(a) There are constants $h_m > 0$ and $\alpha > 0$ which depend on the H considered such that

7 $$\|H(t)\| \leq h_m e^{-\alpha t} \qquad \forall t \geq 0$$

(b) There are constants $h_{md} > 0$ and $\alpha > 0$ such that

$$\|\dot{H}(t) - H(0+)\delta(t)\| < h_{md} e^{-\alpha t}, \qquad \forall t \geq 0$$

($\|H(t)\|$ denotes the norm of the matrix $H(t) \in \mathbb{R}^{n \times n}$, this norm being induced by some chosen norm in $\mathbb{R}^n$.)

Proof Immediate by partial fraction expansion. ∎

To summarize the input–output properties of systems with exponentially stable transfer functions, we state the following theorem.

9 **Theorem** Let the closed-loop transfer function $\hat{H}(s) \in \mathbb{R}^{n \times n}(s)$ be exponentially stable and strictly proper; then

(a) for any minimal representation of $\hat{H}(s)$ (i.e., any minimal state representation of the form $\dot{x} = Ax + Bu$, $y = Cx$), the equilibrium point $x = 0$ is globally, exponentially, uniformly (in t) stable:

(b) if $u \in L_n^1$, then $y = H * u \in L_n^1 \cap L_n^\infty$, $\dot{y} \in L_n^1$, y is absolutely continuous and $y(t) \to 0$ as $t \to \infty$;

(c) if $u \in L_n^2$, then $y = H * u \in L_n^2 \cap L_n^\infty$, $\dot{y} \in L_n^2$, y is continuous and $y(t) \to 0$ as $t \to \infty$;

(d) if $u \in L_n^\infty$, then $y = H * u \in L_n^\infty$, $\dot{y} \in L_n^\infty$, and y is uniformly continuous;

(e) if $u \in L_n^\infty$ and if, as $t \to \infty$, $u(t) \to u_\infty$, a constant vector in $\mathbb{R}^n$, then, in addition $y(t) \to \hat{H}(0)u_\infty$ as $t \to \infty$ and the convergence is exponential;

(f) if $u \in L_n^p$ and $1 < p < \infty$, then $y = H * u \in L_n^p$ and $\dot{y} \in L_n^p$.

Proof Follows immediately from the results of Appendix C. The asymptotic results of (e) follow from Laplace transform. ∎

Exercise 1 In the case of z transforms, we say that the rational transfer function $\hat{H}(z)$ is exponentially stable iff it is proper (bounded at infinity) and has all its poles with absolute value smaller than 1 (i.e., in the open unit disk). Formulate and prove the inequality that corresponds to (7) and a theorem analogous to Theorem (9).

We consider now the relation between the properties of the open-loop transfer function $\hat{G}(s)$ and the poles of the closed-loop transfer function. This subject is basic to stability questions.

10 **Fact** Let $\hat{H}(s)$ and $\hat{G}(s) \in \mathbb{R}^{n \times n}(s)$ and be related by (4); then

11 $$I - F\hat{H}(s) = [I + F\hat{G}(s)]^{-1}$$

If, in addition, $\det F \neq 0$, $p_c \in \overline{\mathbb{C}}$ is a pole of $\hat{H}(s)$ if and only if p_c is a pole of $[I + F\hat{G}(s)]^{-1}$.

Proof Equation (11) is immediate by calculation from (4). The conclusion follows since $\det F \neq 0$. ∎

12 **Theorem** Let $\hat{g}(s) \in \mathbb{R}(s)$ and $\hat{G}(s) \in \mathbb{R}(s)^{n \times n}$. Let $\overline{\mathbb{C}}$ be the extended complex plane. Define $\hat{h}(s)$ and $\hat{H}(s)$ by (4). U.t.c.:

(i) $p_c \in \overline{\mathbb{C}}$ is a pole of $\hat{h}(s)$ if and only if $p_c \in \overline{\mathbb{C}}$ is a zero of $1 + \hat{g}(s)$.

(ii) If $p_c \in \overline{\mathbb{C}}$ is a zero of $\det[I + F\hat{G}(s)]$, then $p_c \in \overline{\mathbb{C}}$ is a pole of $\hat{H}(s)$. (But the converse is not true.)

(iii) If $p_c \in \overline{\mathbb{C}}$ is a pole of $\hat{H}(s)$, then either p_c is a zero of $\det[I + F\hat{G}(s)]$ or p_c is a pole of $\hat{G}(s)$.

(iv) If $\hat{G}(s)$ is exponentially stable, then $\hat{H}(s)$ is exponentially stable if and only if $\det[I + F\hat{G}(s)]$ has no zero at ∞ and has all its zeros with negative real parts.

13 **Remarks** 1. Note that we did *not* assume that $\hat{g}(s)$ or $\hat{G}(s)$ were proper.

2. Here we encounter for the first time the extended complex plane $\overline{\mathbb{C}}$. This is crucial because when $\hat{H}(s)$ has a pole at infinity (equivalently, is not proper, or is not bounded at infinity), it takes some bounded inputs into some unbounded outputs. For example, let $n = 1$, $\hat{g}(s) = -s/(s+1)$, then $\hat{h}(s) = -s$. Now $\hat{h}$ takes the bounded input $t \mapsto \sin(t^2)$ into the output $t \mapsto 2t\cos(t^2)$ which is unbounded. Thus, (i) and (ii) show that if $1 + \hat{g}(\infty) = 0$ (or $\det[I + F\hat{G}(\infty)] = 0$), then the closed-loop system is not L^∞ stable.

3. It is very important to keep in mind that the set of poles of $\hat{H}(s)$ (in $\overline{\mathbb{C}}$) may be larger than the set of zeros of $\det[I + F\hat{G}(s)]$ (in $\overline{\mathbb{C}}$). For example, consider $F = I$ and $I + \hat{G}(s) = \text{diag}[s,\ 1/s,\ (s-1)/(s+1),\ (s+1)/s-1)]$, clearly $\det[I + \hat{G}(s)] = 1$, $\forall s \in \overline{\mathbb{C}}$, and $[I + G(s)]^{-1} = \text{diag}[1/s,\ s,\ (s+1)/(s-1),\ (s-1)/s+1)]$. Therefore, by (10), $\hat{H}(s)$ has a pole at $0, 1, -1, \infty$ even though $\det[I + \hat{G}(s)]$ has no zeros whatsoever.

14 **Example** Consider a simple example where $\hat{G}(s)$ is proper and, in fact, tends to zero as $s \to \infty$. Let

$$\hat{G}(s) = \begin{pmatrix} \dfrac{2s}{(s-1)^2} & \dfrac{1}{s-1} \\[2ex] \dfrac{2}{s-1} & 0 \end{pmatrix}$$

Then

$$[I + \hat{G}(s)]^{-1} = \begin{bmatrix} \dfrac{s+1}{s-1} & \dfrac{-1}{s+1} \\ \dfrac{-2}{s+1} & \dfrac{s^2+1}{s^2-1} \end{bmatrix}; \qquad \hat{H}(s) = \begin{bmatrix} \dfrac{2}{s+1} & \dfrac{1}{s+1} \\ \dfrac{2}{s+1} & \dfrac{1}{s+1} - \dfrac{1}{s-1} \end{bmatrix}$$

and

$$\det[I + \hat{G}(s)] = (s+1)/(s-1)$$

Hence $\det[I + \hat{G}(s)]$ has no zeros in the closed right half-plane nor at infinity; $\hat{G}(s)$ has a *double* pole at $s = 1$; det $[I + \hat{G}(s)]$ has a *simple* pole at $s = 1$; here $\hat{H}(s)$ has a simple pole at $s = 1$. So the closed-loop system is *unstable* even though $\det[I + \hat{G}(s)]$ has no zeros in the closed right half-plane and is equal to 1 at infinity.

Proof of Theorem 12 (i) Note that if p_0 is a pole of $\hat{g}(s)$, so that $|\hat{g}(s)| \to \infty$ as $s \to p_0$, then, by (4), $\hat{h}(s) \to 1$ as $s \to p_0$. Therefore, the only way for the scalar rational function $\hat{h}(s)$ to have a pole at $p_c \in \overline{\mathbb{C}}$ is that $1 + \hat{g}(p_c) = 0$. Conversely, if $1 + \hat{g}(p_c) = 0$, the numerator of (4), namely, $\hat{g}(s)$, tends to -1 as $s \to p_c$; hence no cancellation can occur at p_c, and p_c is a pole of $\hat{h}(s)$. (ii) By assumption $\det[I + F\hat{G}(p_c)] = 0$. For a proof by contradiction, using Fact (10), assume that

15 $\qquad [I + F\hat{G}(s)]^{-1}$ is bounded in some neighborhood of p_c.

Then

$$s \mapsto \det\{[I + F\hat{G}(s)]^{-1}\} = \{\det[I + F\hat{G}(s)]\}^{-1}$$

is bounded in a neighborhood of p_c. This contradicts the assumption $\det[I + F\hat{G}(p_c)] = 0$. Therefore, by (11), $I - F\hat{H}(s)$ has a pole at $p_c \in \mathbb{C}$ whenever $\det[I + F\hat{G}(p_c)] = 0$. Hence $\hat{H}(s)$ also has a pole at p_c.

(iii) Follows immediately from (10) and Cramer's rule.

(iv) $\Rightarrow$ By assumption $\hat{H}(s)$ is exponentially stable, i.e., proper, and has no poles in the closed right half-plane. Hence by (iii), $\det[I + F\hat{G}(s)]$ cannot have a zero at infinity, nor in the closed right half-plane.

$\Leftarrow$ Given the assumptions on $\hat{G}(s)$ and $\det[I + F\hat{G}(s)]$, (iii) implies that all the poles of $\hat{H}(s)$ are finite and have negative real parts. ∎

Exercise 2 Formulate the statements analogous to those of Theorem (12) for the z-transform case.

Exercise 3 Give an example where F is *singular* and the converse of conclusion (ii) of Theorem (12) fails (e.g., $F = \text{diag}(1, 0)$, $\hat{G}(s) = \text{diag}[(s+1)^{-1}, (s-1)^{-1}]$).

2 Necessary and sufficient conditions: factorization method

The purpose of this section is to obtain necessary and sufficient conditions for the stability of feedback systems described by†

1 $$H(s) = G(s)[I + FG(s)]^{-1}$$

where $G(s) \in \mathbb{R}^{n \times n}(s)$ and $F \in \mathbb{R}^{n \times n}$. The system is depicted in Fig. IV.1. The single-input–single-output case is no problem since, when $f \neq 0$,

1a $$h(s) = g(s)/[1 + fg(s)]$$

is exponentially stable if and only if $1 + fg(s)$ has no zeros in Re $s \geq 0$, *including the point at infinity*. In view of Example (1.14), we know that the obvious extension of this result is false for the n-input–n-output case. On the other hand, if we write the *rational* function $g(s)$ as $n(s)/d(s)$, where the *polynomials* $n(s)$ and $d(s)$ are coprime, we know that $h(s)$ [given by (1a)] is exponentially stable if and only if the *polynomial* $d(s) + fn(s)$ has no zeros in the closed right half-plane. We propose to derive in this section a similar criterion for the n-input–n-output case. This will require the factorization of the *rational* function $G(s)$ as a product $N(s)D(s)^{-1}$, where $N(s)$ and $D(s)$ are *polynomial matrices* and $N(s)$ and $D(s)$ are "coprime" in a suitable sense. Then $H(s)$ will be exponentially stable if and only if the *polynomial* det $[D(s) + FN(s)]$ has no zeros in the closed right half-plane.

2.1 Factorization

Let $N(s)$ and $D(s) \in \mathbb{R}^{n \times n}[s]$. The *polynomial* matrix Δ is said to be a **common right divisor** of N and D iff there are *polynomial* matrices N_1 and D_1 such that

2 $$N = N_1 \Delta, \qquad D = D_1 \Delta$$

Note that all matrices in (2) are in $\mathbb{R}^{n \times n}[s]$; therefore, (2) asserts that the polynomial matrices N and $N_1\Delta$ are equal for all $s \in \mathbb{C}$; ditto for D and $D_1\Delta$.

If $P, Q, R \in \mathbb{R}^{n \times n}[s]$ and if $P = QR$, we say that P is a *left-multiple* of R, and R is a *right divisor* of P.

Given two matrices N and $D \in \mathbb{R}^{n \times n}[s]$, we say that $\Delta \in \mathbb{R}^{n \times n}[s]$ is a **greatest common right divisor** (abbreviated gcrd) of N and D iff

† In this section since we deal exclusively with transfer functions, we drop the "^" which we use everywhere else to denote Laplace transforms. Even the best notations have to be abused!

(a) Δ is a common right divisor of N and D and
(b) Δ is a left multiple of every common right divisor of N and D.

A square matrix with elements in $\mathbb{R}[s]$ is said to be **unimodular** iff its determinant is a *nonzero* real *number*. By Cramer's rule, the inverse of a unimodular matrix is a matrix in $\mathbb{R}^{n \times n}[s]$, namely, a *polynomial* matrix. In general, the inverse of a matrix in $\mathbb{R}^{n \times n}[s]$ is not in $\mathbb{R}^{n \times n}[s]$, but is in $\mathbb{R}^{n \times n}(s)$.

When the *polynomial* matrix Δ, a greatest common right divisor of the *polynomial* matrices N and D, is *unimodular*, we say that N and D are **right coprime**. Left coprime and greatest common left divisor are defined similarly.

3 **Factorization Theorem** Let $H(s)$ be a $q \times m$ matrix with elements in $\mathbb{R}(s)$. Then there exists two *polynomial* matrices $N(s)$ and $D(s)$ such that

4
$$H(s) = N(s)D(s)^{-1} \qquad \forall s \in \mathbb{C}$$

such that $N(s)$ and $D(s)$ are *right coprime* [i.e., every greatest common right divisor of $N(s)$ and $D(s)$ is a unimodular matrix].

4a **Remarks** (a) The analogy between (4) and the scalar case is clear. In the scalar case, the polynomials $n(s)$ and $d(s)$ are determined modulo a common factor, which is a *nonzero* number. In the present case, the polynomial matrices N and D are determined modulo a *right* factor, which is a *unimodular* polynomial matrix.

(b) If N and D are right coprime, then it does *not* follow that the polynomials det $N(s)$ and det $D(s)$ are coprime. Consider, for example, $N = \text{diag}(s-1, s-2)$; $D(s) = \text{diag}(s-2, s-1)$.

(c) It is clear that we could just as well have selected a representation in the opposite order:

$$H(s) = \overline{D}(s)^{-1}\overline{N}(s)$$

where $\overline{N}(s)$ and $\overline{D}(s)$ are *left* coprime. This representation will be useful later.

(d) It can be shown that if $H(s)$ is bounded at infinity, then det $D(s) = k \det(sI - A)$, where A is the matrix of any *minimal* realization $[A, B, C, D]$ of $H(s)$, and k a nonzero constant.

(e) All the operations that follow are legitimate because $\mathbb{R}$ is a *field.* No change would be required if we used $\mathbb{C}$ as the field of interest. This occurs, in practice, when polynomials in $\mathbb{R}[s]$ are factored; the factors $(s - z_i)$ belong often to $\mathbb{C}[s]$.

The analogy between the scalar case and (4) is immediate. We establish this canonical form by giving a procedure for calculating N and D.

Procedure Let $H(s)$ be of the form

$$H(s) = \begin{bmatrix} \dfrac{n_{11}(s)}{d_1(s)} & \cdots & \dfrac{n_{1m}(s)}{d_m(s)} \\ \vdots & & \\ \dfrac{n_{q1}(s)}{d_1(s)} & & \dfrac{n_{qm}(s)}{d_m(s)} \end{bmatrix} \tag{5}$$

where the $n_{ij}(s)$ and $d_j(s)$ are polynomials and where $d_j(s)$, for $j = 1, 2, \ldots, m$, is the least common multiple of the denominators of the elements in the jth column of $H(s)$. From (5)

$$H(s) = \begin{bmatrix} n_{11}(s) & \cdots & n_{1m}(s) \\ \vdots & \ddots & \\ n_{q1}(s) & \cdots & n_{qm}(s) \end{bmatrix} \begin{bmatrix} d_1(s) & & 0 \\ & \ddots & \\ 0 & & d_m(s) \end{bmatrix}^{-1} \tag{6}$$

Call these *polynomial* matrices $\bar{N}(s)$ and $\bar{D}(s)$, respectively. Note that $\det[\bar{D}(s)] \not\equiv 0$. Extracting from $\bar{N}$ and $\bar{D}$ a *greatest common right* divisor $\bar{R}(s)$, we have

$$\bar{N}(s) = N(s)\bar{R}(s) \qquad \bar{D}(s) = D(s)\bar{R}(s), \qquad \forall s \in \mathbb{C}$$

where all the matrices have elements in $\mathbb{R}[s]$. Since $\det[\bar{D}(s)] \not\equiv 0$, $\bar{R}(s)$ is necessarily nonsingular; hence the canonical form (4) follows. ∎

The extraction of a greatest common right divisor is obtained as the solution of this.

8 **Problem** Given two *polynomial* matrices $N(s)$ and $D(s)$, where $N(s) \in \mathbb{R}[s]^{q \times m}$ $D(s) \in \mathbb{R}[s]^{m \times m}$, with $\det D(s) \not\equiv 0$. Find

(a) two polynomial matrices $U_{11}(s)$ and $U_{12}(s)$ that satisfy (9) below;
(b) a greatest common right divisor $R(s)$ of $N(s)$ and $D(s)$;
(c) two polynomial matrices $V_{11}(s)$ and $V_{21}(s)$, which are *right coprime*

such that

$$U_{11}(s)D(s) + U_{12}(s)N(s) = R(s), \qquad \forall s \in \mathbb{C} \tag{9}$$

and

$$N(s)D(s)^{-1} = V_{21}(s)V_{11}(s)^{-1}, \qquad \forall s \in \mathbb{C} \text{ except at poles} \tag{10}$$

11 **Procedure** We shall use elementary row operations on matrices whose elements belong to $\mathbb{R}[s]$. There are three types of elementary row operations:

(i) Multiply any row by a *nonzero constant*.
(ii) Interchange any two rows.
(iii) For $i \neq j$, multiply row j by an arbitrary *polynomial* $p(s) \in \mathbb{R}[s]$ and add the result to row i.

The effect of any such elementary row operation on a matrix $M(s) \in \mathbb{R}[s]^{m \times m}$ is equivalent to a multiplication *on the left* by a matrix that is the $m \times m$ unit matrix upon which one has performed the desired elementary row operation. Note that any such elementary row matrix has a determinant that is a nonzero *constant*; hence it is a unimodular matrix, and its inverse is also a polynomial matrix.

12 Let
$$F(s) = \underbrace{\begin{bmatrix} D(s) \\ N(s) \end{bmatrix}}_{m} \begin{matrix} \}m \\ \}q \end{matrix}, \qquad F(s) \in \mathbb{R}[s]^{(m \times q) \times m}$$

Step 1 $M(s) = F(s)$.

Step 2 If all elements of the first column of $M(s)$, except the (1, 1) element are zero, go to Step 6; otherwise, go to Step 3.

Step 3 From the elements in the first column of $M(s)$, pick one nonzero element with least degree. If necessary, interchange two rows to bring this element in the (1, 1) position. Let $\overline{M} = (\overline{m}_{ik})$ be the resulting matrix.

Step 4 For $i = 2, 3, \ldots, j$, where j is the number of rows of $\overline{M}(s)$, divide $\overline{m}_{i1}$ by $\overline{m}_{11}$; thus,

13
$$\overline{m}_{i1} = q_{i1}\overline{m}_{11} + r_{i1} \qquad (i = 2, 3, \ldots, j)$$

where $d^0(r_{i1}) < d^0(\overline{m}_{11})$. For $i = 2, 3, \ldots, j$, subtract from the ith row, the first row of $\overline{M}(s)$ multiplied by q_{i1}. The result is a new matrix, $\tilde{M}(s)$, whose first column is $(\overline{m}_{11}, r_{21}, r_{31}, \ldots, r_{j1})$.

Step 5 $M(s) = \tilde{M}(s)$; go to Step 2.

Step 6 If $M(s)$ has only one row or one column, go to Step 9. Otherwise, go to Step 7.

Step 7 Delete the first row and first column of $M(s) \in \mathbb{R}[s]^{j \times k}$, thus obtaining a new matrix $\hat{M}(s) \in \mathbb{R}[s]^{(j-1) \times (k-1)}$.

Step 8 $M(s) = \hat{M}(s)$; go to Step 2.

Step 9 Stop.

The result of this procedure is to transform $F(s)$ into an upper triangular matrix $\in \mathbb{R}[s]^{(m+q)\times m}$. Equivalently, there exists a matrix $U(s) \in \mathbb{R}[s]^{(m+q)\times(m+q)}$ such that for all $s \in \mathbb{C}$,

14
$$\begin{bmatrix} U_{11}(s) & U_{12}(s) \\ U_{21}(s) & U_{22}(s) \end{bmatrix} \begin{bmatrix} D(s) \\ N(s) \end{bmatrix} = \begin{bmatrix} R(s) \\ 0 \end{bmatrix}$$

(block sizes: rows m, q; columns m, q.)

Since $U(s) \in \mathbb{R}[s]^{(m+q)\times(m+q)}$ and is a product of elementary row matrices, $\det[U(s)] = \text{constant} \neq 0$ and $V(s) \triangleq U(s)^{-1} \in \mathbb{R}[s]^{(m+q)\times(m+q)}$. Note that since $\det D(s) \not\equiv 0$, $\det R(s) \not\equiv 0$. Multiplying (14) on the left by $V(s)$ gives

15
$$D(s) = V_{11}(s)R(s), \qquad N(s) = V_{21}(s)R(s), \qquad \forall s \in \mathbb{C}$$

Furthermore,

16
$$U_{11}(s)D(s) + U_{12}(s)N(s) = R(s), \qquad \forall s \in \mathbb{C}$$

and hence, by (15),

17
$$U_{11}(s)V_{11}(s) + U_{12}(s)V_{21}(s) = I, \qquad \forall s \in \mathbb{C}$$

From (15), $R(s)$ is a common right divisor of $N(s)$ and $D(s)$.

From (16), (17), and lemma (20) in the following, $R(s)$ is a greatest common right divisor of $N(s)$ and $D(s)$.

From (15)

18
$$N(s)D(s)^{-1} = V_{21}(s)V_{11}(s)^{-1}$$

where V_{11} and V_{21} are right coprime as is shown in lemma (20) in the following. ∎

19 **Exercise 1** (a) Write down the form of the elementary row matrices for the three operations.

(b) Write down the matrices corresponding to the inverses of these operations.

(c) Show that the calculation of $U(s)^{-1}$ amounts to the product of *known* elementary row matrices.

20 **Lemma** Let $N(s) \in \mathbb{R}[s]^{q\times m}$, $D(s) \in \mathbb{R}[s]^{m\times m}$. Then there exists two polynomial matrices $P(s) \in \mathbb{R}[s]^{m\times q}$, $Q(s) \in \mathbb{R}[s]^{m\times m}$ such that

21
$$P(s)N(s) + Q(s)D(s) = I_{m\times m}, \qquad \forall \in \mathbb{C}$$

if and only if $N(s)$ and $D(s)$ are right coprime.

Proof $\Rightarrow$ Suppose not; then there is a right common divisor which is not unimodular, say $R(s)$:

22
$$N = \bar{N}R, \qquad D = \bar{D}R$$

where $\bar{N}$, $\bar{D}$ are polynomial matrices and det $R(s)$ is a polynomial of degree ≥ 1. Then (21) gives

23 $$[P(s)\bar{N}(s) + Q(s)\bar{D}(s)]R(s) = I, \qquad \forall s \in \mathbb{C}$$

This is a contradiction. Indeed, the bracketed factor is a polynomial matrix; hence $\det[P(s)\bar{N}(s) + Q(s)\bar{D}(s)]$ is a polynomial, but $\det[R(s)]$ is also a polynomial of degree ≥ 1, hence contradiction with (23).

$\Leftarrow$ The procedure (9) applied to $N(s)$ and $D(s)$ gives a greatest right common divisor $R(s)$ and two polynomial matrices $\bar{P}(s)$, $\bar{Q}(s)$ such that [see (16)]

24 $$\bar{P}(s)N(s) + \bar{Q}(s)D(s) = R(s)$$

Since N and D are right coprime by assumption, $R(s)$ is unimodular; hence $R(s)^{-1} \in \mathbb{R}[s]^{m \times m}$. So multiplying (24) on the left by $R(s)^{-1}$, we obtain

25 $$R(s)^{-1}\bar{P}(s)N(s) + R(s)^{-1}\bar{Q}(s)D(s) = I$$

which is of the form (21). ■

Exercise 2 Show that $N(s) \in \mathbb{R}[s]^{q \times m}$ and $D(s) \in \mathbb{R}[s]^{m \times m}$ are right coprime if and only if the matrix $\left[\begin{smallmatrix} D(s) \\ N(s) \end{smallmatrix}\right] \in \mathbb{R}[s]^{(q+m) \times m}$ is of the full rank (in the commutative ring $\mathbb{R}[s]$); after viewing this matrix as an element of $\mathbb{C}^{(q+m) \times m}$, it must have rank m, $\forall s \in \mathbb{C}$.

2.2 Necessary and sufficient conditions

We consider again the n-input–n-output feedback system with $G(s) \in \mathbb{R}(s)^{n \times n}$ as forward transfer function and $F \in \mathbb{R}^{n \times n}$ as feedback gain. (See Fig. IV.1.) We shall require now that $G(s)$ be proper, i.e., bounded at infinity.

30 **Theorem** Let $G(s) \in \mathbb{R}(s)^{n \times n}$ and be *proper*; let $F \in \mathbb{R}^{n \times n}$ and

31 $$\det[I + FG(\infty)] \neq 0$$

Let $G(s) = N(s)D(s)^{-1}$, where $N(s)$ and $D(s)$ are *polynomial* matrices, which are *right coprime*. U.t.c., the closed-loop transfer function $H(s) = G(s)[I + FG(s)]^{-1}$ is exponentially stable if and only if the *polynomial* $\det[D(s) + FN(s)]$ has all its zeros with negative real parts. (In fact, we show that $H(s)$ is proper and that p_c is a pole of $H(s)$ if and only if p_c is a zero of the polynomial $\det[D(s) + FN(s)]$.)

Exercise 3 State and prove the corresponding theorem for the z-transform case.

Proof Let us note that $H(s)$ is proper:

2 $$H(s) = G(s)[I + FG(s)]^{-1} = G(s)\,\text{Adj}[I + FG(s)]\{\det[I + FG(s)]\}^{-1}$$

Since $G(s)$ is proper, the two matrices in the extreme right-hand side of (32) are bounded at infinity. By (31), the last factor is also bounded at infinity; hence $H(s)$ is proper. Consequently, $H(s)$ can only have poles in the finite plane. The theorem will be proved if we show that

33
$$p_c \in \mathbb{C} \text{ is a pole of } H(s)$$
$$\Leftrightarrow \quad p_c \in \mathbb{C} \text{ is a zero of the } \textit{polynomial} \det[D(s) + FN(s)]$$

$\Rightarrow$ Let $p_c \in \mathbb{C}$ be a pole of $H(s)$. Using the factorization of $G(s)$, we obtain

34
$$H(s) = N(s)[D(s) + FN(s)]^{-1} = N(s)\,\mathrm{Adj}[D(s) + FN(s)]\,\{\det[D(s) + FN(s)]\}^{-1}$$

Now $N(s)$ and $D(s)$ are *polynomial* matrices and F is constant matrix; hence by (34), if $H(s)$ has a pole at p_c, then p_c is a zero of the polynomial $s \mapsto \det[D(s) + FN(s)]$.

$\Leftarrow$ Let $p_c \in \mathbb{C}$ be a zero of $\det[D(s) + FN(s)]$. We have to show that p_c is a pole of $H(s)$.

Since $N(s)$ and $D(s)$ are right coprime, by lemma (20), there are polynomial matrices $P(s), Q(s) \in \mathbb{R}[s]^{n \times n}$ such that

35
$$P(s)N(s) + Q(s)D(s) = I, \qquad \forall s \in \mathbb{C}$$

Adding and subtracting the polynomial matrix $Q(s)FN(s)$, we obtain

36
$$[P(s) - Q(s)F]N(s) + Q(s)[D(s) + FN(s)] = I, \qquad \forall s \in \mathbb{C}$$

So $N(s)$ and $D(s) + FN(s)$ are right coprime. Using (34) in (36), we obtain

37
$$\{[P(s) - Q(s)F]H(s) + Q(s)\}[D(s) + FN(s)] = I, \qquad \forall s \in \mathbb{C}$$

Hence

38
$$\det\{[P(s) - Q(s)F]H(s) + Q(s)\}\,\det[D(s) + FN(s)] = 1, \qquad \forall s \in \mathbb{C}$$

By assumption, $p_c \in \mathbb{C}$ is a zero of the second factor of (38); hence for (38) to hold at p_c, the first factor must have a pole at p_c. Now $P(s)$, $Q(s)$, and F are polynomials; hence have no poles in $\mathbb{C}$. Therefore, $H(s)$ must have a pole at p_c. Thus, (33) is established, and the theorem is proved. ∎

40 **Remark** From (35) we can write

$$\det[P(s)G(s) + Q(s)]\,\det D(s) = 1, \qquad \forall s \in \mathbb{C}$$

Hence

41
$$p_0 \in \mathbb{C} \text{ is a pole of } G(s)$$
$$\Leftrightarrow \quad p_0 \text{ is a zero of the polynomial } \det[D(s)]$$

43 **Corollary** Under the assumptions of Theorem (30), we have

44 $$\det[I + FG(s)] = \frac{\det G(s)}{\det H(s)} = \det[I + FG(\infty)] \frac{\prod_{i=1}^{m}(s - p_{ci})}{\prod_{i=1}^{m}(s - p_{oi})}$$

where $\{p_{oi}\}_1^m$ and $\{p_{ci}\}_1^m$ are the poles of $G(s)$ and $H(s)$ (counting multiplicities), respectively.

Proof By (32), taking determinants

45 $$\det[I + FG(s)] = \frac{\det G(s)}{\det H(s)} = \frac{\det[D(s) + FN(s)]}{\det D(s)} = k \frac{\prod_{i=1}^{m}(s - p_{ci})}{\prod_{i=1}^{m}(s - p_{oi})}$$

The last step follows from (33), (34), and (41). $k = \det[I + FG(\infty)] \neq 0$ as a consequence of (31). Furthermore, the number of poles of $G(s)$ and of $H(s)$ are equal; indeed, if they were not, (45) would either go to zero at infinity [contradicting (31)] or would be unbounded at infinity [contradicting the fact that $G(s)$ is proper]. ∎

46 **Remark** Equation (44) shows that as a result of possible cancellations, the set of zeros of $\det[I + FG(s)]$ may be a *proper subset* of the set $\{p_{ci}\}$ of closed-loop poles. [See Example (1.14.)] This shows that, under the assumptions of Theorem (30), *if $G(s)$ is exponentially stable, then $H(s)$ is exponentially stable if and only if all the zeros of* $\det[I + FG(s)]$ *have negative real parts.*

50 **Alternate Derivation of Corollary (43)** Suppose that the forward transfer function $G(s)$ has $R_0 = [A, B, C, D]$ as a *minimal* representation. Clearly, then

51 $$G(s) = C(sI - A)^{-1}B + D$$

Referrring to Fig. IV.1, note that e is the input to $G(s)$ and $e = u - Fy$. A little calculation leads to the state equations of the closed-loop system:

52 $$\dot{x} = [A - B(I + FD)^{-1}FC]x + B(I + FD)^{-1}u$$

53 $$\begin{aligned} y &= [C - D(I + FD)^{-1}FC]x + D(I + FD)^{-1}u \\ &= (I + DF)^{-1}Cx + (I + DF)^{-1}Du \end{aligned}$$

This is a representation of the closed-loop system. It is a *minimal* representation because, as can easily be checked, by a reasoning based on assuming the contrary, the output feedback cannot destroy the complete controllability and the complete observability of the system in the forward loop. Therefore, the natural frequencies of the closed-loop system are precisely the eigenvalues of $A - B(I + FD)^{-1}FC$. Now using $\det(PQ) = \det P \det Q$, $\det(I + MN) = \det(I + NM)$, we obtain successively:

54 $$\det[sI - A + B(I + FD)^{-1}FC]$$
$$= \det(sI - A)\det[I + (sI - A)^{-1}B(I + FD)^{-1}FC]$$
$$= \det(sI - A)\det[I + (I + FD)^{-1}FC(sI - A)^{-1}B]$$

55 $$= \det(sI - A)\det[(I + FD)^{-1}]\det[I + FC(sI - A)^{-1}B + FD]$$

Now the last two determinants are, respectively, equal to $\det[I + FG(\infty)]$ and $\det[I + FG(s)]$ as can be seen from (51). Therefore, we conclude from (55)

56 $$\det[I + FG(s)] = \det[I + FG(\infty)]\frac{\det[sI - A + B(I + FD)^{-1}FC]}{\det(sI - A)}$$

Equation (44) follows from (56) because the representations $R_0 = [A, B, C, D]$ and that of the closed-loop system in (52) and (53) are minimal.

58 **Remark on Inverses of Matrices in $\mathbb{R}(s)^{n \times n}$** Let $H(s)$ be factored as

59 $$H(s) = N(s)D(s)^{-1}$$

where N and D are in $\mathbb{R}[s]^{n \times n}$ and are right coprime. We have

60 $$p \in C \text{ is a pole of } H(s) \Leftrightarrow p \in \mathbb{C} \text{ is a zero of det } [D(s)]$$

61 $$z \in \mathbb{C} \text{ is a pole of } H(s)^{-1} \Leftrightarrow z \in \mathbb{C} \text{ is a zero of det } [N(s)]$$

Note that no assertion whatsoever is made concerning poles at infinity. Furthermore, since $\det D(s)$ and $\det N(s)$ may have common zeros, it may happen that both $H(s)$ and $H(s)^{-1}$ have a pole at some $s \in \mathbb{C}$. For example, $H(s) = \text{diag}[(s + 1)/(s - 1), (s - 1)/(s + 1)]$.

62 **Remark on Zeros of the $I + F\hat{G}(s)$** Let the assumptions of Theorem (30) hold. The matrix $I + F\hat{G}(s)$, by analogy with the scalar case, will be called the **return difference matrix**. Its factored form is $(D + FN)D^{-1}$, where the two polynomial matrices are right coprime, provided $\det F \neq 0$; then we know that p is a pole of the return difference if and only if $\det D(p) = 0$. For simplicity assume that $\det(D + FN) \not\equiv 0$. Then, by analogy with the scalar case, we say that z **is a zero of the return difference matrix** $I + F\hat{G}(\cdot)$ iff $\det[D(z) + FN(z)] = 0$. Note that, as indicated above, it may happen that some $p \in \mathbb{C}$ is at the *same time* a pole and a zero of $I + F\hat{G}(\cdot)$.

Exercise 4 Suppose that the return difference is factored in two ways

$$I + FG(s) = N_r(s)D_r(s)^{-1} = D_l(s)^{-1}N_l(s)$$

where N_r, D_r (N_l, D_l, resp.) are right coprime (left coprime), polynomial matrices. Show that, for $z \in \mathbb{C}$, det $N_l(z) = 0$ if and only if det $N_r(z) = 0$.

In the scalar case, the zeros and poles of transfer functions have well-known dynamical characterizations. Such characterizations generalize to the matrix case. For simplicity, we consider only the square matrix case. The dynamical characterization is given by the following theorem.

63 **Theorem** Let the assumptions of Theorem (30) hold, then

(i) $p \in \mathbb{C}$ is a pole of $I + F\hat{G}(\cdot)$ if and only if there is an input u to the matrix transfer function $I + F\hat{G}(\cdot)$ of the form

$$u(t) = \sum_{\alpha} u_\alpha \delta^\alpha(t)$$

with each $u_\alpha \in \mathbb{C}^n$, for which the corresponding zero-state response of $I + F\hat{G}(\cdot)$ has the property that

$$e(t) = re^{pt} \qquad \text{for all} \quad t > 0 \tag{64}$$

where $\theta_n \neq r \in \mathbb{C}^n$;

(ii) if $z \in \mathbb{C}$ is a zero of $I + F\hat{G}(\cdot)$, then

(a) there exists a nonzero vector $g \in \mathbb{C}^n$ and a polynomial $\sum_\alpha m_\alpha s^\alpha$ such that for the input

$$u(t) = 1(t)e^{zt}g + \sum_{\alpha} m_\alpha \delta^\alpha(t) \tag{65}$$

the corresponding zero-state reponse of $I + F\hat{G}(\cdot)$ satisfies the relation

$$e[t; 0-, \theta_n; u(\cdot)] = \theta_n, \qquad \text{for} \quad t > 0 \tag{66}$$

(b) if, in addition, z is not a pole of $I + F\hat{G}(\cdot)$, then there exists a nonzero vector $\gamma \in \mathbb{C}^n$ such that

$$\psi(t) \triangleq \gamma' y[t; 0-, \theta_n; u(\cdot)] = 0, \qquad \text{for all} \quad t > 0 \tag{67}$$

where $u(\cdot)$ is defined in (65) with g *arbitrary* in $\mathbb{C}^n$ and the m_α's are appropriate vectors in $\mathbb{C}^n$ which depend on g;

(iii) if $v \in \mathbb{C}$ is neither a zero nor a pole of $I + F\hat{G}(\cdot)$, then for all nonzero vectors $k \in \mathbb{C}^n$ there is a polynomial $\sum_\alpha m_\alpha s^\alpha$ such that the input

$$u(t) = 1(t)e^{vt}k + \sum_{\alpha} m_\alpha \delta^\alpha(t) \tag{68}$$

produces a zero-state response with exponential form

$$e[t; 0-, \theta_n; u(\cdot)] = [I + F\hat{G}(v)]ke^{vt} \neq \theta_n, \qquad \text{for all} \quad t > 0 \tag{69}$$

■

Proof We shall only sketch the proof of (i) and (ii). First use Exercise 4 and write $I + F\hat{G}(s) = D_l(s)^{-1}N_l(s)$; p is a pole if and only if $\det D_l(p) = 0$, and z is a zero if and only if $\det N_l(z) = 0$. Since $N_l(\cdot)$ and $D_l(\cdot)$ are left coprime, we have $N_l(s)P(s) = I - D_l(s)Q(s)$, $\forall s \in \mathbb{C}$.

(i) If p is a pole, there is a vector $r \in \mathbb{C}^n$ such that $D_l(p)r = \theta_n$. Thus, $D_l(s)r = (s - p)k(s)$, where $k(\cdot) \in \mathbb{C}^n[s]$, i.e., is a *polynomial* vector. Choose an input $\hat{u}(s) = P(s)k(s)$, then

$$\begin{aligned}\hat{e}(s) = D_l(s)^{-1}N_l(s)P(s)k(s) &= D_l(s)^{-1}[I - D_l(s)Q(s)]k(s) \\ &= [r/(s - p)] - Q(s)k(s)\end{aligned}$$

Since the last term is a polynomial in s, (64) follows. The converse follows easily by contradiction.

(ii) (a) If z is a zero, then there is a nonzero vector g such that $N_l(z)g = \theta_n$. Hence $N_l(s)g/(s - z)$ is a *polynomial vector*, say, $p(s)$. Choose $m(s)$ in (65) to be $-P(s)p(s)$; then

$$\begin{aligned}\hat{e}(s) &= D_l(s)^{-1}\{N_l(s)[g/(s - z)] + N_l(s)[-P(s)p(s)]\} \\ &= Q(s)p(s), \quad \text{a polynomial in } s\end{aligned}$$

Hence $e(t) = \theta_n$ for all $t > 0$.

(b) The proof follows similar lines by choosing $\gamma' = c'D_l(z)$, where $c'N_l(z) = \theta_n'$. ∎

With this concept of zero and with Theorem (30) in mind, the analogy between the scalar case and the n-input–n-output case is complete.

70 **Theorem** (a) $p_c \in \mathbb{C}$ is a pole of $\hat{h} = \hat{g}(1 + f\hat{g})^{-1}$ if and only if p_c is a zero of the return difference $1 + f\hat{g}$, i.e., $1 + f\hat{g}(p_c) = 0$.

(b) Suppose that $\det F \neq 0$, $\hat{G}(s) \in \mathbb{R}^{n \times n}(s)$ and is proper, and finally that $\det[I + F\hat{G}(\infty)] \neq 0$; then $p_c \in \mathbb{C}$ is a pole of $\hat{H} = \hat{G}(I + F\hat{G})^{-1}$ if and only if p_c is a zero of the return difference matrix $I + F\hat{G}$.

(c) If $\hat{G}$ ($\hat{g}$, resp.) is proper, i.e., bounded at infinity, and if $\det[I + F\hat{G}(\infty)] \neq 0$ $[1 + f\hat{g}(\infty) \neq 0]$, then $\hat{H}$ ($\hat{h}$, resp.) is proper.

Proof (a) and (c) are immediate. For variety, let us use a left-coprime decomposition of $\hat{G}$: $\hat{G} = \bar{D}^{-1}\bar{N}$. Hence

$$\hat{H} = (I + \hat{G}F)^{-1}\hat{G} = (\bar{D} + \bar{N}F)^{-1}\bar{N}$$

Noting that $\bar{D} + \bar{N}F$ and $\bar{N}$ are left coprime [indeed, $\bar{N}P + \bar{D}Q = I$ if and only if $\bar{N}(P - FQ) + (\bar{D} + \bar{N}F)Q = I$], we conclude that p_c is a pole of $\hat{H}$ if and only if p_c is a zero of $\det[\bar{D} + F\bar{N}]$. Since F is nonsingular, $\bar{D} + \bar{N}F$ and $\bar{D}$ are left coprime [indeed, $\bar{N}P + \bar{D}Q = I$ if and only if $(\bar{D} + \bar{N}F)(F^{-1}P) +$

$\bar{D}(Q - F^{-1}P) = I]$, and since $I + \hat{G}F = \bar{D}^{-1}(\bar{D} + \bar{N}F)$, we conclude that p_c is a zero of $I + \hat{G}F$ [and of $I + F\hat{G} = F(I + \hat{G}F)F^{-1}$], if and only if p_c is zero of $\det[\bar{D} + \bar{N}F]$. Thus, p_c is a pole of $\hat{H}$ if and only if it is a zero of $I + F\hat{G}$. ∎

71 **Remark** If F is singular, the equivalence (b) does not hold. To wit $\hat{G} = \mathrm{diag}[(s-1)^{-1}, (s+1)^{-1}]$, $F = \mathrm{diag}(0, 1)$, $\hat{H}$ has a pole at $s = 1$ and $s = -2$, and $I + F\hat{G}$ has a zero only at $s = -2$.

3 Linear feedback systems with dynamics in the feedback path (rational transfer functions case)

Consider a continuous-time, linear, time-invariant, n-input–n-output feedback system with input u, output y, and error e. Call G_0 and G_f the transfer functions of the open-loop system and of the feedback system; we assume that they are rational matrix functions and are *proper*:

$$y = G_0 e; \qquad G_0 \in \mathbb{R}^{n\times n}(s), \quad G_0 \text{ proper} \tag{1}$$

$$e = u - G_f y; \qquad G_f \in \mathbb{R}^{n\times n}(s), \quad G_f \text{ proper} \tag{2}$$

We assume throughout that

$$\det[I + G_0(\infty)G_f(\infty)] = \det[I + G_f(\infty)G_0(\infty)] \neq 0 \tag{3}$$

As a consequence, we know that $(I + G_f G_0)^{-1}$ is a well-defined member of $\mathbb{R}^{n\times n}(s)$ because $\det[I + G_f(s)G_0(s)] \not\equiv 0$.

Our goal is to exhibit necessary and sufficient conditions for the closed-loop transfer functions

$$H_e : u \mapsto e, \; H_e(s) = [I + G_f(s)G_0(s)]^{-1} \tag{4}$$

$$H_y : u \mapsto y, \; H_y(s) = G_0(s)[I + G_f(s)G_0(s)]^{-1} \tag{5}$$

to be exponentially stable.

Exercise Given that G_0, $G_f \in \mathbb{R}^{n\times n}(s)$ are proper (bounded at infinity), show that $\det[I + G_f(\infty)G_0(\infty)] \neq 0$ if and only if H_e and H_y are proper.

One approach to the problem is to pick some minimal realization for G_0 and for G_f, derive from them minimal realizations of H_e and H_y, and require that the characteristic polynomials of the resulting A matrices, A_e and A_y, be stable. We shall use, instead, the factorization technique of Section 2.1.

To start with, consider how one would approach the problem in the single-input–single-output case. First choose irreducible representations of the rational transfer functions g_0 and g_f:

$$g_0 = n_0/d_0, \qquad n_0, d_0 \textit{ coprime} \text{ polynomials} \tag{6}$$

$$g_f = n_f/d_f, \qquad n_f, d_f \textit{ coprime} \text{ polynomials} \tag{7}$$

Then

$$h_e = (1 + g_f g_0)^{-1} = d_0 d_f/(n_f n_0 + d_f d_0) \tag{8}$$

$$h_y = g_0(1 + g_f g_0)^{-1} = n_0 d_f/(n_f n_0 + d_f d_0) \tag{9}$$

The numerator and denominator polynomials in the right-hand sides of (8) and (9) are *not necessarily coprime.* Indeed, for h_e, common factors may cancel out between d_0, n_f and d_f, n_0, respectively. For h_y, cancellation can occur only between d_f and n_0. For this reason it is false to assert that the zeros of $n_f n_0 + d_f d_0$ are the poles of h_e and h_y. Intuitively, it is clear that the same type of phenomenon will occur in the n-input–n-output case; however, the noncommutativity of the product of matrices requires a bit more care.

Consider the n-input–n-output system defined by (1) and (2). We assume that (3) holds. We seek necessary and sufficient conditions under which H_e and H_y, defined in (4) and (5), are exponentially stable. In fact, we shall obtain more, namely, polynomials whose roots are the poles of H_e and H_y, respectively.

Let us factor G_0 and G_f.

$$G_0 = N_0 D_0^{-1}; \qquad N_0, D_0 \in \mathbb{R}^{n\times n}[s]; \quad N_0, D_0 \textit{ right} \text{ coprime} \tag{10}$$

$$G_f = D_f^{-1} N_f; \qquad N_f, D_f \in \mathbb{R}^{n\times n}[s]; \quad N_f, D_f \textit{ left} \text{ coprime} \tag{11}$$

We, of course, have $\det D_0 \not\equiv 0$, $\det D_f \not\equiv 0$.(†)

$$\Omega = D_f D_0 + N_f N_0 \tag{12}$$

Then by (4) and (5)

$$H_e = D_0 \Omega^{-1} D_f, \qquad H_y = N_0 \Omega^{-1} D_f \tag{13}$$

† In most of the analysis of Section 3, the explicit dependence on s is not indicated because it is not necessary. For example, Eq. (12) asserts the equality of two polynomial matrices, i.e., the values taken by the left- and right-hand side, are equal for all $s \in \mathbb{C}$; Eq. (10) asserts the equality of two matrices of rational functions, i.e., the values taken by the left- and right-hand side are equal for all $s \in \mathbb{C}$, except at the poles. Similarly, $\det D_0 \neq 0$ means that the polynomial $\det D_0$ is not the zero element of the ring $\mathbb{R}[s]$; equivalently, the function $s \mapsto \det[D_0(s)]$ is not equal to zero for all $s \in \mathbb{C}$.

Again note that $\det \Omega \not\equiv 0$, because, by (3), H_e tends to a nonsingular constant matrix as $|s| \to \infty$. Let L be a greatest common *left* divisor (gcld) of Ω and D_f; then

14 $$\Omega = L\tilde{\Omega}, \qquad D_f = L\tilde{D}_f$$

where $L, \tilde{\Omega}, \tilde{D}_f \in \mathbb{R}^{n\times n}[s]$, and $\tilde{D}_f$ and $\tilde{\Omega}$ are *left* coprime. Equivalently, there are polynomial matrices $\tilde{P}$ and $\tilde{Q}$ s.t.

15 $$\tilde{D}_f\tilde{P} + \tilde{\Omega}\tilde{Q} = I$$

Thus, H_e can be written

16 $$H_e = D_0\tilde{\Omega}^{-1}\tilde{D}_f$$

Let R_e be a gcrd of D_0 and $\tilde{\Omega}$. Then

17 $$\tilde{\Omega} = \Omega_e R_e$$

18 $$D_0 = \tilde{D}_0 R_e$$

where $R_e, \Omega_e, \tilde{D}_0 \in \mathbb{R}^{n\times n}[s]$, and Ω_e and $\tilde{D}_0$ are *right* coprime. Equivalently, there are polynomial matrices P_e, Q_e s.t.

19 $$P_e\tilde{D}_0 + Q_e\Omega_e = I$$

Substituting (17) in (15), we obtain

$$\tilde{D}_f\tilde{P} + \Omega_e R_e\tilde{Q} = I$$

Hence $\tilde{D}_f$ and Ω_e are *left coprime*. Hence

20 $$\boxed{H_e = \tilde{D}_0\Omega_e^{-1}\tilde{D}_f} \qquad \text{with} \quad \begin{cases}\Omega_e,\ \tilde{D}_f \textit{ left} \text{ coprime}\\ \tilde{D}_0,\ \Omega_e \textit{ right} \text{ coprime}\end{cases}$$

Operating similarly on H_y, we obtain

21 $$H_y = N_0\tilde{\Omega}^{-1}\tilde{D}_f$$

Let R_y be gcrd of N_0 and $\tilde{\Omega}$, then

22 $$\tilde{\Omega} = \Omega_y R_y$$

23 $$N_0 = \tilde{N}_0 R_y$$

where $\Omega_y, R_y, \tilde{N}_0 \in \mathbb{R}^{n\times n}[s]$, and Ω_y and $\tilde{N}_0$ are *right* coprime. Hence there are polynomial matrices P_y and Q_y such that

24 $$P_y\tilde{N}_0 + Q_y\Omega_y = I$$

Again $\tilde{D}_f$ and Ω_y can be shown to be *left* coprime. Thus, we obtain

25 $$\boxed{H_y = \tilde{N}_0\Omega_y^{-1}\tilde{D}_f} \qquad \text{where} \quad \begin{cases}\Omega_y \text{ and } \tilde{D}_f \text{ are } \textit{left} \text{ coprime}\\ \tilde{N}_0 \text{ and } \Omega_y \text{ are } \textit{right} \text{ coprime}\end{cases}$$

26 **Theorem** For the system defined by (1), (2), with assumption (3) and the notations above, we have

$$p_e \in \overline{\mathbb{C}} \text{ is a pole of } H_e \Leftrightarrow p_e \text{ is a zero of } \det \Omega_e \tag{27}$$

$$p_y \in \overline{\mathbb{C}} \text{ is a pole of } H_y \Leftrightarrow p_y \text{ is a zero of } \det \Omega_y \tag{28}$$

Theorem (26) gives immediately the necessary and sufficient conditions for H_e and H_y to be exponentially stable; namely, $\det \Omega_e$ and $\det \Omega_y$ must have all their zeros in the open left-half plane.

Proof Note that (3) and the assumption that G_0 and G_f are proper imply that H_e and H_y are proper. Hence we concern ourselves only with poles in $\mathbb{C}$. We prove (27) only; the proof of (28) is similar.

$\Leftarrow$ By multiplying (19) on the right, we obtain

$$P_e \tilde{D}_0 \Omega_e^{-1} \tilde{D}_f + Q_e \tilde{D}_f = P_e H_e + Q_e \tilde{D}_f = \Omega_e^{-1} \tilde{D}_f \tag{29}$$

By assumption $\det \Omega_e(p_e) = 0$. Since Ω_e and $\tilde{D}_f$ are *left* coprime, the right-hand side of (29) has a pole at p_e [by the proof of Theorem (2.30)]. On the left-hand side, P_e, Q_e, and $\tilde{D}_f \in \mathbb{R}^{n \times n}[s]$, hence are bounded in any neighborhood of p_e; hence H_e has a pole at p_e.

$\Rightarrow$ By Cramer's rule in (20)

$$H_e = \tilde{D}_0 (\text{Adj } \Omega_e) \tilde{D}_f / \det \Omega_e \tag{30}$$

By assumption p_e is a pole of H_e. But $\tilde{D}_0$, Adj Ω_e, and $\tilde{D}_f \in \mathbb{R}^{n \times n}[s]$ (hence have no finite poles); hence (30) requires that $\det \Omega_e(p_e) = 0$. ∎

31 **Interpretation** Let $p = 1$, 2, or ∞. If $\det \Omega_e$ and $\det \Omega_e$ have all their zeros in the open left half-plane, then

(a) H_e and H_y are exponentially stable,
(b) for any $u \in L_n^p$, e and y are in L_n^p,
(c) for any $u \in L_n^p$, and for any *minimal* representation of G_0 and G_f, the corresponding state trajectories $x_0(\cdot)$ and $x_f(\cdot)$ (*starting from the zero state*) are in L_n^p.

Exercise Prove the above statement. [Use Theorem (1.9) and note that any minimal realization is completely observable.]

35 **Remark** With the notations above,

$$\{\text{zeros of } \det[I + G_f G_0]\} \subset \{\text{poles of } H_e\} \tag{36}$$

$$\{\text{zeros of } \det[I + G_f G_0]\} \subset \{\text{poles of } H_y\} \cup \{\text{zeros of } \det R_y\} \tag{37}$$

These inclusion relations show how dangerous it would be to try to ascertain the stability of the closed-loop transfer functions H_e and H_y by considering only the zeros of the rational function $s \mapsto \det[I + G_f(s)G_0(s)]$.

Proof (36) and (37) follow directly from (27), (20), and (4) and from (28), (25), and (5). Indeed,

38 $$\det(I + G_f G_0) = \frac{\det \Omega_e}{\det \tilde{D}_0 \cdot \det \tilde{D}_f}$$

39 $$\det(I + G_f G_0) = \frac{\det \Omega_y \cdot \det R_y}{\det D_0 \cdot \det \tilde{D}_f}$$

41 **Examples** The examples in the following are purposefully simple. Their purpose is to illustrate the relations between the poles of G_0, G_f, H_y, H_y and the zeros of Ω and $\det(I + G_f G_0)$.

42 **Example 1** Neither G_0 nor G_f is exponentially stable; H_e is unstable and H_y is exponentially stable.

$$G_0 = \begin{bmatrix} \dfrac{s-1}{s(s+2)} & 0 \\ 0 & \dfrac{s-2}{s+2} \end{bmatrix}, \qquad G_f = \begin{bmatrix} -\left(\dfrac{s+2}{s-1}\right) & 0 \\ 0 & -2\dfrac{s+1}{s(s-2)} \end{bmatrix}$$

$$G_0 = N_0 D_0^{-1} = \begin{bmatrix} s-1 & 0 \\ 0 & s-2 \end{bmatrix} \begin{bmatrix} s(s+2) & 0 \\ 0 & s+1 \end{bmatrix}^{-1}$$

$$G_f = D_f^{-1} N_f = \begin{bmatrix} s-1 & 0 \\ 0 & s(s-2) \end{bmatrix}^{-1} \begin{bmatrix} -(s+2) & 0 \\ 0 & -2(s+1) \end{bmatrix}$$

$$\det(I + G_f G_0)^{-1} = (s-1)(s-2)/s^2, \qquad \det[I + G_f(\infty)G_0(\infty)] = 1$$

$$H_e = (I + G_f G_0)^{-1} = \begin{bmatrix} \dfrac{s}{s-1} & 0 \\ 0 & \dfrac{s}{s-2} \end{bmatrix}, \qquad \Omega_e = \begin{bmatrix} s-1 & 0 \\ 0 & s-2 \end{bmatrix}$$

$$H_y = G_0(I + G_f G_0)^{-1} = \begin{bmatrix} \dfrac{1}{s+2} & 0 \\ 0 & \dfrac{s}{s+1} \end{bmatrix}, \qquad \Omega_y = \begin{bmatrix} s+2 & 0 \\ 0 & s+1 \end{bmatrix}$$

43 **Example 2** Neither G_0 nor G_f is exponentially stable; H_e is exponentially stable and H_y is unstable.

$$G_0 = \begin{bmatrix} \dfrac{s+2}{s(s-1)} & 0 \\ 0 & \dfrac{s+1}{s-2} \end{bmatrix}, \qquad G_f = \begin{bmatrix} \dfrac{2(s-1)}{s-2} & 0 \\ 0 & \dfrac{s-2}{s(s+1)} \end{bmatrix}$$

$$G_0 = N_0 D_0^{-1} = \begin{bmatrix} s+2 & 0 \\ 0 & s+1 \end{bmatrix} \begin{bmatrix} s(s-1) & 0 \\ 0 & s-2 \end{bmatrix}^{-1}$$

$$G_f = D_f^{-1} N_f = \begin{bmatrix} s+2 & 0 \\ 0 & s(s+1) \end{bmatrix}^{-1} \begin{bmatrix} 2(s-1) & 0 \\ 0 & s-2 \end{bmatrix}$$

$$\det(I + G_f G_0) = (s+1)(s+2)/s^2, \qquad \det[I + G_f(\infty) G_0(\infty)] = 1$$

$$H_e = (I + G_f G_0)^{-1} = \begin{bmatrix} \dfrac{s}{s+2} & 0 \\ 0 & \dfrac{s}{s+1} \end{bmatrix}, \qquad \Omega_e = \begin{bmatrix} s+2 & 0 \\ 0 & s+1 \end{bmatrix}$$

$$H_y = G_0(I + G_f G_0)^{-1} = \begin{bmatrix} \dfrac{1}{s-1} & 0 \\ 0 & \dfrac{s}{s-2} \end{bmatrix}, \qquad \Omega_y = \begin{bmatrix} s-1 & 0 \\ 0 & s-2 \end{bmatrix}$$

50 **Interpretation of the Zeros of det $\Omega(s) = 0$** For the system described by (1) and (2), statements (27) and (28) assert that the stability of the transfer functions H_e and H_y is completely characterized by the location of the zeros of det $\Omega_e(s) = 0$ and det $\Omega_y(s) = 0$, resp. The transfer functions H_e and H_y, however, characterize only the *zero-state response* of the feedback system. To consider responses that do not start from the zero state, we have to adopt a specific state representation. Let $(A_i, B_i, C_i, D_i) = R_i$ where $i = 0, f$, be some *minimal* state representations of G_0 and G_f, resp. Call the corresponding states x_0 and x_f, resp. The vector $(x_0', x_f')'$ is a suitable state vector for the feedback system. Of course, it is not necessarily of minimal dimension. Note that det $D_i(s) = k_i \det(sI - A_i)$, for $i = 0, f$.

We claim that

51 det $\Omega(s) = 0$ is the characteristic equation of the feedback system described by (1) and (2).

This means, in particular, that if, for some λ, $\det \Omega(\lambda) = 0$, then for some initial state c and for $u \equiv 0$, the state trajectory is of the form $ce^{\lambda t}$. To prove (51) we use the factorization (10) and (11) to rewrite the feedback equation as follows:

$$y = G_0 e \qquad \begin{cases} D_0 v = e, \\ y = N_0 v, \end{cases} \qquad u - e = G_f y \qquad \begin{cases} w = N_f y \\ D_f u - D_f e = w \end{cases}$$

where we introduced the new variables v and w. The four equations on the right are *differential* equations since N_0, D_0, N_f, D_f are *polynomial* matrices. Let us eliminate e, w, and y by substitution; then we obtain the following equivalent system

$$(N_f N_0 + D_f D_0)v = D_f u, \qquad y = N_0 v, \qquad e = D_0 v,$$
$$w = N_f y = N_f N_0 v$$

So given u and the appropriate initial conditions, the solution $t \to v(t)$, for $t \geq 0$, is obtained by the first equation; y, e, and w are obtained by substitution. Since these substitutions involve only products by polynomial matrices, no new modes are introduced. Clearly then, the characteristic equation of the feedback system is $\det(N_f N_0 + D_f D_0) = \det \Omega = 0$. ∎

9 **State-Space Representation Formulation** The feedback system described by (1) and (2) consisted of subsystems prescribed by their transfer functions. This allowed us to consider only the *zero-state responses* of the subsystems and of the feedback configuration. In contrast, suppose now that the subsystems are prescribed by their state representations R_0 and R_f, respectively:

$$R_0 = (A_0, B_0, C_0, D_0); \qquad \text{hence} \quad G_0(s) = C_0(sI - A_0)^{-1}B_0 + D_0 \tag{0}$$
$$R_f = (A_f, B_f, C_f, D_f); \qquad \text{hence} \quad G_f(s) = C_f(sI - A_f)^{-1}B_f + D_f \tag{1}$$

These state representations are *not* assumed to be minimal. We wish to be able to study the behavior of the state trajectory of the feedback system when both the *input* and the *initial state* are *arbitrarily chosen.* We assume that

$$\det[I + G_f(\infty)G_0(\infty)] = \det(I + D_f D_0) \neq 0 \tag{2}$$

Let x_0 and x_f denote the states associated with R_0 and R_f, respectively; let us choose x, defined by $x = (x_0', x_f')'$, to be the state of the representation R_c of the closed-loop system. We shall see that under assumption (62), R_c takes the standard form $R_c = (A,B,C,D)$.

Once the representation R_c is obtained, one has a complete description of the relation between input, initial state, and output. In fact, the *zero-state response* y of the closed-loop system is given by

$$\hat{y}(s) = H_y(s)\hat{u}(s) = [C(sI - A)^{-1}B + D]\hat{u}(s) \tag{4}$$

and the state trajectory starting from $x(0)$ at 0 is given by

65 $$\hat{x}(s) = (sI - A)^{-1}x(0) + (sI - A)^{-1}B\hat{u}(s)$$

In order to discuss the boundedness of the state trajectory $t \mapsto x(t)$, we recall the definition (1.5) of exponentially stable transfer functions and their properties [Theorem (1.9)]; thus, we see that we need to relate the closed-loop eigenvalues λ_{ci} (defined as the eigenvalues of A) to the eigenvalues of R_0 and R_f (respectively defined as the eigenvalues of A_0 and A_f). Thus, we need to calculate A.

The matrices A, B, C, D which define R_c are obtained from the equations describing the subsystems and from the equations describing their interconnections. As in (1) and (2) above, let u and y denote the input and output of the closed-loop system. Call e the error; then we have:

(a) For the subsystems

66 $$\begin{aligned} \dot{x}_0 &= A_0 x_0 + B_0 e, & \dot{x}_f &= A_f x_f + B_f y \\ y &= C_0 x_0 + D_0 e, & y_2 &= C_f x_f + D_f y \end{aligned}$$

(We used here the fact that the error e and the output y are, respectively, the input and output of the forward subsystem, and also that y is the input of the feedback subsystem.)

(b) For the interconnection

67 $$e = u - y_2 = u - C_f x_f - D_f y$$

We shall obtain the representation R_c by eliminating e from the first three equations of (66) and from (67). In fact, (67) and the second equation of (66) give

68 $$e = (I + D_f D_0)^{-1}(u - D_f C_0 x_0 - C_f x_f)$$

Using (68) in the first three equations of (66), we obtain, after a few manipulations,

69 $$A = \begin{bmatrix} A_0 - B_0(I + D_f D_0)^{-1} D_f C_0 & -B_0(I + D_f D_0)^{-1} C_f \\ B_f(I + D_0 D_f)^{-1} C_0 & A_f - B_f(I + D_0 D_f)^{-1} D_0 C_f \end{bmatrix}$$

70 $$B = \begin{bmatrix} B_0(I + D_f D_0)^{-1} \\ B_f(I + D_0 D_f)^{-1} D_0 \end{bmatrix}, \qquad D = (I + D_0 D_f)^{-1} D_0$$

71 $$C = [(I + D_0 D_f)^{-1} C_0 \quad -(I + D_0 D_f)^{-1} D_0 C_f]$$

Equations (69)–(71) specify the representation R_c of the closed-loop system. Note the symmetry of the elements of A; by interchanging subscripts 0 and f, one obtains one row from the other. This type of symmetry is not present in

B, C, and D because of the lack of symmetry of the point of application of u as seen from the block diagram representation of the feedback system.

To obtain the desired relation between the eigenvalues of A and those of A_0 and A_f is conceptually very simple. The manipulations are messy; they involve elementary row and column operations performed on blocks of $sI - A$, the observation that $D_0(I + D_f D_0)^{-1} = (I + D_0 D_f)^{-1} D_0$, and if M and N are, resp., $p \times q$ and $q \times p$ matrices, then

$$\det(I_p + MN) = \det(I_q + NM)$$

For the details the reader is referred to Hsu and Chen [Hsu.1]. The result can be expressed as follows:

Let λ_{ci} denote the closed-loop eigenvalues (i.e., the eigenvalues of A); let λ_{oi} and λ_{fi} denote those of A_0 and A_f, resp. Then

72
$$\det(sI - A) = \det(sI - A_0) \cdot \det(sI - A_f) \frac{\det[I + G_f(s)G_0(s)]}{\det[I + G_f(\infty)G_0(\infty)]}$$

or equivalently

73
$$\det[I + G_f(s)G_0(s)] = \det[I + G_f(\infty)G_0(\infty)] \frac{\prod (s - \lambda_{ci})}{\prod (s - \lambda_{oi}) \prod (s - \lambda_{fi})}$$

Note that (72) is a generalization of (2.56), and (73) is a generalization of (2.44).

We note again that the zeros of $\det[I + G_f(s)G_0(s)]$ may be a *proper* subset of $\{\lambda_{ci}\}$, the set of closed-loop eigenvalues; indeed, cancellations may occur in the right-hand side of (73). On the other hand, (73) shows that, in the case where $\text{Re } \lambda_{0i} < 0$ and $\text{Re } \lambda_{fi} < 0$, for all i, the λ_{ci} will all have negative real parts if and only if all the zeros of $\det[I + G_f(s)G_0(s)]$ have negative real parts. Concerning state trajectories, we can state the following fact.

4 **Fact** If all the closed-loop eigenvalues λ_{ci} have negative real parts, then for all initial states $x(0) = [x_0(0)', x_f(0)']'$ and for all bounded inputs, i.e., $u \in L_n^{\infty}$, the state trajectory of the closed-loop system, i.e., $t \mapsto x(t)$, is bounded; this is also true for $e(\cdot)$ and $y(\cdot)$.

Exercise 5 Derive (69), (70), and (71) in the case where D_0 and D_f are zero.

Exercise 6 Show that if R_0 and R_f are minimal, it does not follow that R_c is minimal.

Exercise 7 Let H_y denote, as in (5), the closed-loop transfer junction. Show that

75 (a) $$[I - \hat{G}_f(s)\hat{H}_y(s)][I + \hat{G}_f(s)\hat{G}_0(s)] = I, \qquad \forall s \in \mathbb{C}$$

(b) If

$$\det(I + D_f D_0) = \det(I + D_0 D_f) = 0$$

then (i) as $s \to \infty$, $H_y(s) \to \infty$, and (ii) the closed-loop system does not have a state representation in the standard form (A, B, C, D).

4 Convolution feedback systems

4.1 General results

In the previous sections, we considered only rational transfer functions and hence were restricted to lumped models. We consider now feedback systems made of subsystems whose input–output properties are represented by convolution operators. Thus, our present study includes distributed models. We shall make use without comment of the results of Appendixes C and D.

To appreciate the generality of the convolution assumption, recall that L. Schwartz has shown that any *linear time-invariant* operator that satisfies some slight continuity properties has a convolutional representation, more precisely, a representation of the form $u \mapsto T * u$ where T is a distribution (generalized function). If the operator is, in addition, nonanticipative, then the support of T is in $\mathbb{R}_+$, and conversely.

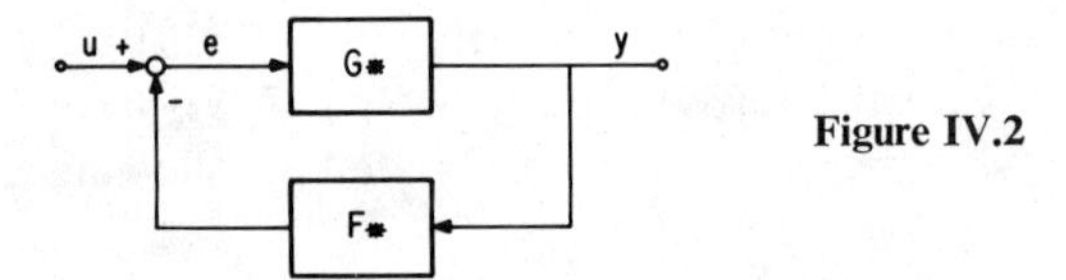

Figure IV.2

The system under study is shown in Fig. IV.2. The input u, the error e, and the output y are functions from $\mathbb{R}_+$ into $\mathbb{R}^n$. We shall also allow them to be generalized functions: δ-functions will appear frequently. The linear time-invariant subsystems **G** and **F** are characterized by their impulse responses $G(\cdot)$ and $F(\cdot)$. The equations are

1
2 $$\begin{cases} y = G * e, \\ u = e + F * G * e, \end{cases} \qquad \text{equivalently,} \qquad \begin{cases} \hat{y} = \hat{G}\hat{e} \\ \hat{u} = \hat{e} + \hat{F}\hat{G}\hat{e} \end{cases}$$

Hence

3a $$\hat{H}(s) = \hat{G}(s)[I + \hat{F}(s)\hat{G}(s)]^{-1}$$

and

3b $$I - \hat{F}(s)\hat{H}(s) = [I + \hat{F}(s)\hat{G}(s)]^{-1}$$

over the common half-plane, where the Laplace transforms $\hat{F}$ and $\hat{G}$ are both defined.

In this section we shall require for stability that the closed-loop impulse response $H(\cdot) \in \mathscr{A}^{n \times n}(0)$. When this is the case,

4 $$\|y\|_p \leq \|H\|_{\mathscr{A}} \cdot \|u\|_p \qquad \text{for} \quad 1 \leq p \leq \infty$$

i.e., the closed-loop system is L^p stable for *all* $p \in [1, \infty]$. The converse is not true, because the class of impulse responses could be enlarged by considering those with singular measure [Tho. 1]. We shall abbreviate $\mathscr{A}(0)$ by $\mathscr{A}$; $\|H\|_{\mathscr{A}}$ denotes the norm of $H(\cdot) \in \mathscr{A}^{n \times n}$. We take the position that the increased technical difficulties are not worth the slight extension.

Throughout this section, we assume that the feedback transfer function matrix $\hat{F}(s)$ belongs to the algebra $\hat{\mathscr{A}}^{n \times n}$, for reasons that are mostly technical. This assumption unfortunately rules out all "unstable" feedbacks, including the commonly found case of rate feedback. This is evidently the price we have to pay for allowing distributed, possibly unstable elements in the forward path.

The first theorem in the following shows that, under very broad conditions, if the closed-loop impulse response $H(\cdot) \in \mathscr{A}^{n \times n}(\sigma)$ for some $\sigma \geq 0$, then $G(\cdot)$ must satisfy certain conditions.

5 **Theorem** Consider a system described by (1) and (2), where the feedback transfer matrix $\hat{F}(\cdot) \in \hat{\mathscr{A}}^{n \times n}$. Let $G(\cdot)$ be a matrix of distributions with support in $\mathbb{R}_+$, and suppose that in some neighborhood of the origin, G contains at most impulse functions. Assume that the closed-loop impulse response $H(\cdot)$ is uniquely determined by the equation

6 $$H + H * F * G = G, \qquad \text{or} \qquad H = G - H * F * G$$

U.t.c., if $H(\cdot) \in \mathscr{A}^{n \times n}(\sigma)$ for some $\sigma \geq 0$, then

(i) $G(\cdot)$ is Laplace transformable; for some $\alpha > 0$, $\hat{G}(\cdot)$ is analytic in $\text{Re}\, s > \alpha$, $\hat{G}(\cdot) \in \hat{\mathscr{A}}^{n \times n}(\alpha)$ and can be continued to a meromorphic function in $\text{Re}\, s > \sigma$.

(ii) $\hat{G}(\cdot)$ is of the form

7 $$\hat{G}(s) = \hat{\mathscr{N}}(s)[\hat{\mathscr{D}}(s)]^{-1} \qquad \text{where} \quad \hat{\mathscr{N}}(s), \hat{\mathscr{D}}(s) \in \hat{\mathscr{A}}^{n \times n}(\sigma)$$

(iii)

8 $$\inf_{\text{Re}\, s \geq \sigma} |\det[I + \hat{F}(s)\hat{G}(s)]| > 0$$

Remark 1. Note that we do not assume that $\hat{F}(\cdot)$ is constant, or even if $\hat{F}(\cdot)$ is constant, that it is nonsingular. This allows us to consider systems whose number of inputs need not necessarily equal the number of outputs. If $F(\cdot)$ is rectangular, it can be made square by adding rows or columns of zeros, as appropriate.

2. This theorem shows that under the mild assumptions on $G(\cdot)$, the solvability of the closed-loop system, and the assumption that $H(\cdot)$ is of exponential order, we can deduce a great deal about the form of $G(\cdot)$.

Proof (i) Balancing impulses in (6) gives

$$H_0 = G_0 - H_0 F_0 G_0, \qquad \text{or} \qquad H_0(I + F_0 G_0) = G_0 \tag{9}$$

where F_0, G_0, and H_0 denote, respectively, the strengths of the impulses at $t = 0$ of $F(\cdot)$, $G(\cdot)$, and $H(\cdot)$. In order for H_0 to be uniquely determined from (9), it is necessary for $I + F_0 G_0$ to be nonsingular. Now define

$$\hat{E}(s) = [I + \hat{F}(s)\hat{G}(s)]^{-1} = I - \hat{F}(s)\hat{H}(s) \tag{10}$$

Since $\hat{E}(s) = I - \hat{F}(s)\hat{H}(s)$ (see Exercise 2) and since $\hat{F}$ and $\hat{H}$ both belong to $\hat{\mathscr{A}}^{n \times n}(\sigma)$, clearly so does $\hat{E}$. Thus, $\hat{E}(s)$ is bounded in $\operatorname{Re} s \geq \sigma$, analytic in $\operatorname{Re} s > \sigma$, and tends to $I + F_0 G_0$ as $\operatorname{Re} s \to \infty$. Hence $s \mapsto 1/\det \hat{E}(s)$ is meromorphic in $\operatorname{Re} s > \sigma$ and is analytic and bounded away from zero in some half-plane $\operatorname{Re} s > \alpha$ for α sufficiently large. Consequently, by Appendix D.3.3, $\hat{E}(s)^{-1} \in \hat{\mathscr{A}}^{n \times n}(\alpha)$. But by (10), this means that $I\delta(\cdot) + F(\cdot) * G(\cdot) \in \mathscr{A}^{n \times n}(\alpha)$. Thus, $F * G$ is Laplace transformable, and $\hat{F}\hat{G}$ is analytic for $\operatorname{Re} s > \alpha$. Furthermore, $\hat{F}\hat{G}$ can be analytically continued to a meromorphic function in $\operatorname{Re} s > \sigma$, since $\det \hat{E}(s)$ can have almost isolated zeros in $\operatorname{Re} s > \sigma$. Since $\hat{G}(\cdot) = \hat{H}(s)[I + \hat{F}(s)\hat{G}(s)]$, the same conclusion holds for $\hat{G}(\cdot)$. Finally, $\hat{G} = \hat{H}\hat{E}^{-1} \in \hat{\mathscr{A}}^{n \times n}(\alpha)$.

(ii) Since $G(\cdot)$ is Laplace transformable, we may write $\hat{H} = \hat{G}(I + \hat{F}\hat{G})^{-1}$. Routine matrix algebra can now be used to show that

$$\hat{G}(s) = \hat{H}(s)[\hat{E}(s)]^{-1} \tag{11}$$

where $\hat{E}(s)$ is defined in (10).

(iii) As we have seen, $H(\cdot) \in \mathscr{A}^{n \times n}(\sigma)$ implies that $E(\cdot) \in \mathscr{A}^{n \times n}(\sigma)$, whence $\det \hat{E}(\cdot) \in \hat{\mathscr{A}}(\sigma)$. Thus, there exists a finite constant k such that $|\det \hat{E}(s)| \leq k$ whenever $\operatorname{Re} s \geq \sigma$. But this, in turn, implies that

$$1/|\det \hat{E}(s)| = |\det[I + \hat{F}(s)\hat{G}(s)]| \geq 1/k \qquad \text{whenever} \quad \operatorname{Re} s \geq \sigma \tag{12}$$

which is enough to prove (8). ∎

The factorization (7) is the first hint of a similarity between the theory for systems with rational transfer functions and the general case of convolution feedback systems.

Exercise 1 Suppose that $n = 1$, that $g(t) = g_0\,\delta(t) + g_a(t)$, with $g_a(\cdot) \in L^1$, and $\hat{f}(s) = f_0$, a nonzero constant. Show that (8) is equivalent to the statement: $s \mapsto 1 + f_0\,\hat{g}(s)$ has no zeros in $\operatorname{Re} s \geq \sigma$. This holds if and only if the Nyquist diagram of $\hat{g}$ [i.e., the graph of $\omega \mapsto \hat{g}(\sigma + j\omega)$, $\omega \in \mathbb{R}$] does not intersect or encircle the point $(-1/f_0, 0)$ in $\mathbb{C}$. For other graphical tests, see Section 5.

[The significance of this exercise is as follows. There are clearly two possible ways in which the condition (8) can be violated: (i) $\det[I + \hat{F}(s_0)\hat{G}(s_0)] = 0$ for some s_0 with $\operatorname{Re} s_0 \geq \sigma$, or (ii) no such s_0 may exist, but there may exist a sequence $\{s_i\}$ with $\operatorname{Re} s_i \geq \sigma$ such that $\det[I + \hat{F}(s_i)\hat{G}(s_i)] \to 0$ as $i \to \infty$. This exercise shows that under the stated conditions, the second possibility cannot occur. Furthermore, it provides a means for verifying whether or not the first possibility occurs by studying only the behavior of the function $\omega \mapsto \hat{g}(\sigma + j\omega)$.]

Exercise 2 Show that the following relationships hold for the system described in Theorem (5):

3a $$\hat{H} = \hat{G}(I + \hat{F}\hat{G})^{-1} = (I + \hat{G}\hat{F})^{-1}\hat{G}$$

3b $$\hat{G} = \hat{H}(I - \hat{F}\hat{H})^{-1} = (I - \hat{H}\hat{F})^{-1}\hat{H}$$

3c $$(I - \hat{F}\hat{H})(I + \hat{F}\hat{G}) = I$$

3d $$(I - \hat{H}\hat{F})(I + \hat{G}\hat{F}) = I$$

The relation between (13a) and (13b) is made clearer by the observation that H is obtained from G by putting a feedback F around G, while G is obtained from H by putting a feedback of $-F$ around H.

Exercise 3 Show that if $\hat{H} \in \hat{\mathscr{A}}^{n\times n}$ and $\hat{F} \in \hat{\mathscr{A}}^{n\times n}$, then so does $\hat{E}$. Show that if in addition $\hat{F}^{-1} \in \hat{\mathscr{A}}^{n\times n}$, then $\hat{H} \in \hat{\mathscr{A}}^{n\times n}$ if and only if $\hat{E} \in \hat{\mathscr{A}}^{n\times n}$.

Knowing that in order for the closed-loop impulse response to be of exponential order, $\hat{G}(\cdot)$ must be of the form (7), we can now formulate a very general theorem that can, in turn, be specialized to various practically significant situations.

4 **Theorem** Consider a feedback system described by (1) and (2). Suppose that $\hat{F}(\cdot) \in \hat{\mathscr{A}}^{n\times n}$, that the system has a uniquely defined closed-loop impulse response $H(\cdot)$, that $G(\cdot)$ is Laplace transformable, and hence that $\hat{H}(s) = \hat{G}(s)[I + \hat{F}(s)\hat{G}(s)]^{-1}$ over the common half-plane of convergence. U.t.c., $H \in \mathscr{A}^{n\times n}$ if and only if

(i) there exist $\hat{\mathscr{N}}(\cdot)$ and $\hat{\mathscr{D}}(\cdot)$ in $\hat{\mathscr{A}}^{n\times n}$ such that

5 $$\hat{G}(s) = \hat{\mathscr{N}}(s)\hat{\mathscr{D}}^{-1}(s)$$

Moreover, the following non-cancellation condition is satisfied: Whenever (s_i) is a sequence with Re $s_i \geq 0$ such that $\lim_{i\to\infty} |\det \hat{\mathscr{D}}(s_i)| = 0$, we have $\liminf_{i\to\infty} |\det[\hat{\mathscr{D}}(s_i) + \hat{F}(s_i)\hat{\mathscr{N}}(s_i)]| > 0$.
[This condition is hereafter referred to in abbreviated form as follows: The ordered pair of functions [det $\hat{\mathscr{D}}$, $\det(\hat{\mathscr{D}} + \hat{F}\hat{\mathscr{N}})$] satisfy condition (N).]

(ii)

16
$$\inf_{\operatorname{Re} s \geq 0} |\det[I + \hat{F}(s)\hat{G}(s)]| > 0$$

Proof $\Rightarrow$ Rewrite the relation between $\hat{G}$ and $\hat{H}$ as follows

$$\hat{G} = \hat{H}(I - \hat{F}\hat{H})^{-1}$$

Hence with $\hat{\mathscr{N}} = \hat{H}$, $\hat{\mathscr{D}} = I - \hat{F}\hat{H}$, we have (15), Furthermore, the no-cancellation condition (N) also holds since

$$\det(\hat{\mathscr{D}} + \hat{F}\hat{\mathscr{N}}) = \det I = 1, \qquad \forall s \text{ in } \operatorname{Re} s \geq 0$$

Thus, statement (i) is established.

Consider now (13c) and take determinant of both sides; then

17
$$\det[I + \hat{F}\hat{G}] = 1/\det(I - \hat{F}\hat{H})$$

Since $I - \hat{F}\hat{H} \in \hat{\mathscr{A}}^{n\times n}$, it is bounded in Re $s \geq 0$, and so is its determinant. Hence (16) follows from (17).

$\Leftarrow$ We show first of all that (16) and (15) together imply that

18
$$\inf_{\operatorname{Re} s \geq 0} |\det[\hat{\mathscr{D}}(s) + \hat{F}(s)\hat{\mathscr{N}}(s)]| > 0$$

To prove (18), suppose by way of contradiction that (18) is false, and let $(s_i)_1^\infty$ be a sequence with Re $s_i \geq 0$ such that $\det[\hat{\mathscr{D}}(s_i) + \hat{F}(s_i)\hat{\mathscr{N}}(s_i)] \to 0$. Since $\det(\hat{\mathscr{D}} + \hat{F}\hat{\mathscr{N}}) = \det \hat{\mathscr{D}} \cdot \det(I + \hat{F}\hat{G})$, we see that if $\det(\hat{\mathscr{D}} + \hat{F}\hat{\mathscr{N}}) \to 0$, then either $\det \hat{\mathscr{D}} \to 0$ or $\det(I + \hat{F}\hat{G}) \to 0$ [after taking subsequences of $(s_i)_1^\infty$ if necessary]. The latter possibility is ruled out by (16). As to the former possibility, suppose $\det \hat{\mathscr{D}}(s_i) \to 0$. Then since the pair (det $\hat{\mathscr{D}}$, $\det(\hat{\mathscr{D}} + \hat{F}\hat{\mathscr{N}})$) satisfies condition (N), it follows that $\liminf |\det[\hat{\mathscr{D}}(s_i) + \hat{F}(s_i)\hat{\mathscr{N}}(s_i)]| > 0$, which is a contradiction. Thus, (18) is established. Now, by matrix algebra, we have $\hat{H} = \hat{G}(I + \hat{F}\hat{G})^{-1} = \hat{\mathscr{N}}(\hat{\mathscr{D}} + \hat{F}\hat{\mathscr{N}})^{-1}$. In view of (18) and Appendix D.3.3, we see that $(\hat{\mathscr{D}} + \hat{F}\hat{\mathscr{N}})^{-1} \in \hat{\mathscr{A}}^{n\times n}$, whence $\hat{H} \in \hat{\mathscr{A}}^{n\times n}$. ∎

Exercise 4 Prove the following alternate version of Theorem (14). Let $\hat{F} \in \hat{\mathscr{A}}^{n\times n}$. Then $\hat{H} = \hat{G}(I + \hat{F}\hat{G})^{-1} \in \hat{\mathscr{A}}^{n\times n}$ if and only if there exist $\hat{\mathscr{N}}$ and $\hat{\mathscr{D}}$ in $\hat{\mathscr{A}}^{n\times n}$ such that (i) $\hat{G} = \hat{\mathscr{N}}\hat{\mathscr{D}}^{-1}$, and (ii)

$$\inf_{\operatorname{Re} s \geq 0} |\det[\hat{\mathscr{D}}(s) + \hat{F}(s)\hat{\mathscr{N}}(s)]| > 0$$

19 **Corollary** Suppose $\hat{F} \in \hat{\mathscr{A}}^{n \times n}$ and that $\hat{G} = \hat{\mathscr{N}}\hat{\mathscr{D}}^{-1}$, where $\hat{\mathscr{N}}$, $\hat{\mathscr{D}} \in \hat{\mathscr{A}}^{n \times n}$, and the pair [det $\hat{\mathscr{D}}$, det $(\hat{\mathscr{D}} + \hat{F}\hat{\mathscr{N}})$] satisfies condition (N). Then $\hat{H} = \hat{G}(I + \hat{F}\hat{G})^{-1} \in \hat{\mathscr{A}}^{n \times n}$ if and only if (16) is satisfied.

Theorem (14), though quite easy to state and prove, has many interesting implications. Suppose we are given $\hat{F} \in \hat{\mathscr{A}}^{n \times n}$ and $\hat{G}$, and we wish to determine whether $\hat{H} = \hat{G}(I + \hat{F}\hat{G})^{-1} \in \hat{\mathscr{A}}^{n \times n}$ or not. How would we proceed? We would first check the condition (16). If (16) fails, then definitely $\hat{H} \notin \hat{\mathscr{A}}^{n \times n}$, because (16) is necessary for $\hat{H}$ to belong to $\hat{\mathscr{A}}^{n \times n}$ [recall Theorem (5)]. On the other hand, suppose (16) is satisfied. This does not mean that $\hat{H} \in \hat{\mathscr{A}}^{n \times n}$. In fact, one need not look far to find a counterexample. Let

$$\hat{G} = \begin{bmatrix} \dfrac{1}{s+1} & 0 \\ 0 & \dfrac{1}{s-1} \end{bmatrix}, \qquad \hat{F} = \begin{bmatrix} 0 & 0 \\ 0 & \dfrac{s-1}{s+1} \end{bmatrix}$$

Then

$$I + \hat{F}\hat{G} = \begin{bmatrix} 1 & 0 \\ 0 & \dfrac{s+2}{s+1} \end{bmatrix}$$

and hence (16) is satisfied. However,

$$\hat{H} = \begin{bmatrix} \dfrac{1}{s+1} & 0 \\ 0 & \dfrac{s+1}{(s-1)(s+2)} \end{bmatrix}$$

and clearly $\hat{H} \notin \hat{\mathscr{A}}^{n \times n}$. Thus, in order to conclude that $\hat{H} \in \hat{\mathscr{A}}^{n \times n}$, in addition to (16), we use the added assumption that $\hat{G}$ is of the form (15), where the appropriate condition (N) is satisfied. This brings us to the following question: Suppose we express $\hat{G}$ in the form (15), where $\hat{\mathscr{N}}$, $\hat{\mathscr{D}} \in \hat{\mathscr{A}}^{n \times n}$, but suppose the condition (N) fails to hold. What, if anything, can we conclude? The answer is, in general, nothing—one simply has to try to find a different factorization for $\hat{G}$. On the other hand, if $\hat{\mathscr{N}}$ and $\hat{\mathscr{D}}$ constitute a so-called pseudo-right-coprime factorization, then definite conclusions can be drawn. We now proceed to study this last concept in detail.

.0 **Definition** Two elements $\hat{\mathscr{N}}$, $\hat{\mathscr{D}} \in \hat{\mathscr{A}}^{n \times n}$ are said to be **pseudo-right-coprime** (prc) if there exist $\hat{\mathscr{U}}, \hat{\mathscr{V}}, \hat{\mathscr{W}} \in \hat{\mathscr{A}}^{n \times n}$ such that

(i) det $\hat{\mathscr{W}}(s) \neq 0$ for all s with Re $s \geq 0$, $|s| < \infty$, and
(ii) $\hat{\mathscr{U}}\hat{\mathscr{N}} + \hat{\mathscr{V}}\hat{\mathscr{D}} = \hat{\mathscr{W}}$.

21 **Definition** Given a Laplace transform $\hat{G}(\cdot)$, the pair $(\hat{\mathcal{N}}, \hat{\mathcal{D}})$ is said to be a **pseudo-right-coprime factorization** (prcf) of $\hat{G}$ if

(i) $\hat{G} = \hat{\mathcal{N}}\hat{\mathcal{D}}^{-1}$,
(ii) $\hat{\mathcal{N}}$ and $\hat{\mathcal{D}}$ are prc, and
(iii) whenever $(s_i)_1{}^\infty$ is a sequence with $\text{Re } s_i \geq 0$ and $|s_i| \to \infty$, we have $\liminf_{i\to\infty} |\det \hat{\mathcal{D}}(s_i)| > 0$.

22 **Fact** Let $\hat{G}(s) \in \mathbb{R}^{n\times n}(s)$ and be proper. Then $\hat{G}$ has a prcf.

Proof If $\hat{G}(s) \in \mathbb{R}^{n\times n}(s)$ and is proper, then there exist polynomial matrices N and D such tht N and D are right coprime and such that $ND^{-1} = G$. Moreover, we can assume that D is column proper. Let $\det D(s) = \prod_{i=1}^k (s - p_i)^{m_i}$, and let δ_i denote the highest power of s appearing in the ith column of $D(s)$. Since D is column proper, we have $\sum_{i=1}^n \delta_i = \sum_{i=1}^k m_i$. Let $M(s) = \text{diag}[(s+1)^{\delta_1}, \ldots, (s+1)^{\delta_n}]$, and define

$$\hat{\mathcal{N}} = NM^{-1}, \qquad \hat{\mathcal{D}} = DM^{-1} \tag{23}$$

Then $\hat{\mathcal{N}}$ and $\hat{\mathcal{D}}$ are proper rational matrices with poles at $s = -1$, and hence $\hat{\mathcal{N}}, \hat{\mathcal{D}} \in \hat{\mathcal{A}}^{n\times n}$. Moreover, $\hat{G} = \hat{\mathcal{N}}\hat{\mathcal{D}}^{-1}$. Thus, (i) of Definition (21) is satisfied. Since N and D are right coprime, there exist polynomial matrices P and Q such that

$$PN + QD = I, \qquad \text{for all} \quad s \tag{24}$$

Now let α be an integer greater than or equal to the degree of any element of P and Q. Then the rational matrices

$$\hat{\mathcal{U}} = P \cdot (s+1)^{-\alpha}, \qquad \hat{\mathcal{V}} = Q(s+1)^{-\alpha} \tag{25}$$

both belong to $\hat{\mathcal{A}}^{n\times n}$. Moreover, from (24) we have

$$\hat{\mathcal{U}}\hat{\mathcal{N}} + \hat{\mathcal{V}}\hat{\mathcal{D}} = (PN + QD)M^{-1}(s+1)^{-\alpha} = M^{-1}(s+1)^{-\alpha} = \hat{\mathcal{W}}(s), \quad \text{say} \tag{26}$$

Clearly, $\hat{\mathcal{W}}(s) \in \hat{\mathcal{A}}^{n\times n}$. Moreover, $\det \hat{\mathcal{W}}(s) = (s+1)^{-l}$, where l is an integer. (In fact, $l = \alpha n + \sum_{i=1}^k m_i$.) So $\det \hat{\mathcal{W}}(s) \neq 0$ whenever $\text{Re } s \geq 0$ and $|s| < \infty$. Thus, the condition (ii) of Definition (21) is satisfied. Finally, we have

$$\det \hat{\mathcal{D}}(s) = \det D(s) \cdot [\det M(s)]^{-1} = \prod_{i=1}^{k} (s - p_i)^{m_i} \cdot \prod_{i=1}^{n} (s-1)^{-\delta_i}$$

So clearly $\det \hat{\mathcal{D}}(s) \to 1$ whenever $|s| \to \infty$. Thus, the pair $(\hat{\mathcal{N}}, \hat{\mathcal{D}})$ defined by (23) constitutes a prcf of $\hat{G}$, according to Definition (21). ∎

Exercise 5 Show that $\hat{\mathcal{N}}$ defined in (23) is proper.

Exercise 6 Let $(\hat{\mathcal{N}}, \hat{\mathcal{D}})$ be a prcf of $\hat{G}$. Show that $\hat{G}$ is a meromorphic in $\mathbb{C}_+$ and that p, with Re $p > 0$ is a pole of $\hat{G}$ if and only if det $\hat{\mathcal{D}}(p) = 0$.

Exercise 7 Let $\hat{G}$ possess a prcf $(\hat{\mathcal{N}}, \hat{\mathcal{D}})$. Show that whenever $(s_i)_1^\infty$ is a sequence with Re $s_i \geq 0$ and $\lim_{i\to\infty}|s_i| = \infty$, we have $\lim\sup|\hat{G}(s_i)| < \infty$. Loosely speaking, if $\hat{G}$ possesses a prcf, then $\hat{G}(s)$ must remain bounded as $|s| \to \infty$ with Re $s \geq 0$.

The importance of pseudo-right-coprime factorizations is brought out in the following theorem.

27 **Theorem** Let $\hat{F} \in \hat{\mathscr{A}}^{n\times n}$, and let $\hat{G} = \hat{\mathcal{N}}\hat{\mathcal{D}}^{-1}$, where $(\hat{\mathcal{N}}, \hat{\mathcal{D}})$ s a prcf of $\hat{G}$. U.t.c., $\hat{H} = \hat{G}(I + \hat{F}\hat{G})^{-1} \in \hat{\mathscr{A}}^{n\times n}$ if and only if

28 (i)
$$\inf_{\text{Re}\, s\geq 0} |\det[I + \hat{F}(s)\hat{G}(s)]| > 0$$

and

29 (ii) $\det[\hat{\mathcal{D}}(s) + \hat{F}(s)\hat{\mathcal{N}}(s)] \neq 0$ whenever $\det \hat{\mathcal{D}}(s) = 0$ and Re $s \geq 0$

Proof $\Rightarrow$ Suppose $\hat{H} \in \hat{\mathscr{A}}^{n\times n}$. Then (28) follows, by Theorem (14). To prove (29), we show that if (29) fails, then $\hat{H} \notin \hat{\mathscr{A}}^{n\times n}$. So let s_0 be such that $\det[\hat{\mathcal{D}}(s_0) + \hat{F}(s_0)\hat{\mathcal{N}}(s_0)] = 0$ and Re $s_0 \geq 0$. Since $\hat{\mathcal{N}}$ and $\hat{\mathcal{D}}$ are prc, there exist $\hat{\mathcal{U}}$, $\hat{\mathcal{V}}$, and $\hat{\mathcal{W}}$ in $\hat{\mathscr{A}}^{n\times n}$ such that

30
$$\hat{\mathcal{U}}\hat{\mathcal{N}} + \hat{\mathcal{V}}\hat{\mathcal{D}} = \hat{\mathcal{W}}$$

and det $\hat{\mathcal{W}}(s) \neq 0$ whenever Re $s \geq 0$. Now, starting from (30), we get

$$\begin{aligned}\hat{\mathcal{U}}\hat{\mathcal{N}} + \hat{\mathcal{V}}\hat{\mathcal{D}} + \hat{\mathcal{V}}\hat{F}\hat{\mathcal{N}} &= \hat{\mathcal{W}} + \hat{\mathcal{V}}\hat{F}\hat{\mathcal{N}} \\ (\hat{\mathcal{U}} - \hat{\mathcal{V}}\hat{F})\hat{\mathcal{N}} + \hat{\mathcal{V}}(\hat{\mathcal{D}} + \hat{F}\hat{\mathcal{N}}) &= \hat{\mathcal{W}} \\ (\hat{\mathcal{U}} - \hat{\mathcal{V}}\hat{F})\hat{H} + \hat{\mathcal{V}} &= \hat{\mathcal{W}} \cdot (\hat{\mathcal{D}} + \hat{F}\hat{\mathcal{N}})^{-1}\end{aligned} \tag{31}$$

Now as $s \to s_0$, the right side of (31) becomes unbounded, because det $(\hat{\mathcal{D}} + \hat{F}\hat{\mathcal{N}}) \to 0$, while det $\hat{\mathcal{W}}(s_0) \neq 0$. Thus, the left side of (31) must also become unbounded. But $\hat{\mathcal{U}} - \hat{\mathcal{V}}\hat{F}$ and $\hat{\mathcal{V}}$ are both bounded over the region Re $s \geq 0$. Hence $\hat{H}$ must become unbounded as $s \to s_0$, so that $\hat{H} \notin \hat{\mathscr{A}}^{n\times n}$. Hence $\hat{H} \in \hat{\mathscr{A}}^{n\times n}$ implies (29).

$\Leftarrow$ Suppose (28) and (29) hold. We must show that $\hat{H} \in \hat{\mathscr{A}}^{n\times n}$. We begin by showing that the pair (det $\hat{\mathcal{D}}$, $\det(\hat{\mathcal{D}} + \hat{F}\hat{\mathcal{N}})$ satisfies condition (N). Let $(s_i)_1^\infty$ be a sequence with Re $s_i \geq 0$ such that det $\hat{\mathcal{D}}(s_i) \to 0$ as $i \to \infty$. Since lim inf$|\det \hat{\mathcal{D}}(s_i)| > 0$ as $|s_i| \to \infty$, it follows that the sequence (s_i) is bounded. Therefore, it contains a convergent subsequence, which we renumber again as (s_i), and denote the limit of (s_i) by s_0. Then Re $s_0 \geq 0$ and det $\hat{\mathcal{D}}(s_0) = 0$. But by (29), this implies that $\det[\hat{\mathcal{D}}(s_0) + \hat{F}(s_0)\hat{\mathcal{N}}(s_0)] \neq 0$. Thus, the pair (det $\hat{\mathcal{D}}$, $\det(\hat{\mathcal{D}} + \hat{F}\hat{\mathcal{N}})$) satisfies condition ($N$). This fact, together with (28), implies by Theorem (14) that $\hat{H} \in \hat{\mathscr{A}}^{n\times n}$. ∎

Exercise 8 Prove the following alternate version of the Theorem (27). Given that $(\hat{\mathcal{N}}, \hat{\mathcal{D}})$ is prcf of $\hat{G}$ and that $\hat{F} \in \hat{\mathscr{A}}^{n\times n}$, we have that $\hat{H} = \tilde{G}(I + \tilde{F}\hat{G})^{-1} \in \hat{\mathscr{A}}^{n\times n}$ if and only if

$$\inf_{\operatorname{Re} s \geq 0} |\det[\hat{\mathcal{D}}(s) + \hat{F}(s)\hat{\mathcal{N}}(s)]| > 0$$

32 **Remark** As mentioned after Corollary (19), the condition (28) [or (16), which is the same thing] is necessary for $\hat{H}$ to belong to $\hat{\mathscr{A}}^{n\times n}$, but is not sufficient. The present theorem more clearly brings out when (28) is sufficient for stability. Let $(\hat{\mathcal{N}}, \hat{\mathcal{D}})$ be a prcf of $\hat{G}$ and suppose $\hat{F} \in \hat{\mathscr{A}}^{n\times n}$ and that (28) holds. Then $\hat{H} \in \hat{\mathscr{A}}^{n\times n}$ if and only if (29) is satisfied. This condition is to be interpreted as follows. We have $\det(\hat{\mathcal{D}} + \hat{F}\hat{\mathcal{N}}) = \det \hat{\mathcal{D}} \cdot \det(I + \hat{F}\hat{G})$. Now suppose $\det \hat{\mathcal{D}}(s) = 0$ with $\operatorname{Re} s \geq 0$. If $\det(I + \hat{F}\hat{G})$ is finite, then $\det(\hat{\mathcal{D}} + \hat{F}\hat{\mathcal{N}}) = 0$, and $\hat{H} \notin \hat{\mathscr{A}}^{n\times n}$. [This is, in fact, the case in the example following Corollary (19).] On the other hand, if $\det(I + \hat{F}\hat{G})$ has a pole at s, then the product $\det \hat{\mathcal{D}} \cdot \det(I + \hat{F}\hat{G})$ is indeterminate, and one has to evaluate $\det(\hat{\mathcal{D}} + \hat{F}\hat{\mathcal{N}})$ directly.

This theorem shows the importance of finding a prcf of a given transfer function $\hat{G}(\cdot)$. This problem is made simpler by the following fact, which shows that it is only necessary to find a prcf of the "unstable part" of $\hat{G}(\cdot)$.

33 **Fact** Let $(\hat{\mathcal{N}}, \hat{\mathcal{D}})$ be a prcf of $\hat{G}(\cdot)$, and suppose $\hat{G}_1(\cdot) \in \hat{\mathscr{A}}^{n\times n}$. Then $(\hat{\mathcal{N}} + \hat{G}_1\hat{\mathcal{D}}, \hat{\mathcal{D}})$ is a prcf of $\hat{G} + \hat{G}_1$.

Proof By hypothesis, $\hat{G} = \hat{\mathcal{N}}\hat{\mathcal{D}}^{-1}$, so clearly $\hat{G} + \hat{G}_1 = (\hat{\mathcal{N}} + \hat{G}_1\hat{\mathcal{D}}) \cdot \hat{\mathcal{D}}^{-1}$. Also by hypothesis, $\lim\inf |\det \hat{\mathcal{D}}(s)| > 0$ whenever $|s| \to \infty$ with $\operatorname{Re} s \geq 0$. So all that remains to be shown is that $\hat{\mathcal{N}} + \hat{G}_1\hat{\mathcal{D}}$ and $\hat{\mathcal{D}}$ are prc. Since $\hat{\mathcal{N}}$ and $\hat{\mathcal{D}}$ are prc by hypothesis, there exist $\hat{\mathcal{U}}$, $\hat{\mathcal{V}}$, and $\hat{\mathcal{W}}$ in $\hat{\mathscr{A}}^{n\times n}$ such that $\det |\hat{\mathcal{W}}(s)| \neq 0$ whenever $\operatorname{Re} s \geq 0$ and $|s| < \infty$, and such that

$$\hat{\mathcal{U}}\hat{\mathcal{N}} + \hat{\mathcal{V}}\hat{\mathcal{D}} = \hat{\mathcal{W}} \tag{34}$$

So from (34) it follows that

$$\hat{\mathcal{U}}(\hat{\mathcal{N}} + \hat{G}_1\hat{\mathcal{D}}) + (\hat{\mathcal{V}} - \hat{\mathcal{U}}\hat{G}_1)\hat{\mathcal{D}} = \hat{\mathcal{W}} \tag{35}$$

which shows that $\hat{\mathcal{N}} + \hat{G}_1\hat{\mathcal{D}}$ and $\hat{\mathcal{D}}$ are prc. ∎

As an application of Theorem (27), we derive completely explicit, necessary, and sufficient conditions for a class of multivariable feedback systems to be stable.

36 **Theorem** Let $\hat{G}(\cdot)$ be of the form

$$\hat{G}(s) = \sum_{i=1}^{k} \sum_{j=1}^{m_i} R_{ij}/(s - p_i)^j + \hat{G}_b(s) = \hat{G}_u(s) + \hat{G}_b(s) \tag{37}$$

where Re $p_i \geq 0$ for all i, and $\hat{G}_b \in \hat{\mathscr{A}}^{n \times n}$. Let

38 $$\hat{G}_u(s) = N(s)D(s)^{-1}$$

where N and D are right-coprime polynomial matrices, and further D is column proper. Suppose $\hat{F} \in \hat{\mathscr{A}}^{n \times n}$. Then $\hat{H} = \hat{G}(I + \hat{F}\hat{G})^{-1} \in \hat{\mathscr{A}}^{n \times n}$ if and only if

39 (i) $$\inf_{\operatorname{Re} s \geq 0} |\det[I + \hat{F}(s)\hat{G}(s)]| > 0$$

and

40 (ii) $$\det[D(p_i) + \hat{F}(p_i)N(p_i) + \hat{F}(p_i)\hat{G}_b(p_i)D(p_i)] \neq 0 \quad \text{for} \quad i = 1, \ldots, k$$

Proof Given N and D, define $\hat{\mathscr{N}}$ and $\hat{\mathscr{D}}$ as in (23). Then $(\hat{\mathscr{N}}, \hat{\mathscr{D}})$ is a prcf of $\hat{G}_u$, and therefore, by Fact (33), $(\hat{\mathscr{N}} + \hat{G}_b\hat{\mathscr{D}}, \hat{\mathscr{D}})$ is a prcf of $\hat{G}$. Hence by Theorem (27), $\hat{H} \in \hat{\mathscr{A}}^{n \times n}$ if and only if (39) holds, and in addition

41 $$\det[\hat{\mathscr{D}}(s) + \hat{F}(s)\hat{\mathscr{N}}(s) + \hat{F}(s)\hat{G}_b(s)\hat{\mathscr{D}}(s)] \neq 0 \quad \text{whenever} \quad \det \hat{\mathscr{D}}(s) = 0 \quad \text{and} \quad \operatorname{Re} s \geq 0$$

However, it is clear from the way that $\hat{\mathscr{N}}$ and $\hat{\mathscr{D}}$ are constructed that det $\hat{\mathscr{D}}(s) = 0$ with Re $s \geq 0$ if and only if $s = p_i$, $i = 1, \ldots, k$. Furthermore, $\hat{\mathscr{N}}(s) = N(s)M^{-1}(s)$, $\hat{\mathscr{D}}(s) = D(s)M^{-1}(s)$, and det $M(p_i) \neq 0$ for $i = 1, \ldots, k$. Therefore, (41) simplifies to (40). ∎

42 **Corollary** Suppose $n = 1$ (scalar case), that

43 $$\hat{g}(s) = \sum_{i=1}^{k} \sum_{j=1}^{m_i} r_{ij}/(s - p_i)^j + \hat{g}_b(s) = \hat{g}_u(s) + \hat{g}_b(s)$$

and suppose $\hat{f}$, $\hat{g}_b \in \hat{\mathscr{A}}$. Then $\hat{h} = \hat{g}/(1 + \hat{f}\hat{g}) \in \hat{\mathscr{A}}$ if and only if

44 $$\inf_{\operatorname{Re} s \geq 0} |1 + \hat{f}(s)\hat{g}(s)| > 0$$

45 $$\hat{f}(p_i) \neq 0, \qquad i = 1, \ldots, k$$

Proof Let $\hat{g}_u(s) = n(s)/d(s)$, where $n(s)$ and $d(s)$ are polynomials with no common zeros. Then (39) reduces to (44), while (40) becomes

46 $$d(p_i) + \hat{f}(p_i)n(p_i) + \hat{f}(p_i)\hat{g}_b(p_i)d(p_i) \neq 0, \qquad i = 1, \ldots, k$$

However, since $d(p_i) = 0$ and $n(p_i) \neq 0$, (46) reduces to (45). ∎

48 **Remark** When $\hat{G}$ has several right half-plane poles, the right-coprime factorization (38) may be quite cumbersome. Since the condition (40) is purely local, it is possible to deal with each pole successively. Call $\hat{R}_i(s)$ the singular part of the Laurent expansion of $\hat{G}$ about p_i, $i = 1, 2, \ldots, k$. Call $\hat{M}_i$ the

difference between $\hat{G}$ and $\hat{R}_i$; $\hat{M}_i$ is analytic in a small disk centered at p_i. We have

$$\hat{G}(s) = [\hat{R}_i(s) + \hat{M}_i(p_i)] + [\hat{M}_i(s) - \hat{M}_i(p_i)]$$

The first bracket is a proper rational matrix, hence has a right-coprime factorization, say, $\hat{N}_i \hat{D}_i^{-1}$; the second bracket, say $\hat{\Phi}_i$, is locally analytic and $\hat{\Phi}_i(p_i) = 0$. Thus,

$$\hat{G}(s) = \hat{N}_i(s)\hat{D}_i(s)^{-1} + \hat{\Phi}_i(s)$$

We leave it as an exercise to show that (40) can be replaced by

50 $$\det[\hat{D}_i(p_i) + \hat{F}(p_i)\hat{N}_i(p_i)] \neq 0, \qquad \text{for} \quad i = 1, 2, \ldots, k$$

Exercise 9 With the notations and assumptions of Remark (48), show that $\hat{H}$ has a pole at p_i if and only if (50) fails.

5. Graphical test

It is well known that the Nyquist graphical test is important for three reasons:

(i) It is based on directly measured experimental data, which can be obtained with great accuracy. It is not like the Routh–Hurwitz test or the Liénard–Chipart test, which are applied to data *derived* by interpolation from the measurements.

(ii) It applies to distributed systems.

(iii) In case the criterion is not satisfied, the required design modifications are readily apparent.

In this section we present the graphical test for the distributed n-input–n-output case and also for the scalar case.

We consider a particular case of the system of Theorem (4.36) in that the feedback transfer function is a *constant matrix F*. As before,

1 $$\hat{G}(s) = \sum_{i=1}^{k} \sum_{j=1}^{m_i} R_{ij}/(s - p_i)^j + \hat{G}_b(s)$$

The graphical test is used to check the inequality (4.39). The following equation describes our notation

2 $$\det[I + FG(s)] \triangleq 1 + \hat{g}(s) \triangleq 1 + \hat{g}_a(s) + \sum_{i=0}^{\infty} \hat{g}_i^{-st_i} + \sum_{k=1}^{l} \sum_{\alpha=1}^{\mu_k} r_{k\alpha}/(s - p_k)^\alpha$$

where $g_a \in L^1$, $\sum_0^\infty |g_i| < \infty$, $\operatorname{Re} p_k \geq 0$ for $k = 1, 2, \ldots, l$, and μ_k, the order of the pole p_k of $\det[I + F\hat{G}(s)]$, need not be equal to m_k. In fact, $0 \leq \mu_k \leq nm_k$. We assume $0 = t_0$, $t_i > 0$ for all $i > 0$. In the scalar case, as in Corollary (4.42), the expression to be tested is of the same form as (2), except for the fact that we have taken $f = 1$, for simplicity.

Roughly speaking, the graphical test is based on the image of the $j\omega$ axis under the map $s \mapsto 1 + \hat{g}(s)$. We must first define the phase of $1 + \hat{g}(j\omega)$ for all $\omega \in \mathbb{R}$:

$$\theta(j\omega) \triangleq \arg[1 + \hat{g}(j\omega)] = \operatorname{Im}\{\log[1 + \hat{g}(j\omega)]\} \tag{4}$$

There are two difficulties with this expression. First, $1 + \hat{g}(j\omega)$ may be zero for some ω. In that case, the test (4.39) fails; i.e., the closed-loop transfer function $\notin \hat{\mathscr{A}}^{n \times n}$, and no further work is required. Second, one or more of the poles p_k may be on the $j\omega$-axis. In that case, we "indent" the $j\omega$ axis at every pole. More precisely, let I_k denote the line segment centered on the $j\omega$-axis pole p_k and of length 2ρ, where $\rho > 0$ and sufficiently small; for all $j\omega$-axis poles we replace these line segments I_k by half-circles of radius ρ, centered on the pole and lying in the right half-plane. Along the indented $j\omega$ axis, the function $s \mapsto 1 + \hat{g}(s)$ is uniformly continuous, and the phase θ is well defined. To every point on the indented $j\omega$ axis associate its ordinate ω; this defines a bijection between the real line, $-\infty < \omega < \infty$, and the indented $j\omega$ axis. For this reason, we abuse notations and denote by $\theta(j\omega)$ the phase of $1 + \hat{g}(s)$ at the point s of the indented $j\omega$ axis whose ordinate is ω. Thus, as ω increases and goes around the pole $p_k = j\omega_k$ of order m_k, we have $\theta[j(\omega_k + \rho)] - \theta[j(\omega_k + \rho)] = -m_k\pi + O(\rho)$; i.e., $\theta(\cdot)$ *decreases* by $m_k \pi$.

At this point, we have $\theta(j\omega)$ well defined as a continuous function of ω except that we have to specify the branch of the logarithm we use in (4). We choose it as follows:

if $0 < |1 + \hat{g}(j0)| < \infty$, then $\theta(j0)$ is equal to zero or π

according as $1 + \hat{g}(j0)$ is positive or negative, respectively;

if $1 + \hat{g}(\cdot)$ has a pole at 0, then $\theta(j0)$ is equal to zero or π

according as whether $1 + \hat{g}(\sigma)$ is positive or negative for all σ restricted to $(0, \rho)$ where ρ is chosen sufficiently small. Thus, we have a well-defined continuous function $\omega \mapsto \theta(j\omega)$, which is the phase of $1 + \hat{g}(s)$ along the indented $j\omega$ axis.

Let V_0 denote the $j\omega$ axis duly indented in the manner described above. The graphical test is based on the image of V_0 under the map $1 + \hat{g}(\cdot)$. Let $\mathscr{N}$ (for Nyquist diagram) denote this image. It will help us to consider in succession three increasingly complicated cases.

Case I All the $\hat{g}_i$'s in (2) are zero Then $1 + \hat{g}(s)$ is analytic for $\operatorname{Re} s > 0$, except at the poles p_k, and, by the Riemann–Lebesgue lemma, it tends to 1 as $|s| \to \infty$ with $\operatorname{Re} s \geq 0$. This limit is attained uniformly in arg s for $|\arg s| \leq \pi/2$. Therefore, for any $\varepsilon > 0$, there is an $r > 0$ sufficiently large so that

(a) all poles p_k are included in $B(0; r) \cap \mathbb{C}_+$, namely, the right half of the disk centered on the origin and of radius r;

(b) for all $|\alpha| \leq \pi/2$, $|1 + \hat{g}(re^{j\alpha})| \leq 1 + \varepsilon$.

Call $\mathscr{C}_r$ the right half-circle, which is on the boundary of the above half-disk. The function $1 + \hat{g}(\cdot)$ is meromorphic in the interior of $B(0; r) \cap \mathbb{C}_+$ and uniformly continuous on its boundary, namely, $V_0 \cup \mathscr{C}_r$. Therefore, the principle of the argument applies: $1 + \hat{g}(\cdot)$ has no zeros in the interior of $V_0 \cup \mathscr{C}_r$ if and only if the net increase in its argument θ as we traverse $V_0 \cup \mathscr{C}_r$ in the *clockwise* direction is $\Delta\theta = \sum_1^k \mu_k$. Since by statement (b) above, $1 + \hat{g}$ is bounded away from zero outside $B(0, r)$, we conclude with the following theorem.

5 **Theorem** With the notations of (1), (2), and (3), and assuming that $\hat{g}_i = 0$ for all $i > 0$,

$$\inf_{\operatorname{Re} s \geq 0} |\det[I + F\hat{G}(s)]| > 0 \tag{6}$$

if and only if

$$1 + \hat{g}(j\omega) \neq 0, \qquad \text{for all} \quad \omega \in \mathbb{R} \tag{7}$$

and

$$\Delta\theta = \lim_{\Omega \to \infty} [\theta(j\Omega) - \theta(-j\Omega)] = \sum_k \mu_k \triangleq n_p \tag{8}$$

where the summation is over all poles p_k that lie in the *open* right half-plane.

The interpretation of (8) is the following: As ω increases from $-\infty$ to $+\infty$, following the required indentations at the $j\omega$-axis poles of $1 + \hat{g}(\cdot)$, the corresponding point traverses $\mathscr{N}$ and encircles the origin $\sum \mu_k = n_p$ times in the *counterclockwise* direction. Note that n_p denotes the number of poles in the *open* right half-plane, where multiple poles are counted according to their multiplicity. Note also that (7) asserts that $\mathscr{N}$ does not go through the origin.

Case II The $\hat{g}_i$'s are not required to be zero, but we assume that there is a sequence of nonnegative integers $(n_i)_0^\infty$ and a positive number $\tau > 0$ such that $n_0 = 0$ and

$$t_i = n_i \tau, \qquad \forall i \in \mathbb{Z}_+ \tag{10}$$

This is an important special case because it occurs

(a) in circuits which include one uniform lossless transmission line or a number of such transmission lines whose lengths are rationally related;
(b) in control systems and in bioengineering models where there is only one transportation lag or a number of transportation lags whose time delays are rationally related.

Condition (10) has two interpretations:

(a) The t_i's are rationally related: $t_i = t_k n_i / n_k$, $\forall i, k \in \mathbb{Z}_+$.
(b) The function $\omega \mapsto \sum \hat{g}_i \exp(-jn_i \omega \tau)$ is a *periodic function of period* $2\pi/\tau$.

Let

11 $$\hat{f}(s) \triangleq 1 + \sum_{i=0}^{\infty} \hat{g}_i e^{-t_i s} = 1 + \sum_{i=0}^{\infty} \hat{g}_i e^{-n_i s \tau}$$

By the Riemann–Lebesgue lemma, as $|s| \to \infty$ with Re $s \geq 0$, we have

12a $$1 + \hat{g}(s) \to \hat{f}(s) \qquad \text{uniformly in arg } s \text{ on } \quad [-\pi/2, \pi/2]$$

and

12b $$1 + \hat{g}(s) \to 1 + \hat{g}_0 \qquad \text{for} \quad s \to \infty \text{ along the real axis}$$

Let

13 $$\phi(\omega) \triangleq \arg \hat{f}(j\omega)$$

Since $\omega \mapsto \hat{f}(j\omega)$ is periodic with period $2\pi/\tau$, we have

14 $$\phi(\omega + 2\pi/\tau) - \phi(\omega) = m2\pi, \qquad \forall \omega \in \mathbb{R}$$

where m is an *integer*. If $m = 0$, there is no increase in ϕ over one period and $\omega \mapsto \phi(\omega)$ is *periodic*. If $m \neq 0$, then there is a net increase in phase of $m2\pi$ per period, and we have

15 $$\phi(\omega) = \lambda\omega + \phi_p(\omega)$$

where $\lambda = m\tau$ and $\phi_p(\cdot)$ is periodic.

Graphically, (12a) implies that the image of V_0 under the map $s \mapsto 1 + \hat{g}(s)$ approaches, as $|\omega| \to \infty$, a closed curve $\mathcal{N}_\infty$, which is represented by

16 $$\mathcal{N}_\infty \triangleq \{\hat{f}(j\omega) \mid 0 \leq \omega < 2\pi/\tau\}$$

If, in (15), λ is different from zero, or equivalently $m \neq 0$ in (14), then, as $\omega \to \infty$, the curve $\mathcal{N}$ tends to the closed curve $\mathcal{N}_\infty$ and $\theta(j\cdot)$ is unbounded on $\mathbb{R}$ because for ω sufficiently large, $\mathcal{N}$ becomes arbitrarily close to $\mathcal{N}_\infty$ and in the limit the phase θ increases by $m2\pi$ per period.

The graphical test for Case II is a special instance of Case III in the following. Case II can also be established independently by conformal mapping techniques using the transformation $z = \exp(-s\tau)$ [Wil. 5]. The test can be expressed as follows.

18 **Theorem** With the notations (1), (2), and (3) and assuming that the t_i's are rationally related [(10)], we have

$$\inf_{\text{Re } s \geq 0} |\det[I + F\hat{G}(s)]| > 0 \tag{19}$$

if and only if

$$1 + \hat{g}_0 \quad \neq 0 \tag{20}$$

$$1 + \hat{g}(j\omega) \neq 0, \qquad \text{for all} \quad \omega \in \mathbb{R} \tag{21}$$

$$\Delta\theta = \sum_k \mu_k \tag{22}$$

where the summation is taken over all *open* right-half-plane poles, counting their multiplicity.

Condition (22) implies that $\lambda = 0$, or equivalently $m = 0$; graphically, it means that the closed curve $\mathcal{N}_\infty$ does *not* encircle the origin. Furthermore, (21) and (12a) require that both $\mathcal{N}$ and $\mathcal{N}_\infty$ do not go through the origin.

Case III General Case: No Specializing Assumptions We shall not prove this case. We shall only describe what the test involves and in what way it differs from the preceding cases.

In the present case, the function $\hat{f}$ defined, as in (11), by

$$\hat{f}(s) \triangleq 1 + \sum_{i=0}^{\infty} \hat{g}_i e^{-t_i s} \tag{25}$$

turns out to be an *almost periodic function* in the right half-plane. (For definition see [Cor.1].) The limiting conditions (12a) and (12b) still hold. Since $\omega \mapsto \hat{f}(j\omega)$ is almost periodic, given any $\varepsilon > 0$, there are ε-translation numbers τ_ε which satisfy the condition

$$|\hat{f}(j\omega) - \hat{f}(j\omega + j\tau_\varepsilon)| < \varepsilon, \qquad \text{for all} \quad \omega \in \mathbb{R} \tag{26}$$

Furthermore, these translation numbers are $l(\varepsilon)$ *relatively dense* on $\mathbb{R}$. This means that any interval of length $l(\varepsilon)$ contains at least one ε-translation number. For these facts consult [Cor.1]. These facts have a very important consequence—consider the image under $\hat{f}(j\cdot)$ of the compact interval $[0, l(\varepsilon)]$, namely,

$$\mathcal{N}_l \triangleq \{z \in \mathbb{C} \,|\, z = \hat{f}(j\omega),\ 0 \leq \omega \leq l(\varepsilon)\} \tag{27}$$

Let $\alpha \in \mathbb{Z}$ and consider

28 $$\mathcal{N}_{\alpha l} \triangleq \{z \in \mathbb{C} \mid z = \hat{f}(j\omega),\ \alpha l(\varepsilon) \leq \omega \leq (\alpha + 1)l(\varepsilon)\}$$

By definition of $l(\varepsilon)$, we have the important fact that for all $\alpha \in \mathbb{Z}$, $\mathcal{N}_{\alpha l}$ is within an ε neighborhood of $\mathcal{N}_l$. Consequently, the image of the $j\omega$ axis under $\hat{f}(\cdot)$ lies within an ε neighborhood of $\mathcal{N}_l$. Using the same ε as in (26) and (28) and invoking the Riemann–Lebesgue lemma, there is an $\Omega_\varepsilon > 0$ such that for all $|\omega| > \Omega_\varepsilon$, the image of V_0 under $1 + \hat{g}(\cdot)$ lies within a 2ε neighborhood of $\mathcal{N}_l$. As $|\omega|$ becomes very large, $\mathcal{N}$ enters and remains within 2ε neighborhood of $\mathcal{N}_l$.

It can be shown that the phase ϕ of the almost periodic function $\hat{f}(j\omega)$ is necessarily of the form

29 $$\phi(\omega) = \lambda\omega + h(\omega), \qquad \omega \in \mathbb{R}$$

where $\lambda \in \mathbb{R}$ and $h(\cdot)$ is *almost periodic*, hence bounded on $\mathbb{R}$. Note that $\lambda \neq 0$ if and only if, for ε sufficiently small, the corresponding curve $\mathcal{N}_l$ encircles the origin. To state the graphical test, it is convenient to denote by $N(\mathcal{N}_l; 2\varepsilon)$ the 2ε neighborhood of $\mathcal{N}_l$, with $\mathcal{N}_l$ being the curve defined by (27).

Using these facts, we can state the graphical test as follows.

30 **Theorem** With the notations of (1), (2), and (3),

31 $$\inf_{\operatorname{Re} s \geq 0} |\det[I + F\tilde{G}(s)]| > 0$$

if and only if

(i) $1 + \hat{g}_0 \neq 0$

(ii) the position of the curves $\{z \in \mathbb{C} \mid z = \hat{f}(j\omega),\ \omega \in \mathbb{R}\}$ and $\{z \in \mathbb{C} \mid z = 1 + \hat{g}(j\omega),\ \omega \in \mathbb{R}\}$ with respect to the origin O of the complex plane is such that

(a) for an $\varepsilon > 0$, sufficiently small, the point O does not belong to $N(\mathcal{N}_l;\ 2\varepsilon)$ and to $\{z \in \mathbb{C} \mid z = 1 + \hat{g}(j\omega),\ 0 \leq \omega \leq \Omega(\varepsilon)\}$, where $\Omega(\varepsilon)$ is defined above;

(b) for the same ε, with τ_ε denoting a corresponding translation number, it is required that

$$|\phi(\tau_\varepsilon) - \phi(0)| < \pi/2$$

(c) $$\lim_{\omega \to \infty} [\theta(j\omega) - \phi(j\omega)] = \theta(j0) - \phi(j0) + n_p\pi$$

where n_p is the number of open right-half-plane poles counting multiplicities of $\hat{g}$, θ is the phase of $1 + \hat{g}$, and ϕ is the phase of $\hat{f}$.

32 **Remarks** 1. The graphical test (30) requires the knowledge of the sequences $(\hat{g}_i)_0^\infty$ and $(t_i)_0^\infty$ in order to plot $\mathcal{N}_l$ and obtain $\phi(\cdot)$.

2. Condition (b) essentially says that $\mathcal{N}_l$ does not encircle the origin. Indeed, by (13), ϕ is the phase of $\hat{f}$; by (26), $|\hat{f}(j\tau_\varepsilon) - \hat{f}(0)| < \varepsilon$; by condition (a) $|\hat{f}(j\tau_\varepsilon)|$ and $|\hat{f}(0)|$ are both larger than 2ε. So condition (b) says that as ω increases from 0 to τ_ε, the point $\hat{f}(j\omega)$ does not encircle the origin.

3. In simple cases, having chosen an $\varepsilon > 0$, it is easy to obtain an estimate for $\Omega(\varepsilon)$ and $l(\varepsilon)$. Then, only images of compact intervals need to be plotted. In complicated cases, it is not easy to give a lower bound on $l(\varepsilon)$; there is the possibility that in (29) λ is, say, positive and very small so that over $[0, l(\varepsilon)]$, the contribution of $\lambda\omega$ is not apparent. Using $(\hat{g}_i)_0^\infty$ and $(t_i)_0^\infty$ and Diophantine analysis, we can obtain a lower bound on λ if λ were positive; hence this gives a lower bound on $l(\varepsilon)$ so that the condition (b) will guarantee $\lambda = 0$.

Exercise Use the graphical test to discuss the stability of the following system: $u_1, e_1, y_1 : \mathbb{R}_+ \to \mathbb{R}$; $u_2 \equiv 0$; the forward gain is a real constant k; the feedback subsystem has e^{-s} as transfer function; the constant k takes values in $(0, \infty)$. Check your answer by calculating the impulse response of the system.

6 Discrete-time systems

Discrete-time systems arise

(a) from modeling systems that are inherently digital such as digital filters and computer-controlled systems where the inputs and outputs are periodically sampled;

(b) from approximations of continuous-time models where the inputs and outputs are approximated as piecewise constant functions; for example, $u(t) = a_k$, for $kT < t < (k+1)T$, a_k constant, and $k = 0, 1, \ldots$;

(c) in computer algorithms for solving continuous-time problems.

In all these cases, the inputs and outputs can be viewed as *sequences* defined on $\mathbb{Z}_+$ (the set of nonnegative integers) taking values in a Banach space E (i.e., complete normed space). Typically this Banach space will be $\mathbb{R}$, $\mathbb{C}$, $\mathbb{R}^n$, $\mathbb{C}^n$, $\mathbb{R}^{n\times n}$, etc., ...

6.1 Existence and uniqueness

We consider once again a system whose configuration is as shown in Fig. IV.1. Since we are dealing now with the discrete-time case, u, e, and y represent sequences in $\mathbb{R}^n$. We study the conditions under which there exists a unique sequence e corresponding to each sequence u. In what follows, we allow both F and G to be time-varying operators with memory, but we restrict them to be *linear* and *nonanticipative*. So, to establish our notation, we have

1 $$S^n = \text{the set of all maps } x \text{ from } \mathbb{Z}_+ \text{ into } \mathbb{R}^n$$

2 $$u, e, y \in S^n, \quad \text{or equivalently,} \quad u, e, y: \mathbb{Z}_+ \to \mathbb{R}^n, \quad \text{e.g.,} \quad u = (u_0, u_1, u_2, \ldots)$$

3 $$F: S^n \to S^n, \quad \text{and} \quad (Fx)_i = \sum_{j=0}^{i} F_{i,j} x_j$$

4 $$G: S^n \to S^n, \quad \text{and} \quad (Gx)_i = \sum_{j=0}^{i} G_{i,j} x_j$$

Notice that there is no real restriction in assuming that the input, error, and output all have the same number of components; for if this were not the case, then one can always add rows or columns of zeros, as appropriate, to the matrices $F_{i,j}$ and $G_{i,j}$.

5 **Theorem** There exists a unique $e \in S^n$ satisfying the equation

6 $$e = u - FGe$$

corresponding to each $u \in S^n$, if and only if

7 $$\det(I + F_{m,m} G_{m,m}) \neq 0, \qquad \forall m \in \mathbb{Z}_+$$

Proof Since the system in Fig. IV.1 is characterized by the equations

8a $$e = u - Fy$$

8b $$y = Ge$$

it is clear that there exists a unique pair (e, y) in $S^n \times S^n$ satisfying (8a) and (8b) corresponding to each $u \in S^n$, if and only if (6) has a unique solution $e \in S^n$ corresponding to each $u \in S^n$. Thus, we justify concentrating on the existence and uniqueness of solutions to (6).

$\Leftarrow$ If we expand out the equations forming (6) and write them out as simultaneous equations in the infinite number of unknowns $e_0, e_1, \ldots, e_m, \ldots$, we see that the matrix of coefficients multiplying $(e_0, e_1, \ldots)$ is lower triangular, and that the diagonal elements are $I + F_{0,0} G_{0,0}, \ldots, I + F_{m,m} G_{m,m}, \ldots$. Thus, if (7) holds, then for any $u \in S^n$, we can find a unique $e \in S^n$ satisfying (6).

$\Rightarrow$ By contradiction. Suppose (7) is false, and let k be the smallest integer m such that $\det(I + F_{m,m} G_{m,m}) = 0$. Then, given any $u \in S^n$, the quantities $e_0, e_1, \ldots, e_{k-1}$ can be uniquely determined. Now the equation for e_k is

$$e_k = u_k - \sum_{i=0}^{k} \sum_{j=0}^{k} F_{k,i} G_{i,j} e_j \tag{9}$$

or, collecting all unknown quantities on one side and all known quantities on the other,

$$(I + F_{k,k} G_{k,k}) e_k = u_k - \sum_{i=0}^{k-1} \sum_{j=0}^{i} F_{k,i} G_{i,j} e_j - \sum_{j=0}^{k-1} F_{k,k} G_{k,j} e_j \tag{10}$$

Depending on the particular sequence u under consideration, the right side of (10) may not be in the range of $I + F_{k,k} G_{k,k}$, in which case (10) has no solution; or it may be in the range of $I + F_{k,k} G_{k,k}$, in which case (10) has infinitely many solutions. But in either case, (10) does not have a unique solution, whence neither does (6). ∎

The importance of Theorem (5) lies in the fact that it provides a very simple, necessary, and sufficient condition for the closed-loop system characterized by (8a) and (8b) to be solvable, under relatively mild assumptions on F and G. The only crucial assumptions on F and G are that they are (i) linear, and (ii) nonanticipative. But other than that, F and G may be time invariant or time varying, and they may have memory or be memoryless.

Exercise 1 Based on Theorem (5), one can readily derive a large number of criteria for various classes of discrete feedback systems to be solvable. We give one of the most important cases as an exercise. Let $G: S^n \to S^n$ be time invariant, i.e., $G_{i,j} = \mathcal{G}(i-j) = \mathcal{G}_{i-j}$, say (the causality assumption on G, of course, implies that $\mathcal{G}_i = 0$ for $i < 0$), and let $F: S^n \to S^n$ be a memoryless time-varying gain, i.e., $F_{i,i} = \mathcal{F}_i$, $F_{i,j} = 0$ for $i > j$. Then (6) has a unique solution $e \in S^n$ corresponding to each $u \in S^n$ if and only if

$$\det(I + \mathcal{F}_m \mathcal{G}_0) \neq 0, \qquad \forall m \in \mathbb{Z}_+ \tag{11}$$

6.2 Z-transforms

The main properties of z transforms are a direct consequence of properties of power series. Given a sequence $a = (a_0, a_1, a_2, \ldots)$ with the a_i's in a Banach space E, we define its z transform by

$$\mathscr{Z}(a) = \tilde{a}(z) = \sum_{k=0}^{\infty} a_k z^{-k} \tag{12}$$

This is a *power series* in z^{-1}; it has a radius of convergence r_a and converges *outside* $\bar{B}(0; r_a)$, the *closed* disk of center 0, and radius r_a. It is a well-known result that

13
$$r_a = \limsup_{k\to\infty} \|a_k\|^{1/k}$$

Furthermore,

(a) the right-hand side of (12) converges *absolutely* for any $|z| > r_a$;

(b) for any $\delta > 0$, it converges *uniformly* in the complement of $B(0; r_a + \delta)$, the *open* disk of center 0 and radius $r_a + \delta$.

(c) the right-hand side of (12) is an analytic function in the open set $|z| > r_a$.

In the following we shall use the superscript tilde($\sim$) to denote z transforms; viz., $\tilde{a} = \mathscr{Z}(a)$, $\tilde{G} = \mathscr{Z}(G)$.

The connection between z transforms and the Laplace transform is the following: To the sequence $a = (a_0, a_1, \ldots)$ associate the time "function" $\sum_0^\infty a_k\,\delta(t-k)$. Its Laplace transform is $\sum_{k=0}^\infty a_k e^{-ks}$. By comparison with (12), we see that z corresponds to e^s. Thus, the open left half-plane, Re $s < 0$, corresponds to $B(0; 1)$, the open unit disk $|z| < 1$; the closed right half-plane $\mathbb{C}_+$, Re $s \geq 0$, corresponds to the complement of $B(0; 1)$, i.e., $|z| \geq 1$. This observation is very useful in translating a proof of the continuous-time case into one for the discrete-time case.

To recover the sequence from its z transform, we use a classical result on Laurent expansions as in the following theorem.

14 **Theorem** Let $a = (a_0, a_1, \ldots)$ be a sequence in a Banach space E. Let $\tilde{a}$ be its z transform and r_a its radius of convergence. Then, for any simple closed rectifiable curve γ which lies in $|z| > r_a$ and which encircles the origin once in the counter clockwise direction,

15
$$a_k = (1/2\pi j) \oint_\gamma \tilde{a}(z) z^{k-1}\, dz, \qquad k = 0, 1, \ldots$$

These results are to be found in Dieudonné [Die.1, Chap.9], Hille and Phillips, [Hil.1, Chap.5.4].

6.3 Stability of discrete-time feedback systems

In this subsection, we leave the proofs of the various theorems as exercises to the reader because they can be easily constructed from those of the corresponding theorems for the continuous-time case. It is a fact, however, that in many instances the theorems for the discrete case are more intuitively clear, and less cluttered, than their continuous analogues. Where this happens, it is pointed out.

We consider a discrete-time linear feedback system as shown in Fig. IV.2. The subsystems G and F are both time invariant, and as such they are characterized by their "unit pulse responses" G and F, respectively. Specifically, we have

18a $$S^{n \times n} = \{\text{set of all mappings from } \mathbb{Z}_+ \text{ into } \mathbb{R}^{n \times n}\}$$

18b $$G, F \in S^{n \times n}; \qquad \text{e.g.,} \quad G = (G_0, G_1, \ldots .), \quad G_i \in \mathbb{R}^{n \times n}, \qquad \forall i \in \mathbb{Z}_+$$

The equations characterizing the feedback system are

19a $$e = u - F * y, \qquad \text{or} \quad e_m = u_m - \sum_{i=0}^{m} F_{m-i} y_i$$

19b $$y = G * e, \qquad \text{or} \quad y_m = \sum_{i=0}^{m} G_{m-i} e_i$$

If u, e, y, G, and F are all z transformable, then (19a) and (19b) can also be rewritten as

20a $$\tilde{e}(z) = \tilde{u}(z) - \tilde{F}(z)\tilde{e}(z)$$

20b $$\tilde{y}(z) = \tilde{G}(z)\tilde{e}(z)$$

Note that if both G and F are z transformable, then the closed-loop transfer function satisfies

21a $$\tilde{H} = \tilde{G}(I + \tilde{F}\tilde{G})^{-1}$$

21b $$(I - \tilde{F}\tilde{H})(I + \tilde{F}\tilde{G}) = (I + \tilde{F}\tilde{G})(I - \tilde{F}\tilde{H}) = I$$

But in any case, H satisfies the time domain equation

22 $$H = G - H * F * G$$

If $\tilde{G}(z)$ is rational and $\tilde{F}(z)$ equals a constant F, we can state a theorem analogous to Theorem (2.30) and Corollary (2.43).

23 **Theorem** Let $\tilde{G}(z)$ be rational and proper; let $\tilde{F}(z) = F$ be a constant and suppose

24 $$\det[I + F\tilde{G}(\infty)] = \det(I + FG_0) \neq 0$$

Let $\tilde{G}(z) = \tilde{N}(z)\tilde{D}(z)^{-1}$, where the polynomial matrices $\tilde{N}(z)$ and $\tilde{D}(z)$ are right coprime. U.t.c.,

(a) the closed-loop transfer function $H(z)$ is exponentially stable [i.e., all of its poles are in $B(0; \rho)$ for some $\rho < 1$] if and only if the polynomial $\det[\tilde{D}(z) + F\tilde{N}(z)]$ has all of its zeros in $B(0; 1)$, the open unit disk;

25 (b)
$$\det[I + F\tilde{G}(z)] = \frac{\det \tilde{G}(z)}{\det \tilde{H}(z)} = \frac{\det[\tilde{D}(z) + F\tilde{N}(z)]}{\det \tilde{D}(z)}$$
$$= \det(I + FG_0) \frac{\prod_{i=1}^{n} (z - p_{ci})}{\prod_{i=1}^{n} (z - p_{0i})}$$

where $(p_{0i})_1{}^n$ and $(p_{ci})_1{}^n$ are the poles of $\tilde{G}(\cdot)$ [i.e., the zeros of $\det \tilde{D}(z)$] and the poles of $\tilde{H}(\cdot)$ (i.e., zeros of $\det[\tilde{D}(z) + F\tilde{N}(z)]$), respectively. In both cases, multiple poles are counted according to their multiplicity. Note that the remarks (2.46), (2.58), (2.62), and Theorem (2.70) also apply in the present case. Note also that the assumption (24) is quite reasonable since, by Theorem (5), (24) is necessary and sufficient for the closed-loop system to have a unique solution.

26 **Corollary** If $\tilde{H}(\cdot) \in \mathbb{R}(z)^{n \times n}$ and if it is exponentially stable, then

(a) for any minimal representation [of the form $x_{k+1} = Ax_k + Bu_k$, $y_k = Cx_k + Du_k$] of $\tilde{H}(z)$, the equilibrium point $x = 0$ is globally, exponentially, uniformly (in k) stable;

(b) for any $p \in [1, \infty]$, if $u \in l_n{}^p$, then $y = H * u \in l_n{}^p$, and both u_k and $y_k \to 0$ as $k \to \infty$ whenever $p < \infty$;

(c) if $u \in l_n{}^\infty$ and $u_k \to u_\infty$, a constant vector in R^n, then $y_k \to \tilde{H}(1)u_\infty$ as $k \to \infty$, and the convergence is exponential. ∎

In the case where $\tilde{G}(z)$ is not necessarily rational, our results are based on a straightforward extension of Wiener's theorem (Appendix D.3.6.). Let $|\cdot|$ denote any suitable norm on $\mathbb{R}^n$ and also the corresponding induced norm on $\mathbb{R}^{n \times n}$. A sequence $(a_0, a_1, \ldots)$ of vectors in $\mathbb{R}^n$ (resp. of matrices in $\mathbb{R}^{n \times n}$) is said to be in $l_n{}^1$ (resp., $l_{n \times n}^1$) if $\sum_{i=0}^{\infty} |a_i| < \infty$, and its z transform is said to be in $\tilde{l}_n{}^1$ (resp., $\tilde{l}_{n \times n}^1$). The following lemma is an important tool in the subsequent work.

27 **Lemma** Let $M = (M_0, M_1, \ldots)$ be a sequence in $\mathbb{R}^{n \times n}$. Assume that $M \in l_{n \times n}^1$; i.e., $\|M\|_1 \triangleq \sum_{k=0}^{\infty} |M_k| < \infty$. U.t.c.,

(a) its z transform $z \mapsto \tilde{M}(z)$ is analytic in $|z| > 1$, uniformly continuous on the unit circle $e^{i\theta}$, $0 \leq \theta \leq 2\pi$; $|\tilde{M}(z)| \leq \|M\|_1$ for all $|z| \geq 1$, and $\tilde{M}(z) \to M_0$ as $|z| \to \infty$;

(b) M has an inverse in $l^1_{n\times n}$ [i.e., there is a $P = (P_0, P_1, \ldots)$, with $\|P\|_1 < \infty$, such that $M * P = P * M = (I, 0, 0, \ldots)$] if and only if

28a $$\inf_{|z|\geq 1} |\det \tilde{M}(z)| > 0$$

(c) for any $u \in l_n^p$ [i.e., $u = (u_0, u_1, \ldots)$ with $\sum_0^\infty |u_k|^p \triangleq (\|u\|_p)^p < \infty$],

28b $$\|M * u\|_p \leq \|M\|_1 \|u\|_p, \qquad 1 \leq p < \infty$$

First, we state a general set of necessary conditions.

29 **Theorem** Consider the system characterized by (19a) and (19b). Suppose $F \in l^1_{n\times n}$, and that the closed-loop system has a unique solution (e, y) in $S^n \times S^n$ corresponding to each input $u \in S^n$ [or, equivalently, that H is uniquely determined by (22)]. U.t.c., if $H \in l^1_{n\times n}$ then

30 (i) G is z transformable;

31 (ii) $\tilde{G}$ is analytic outside some finite ball $B(0; r)$, where $r < \infty$;

32 (iii) $\tilde{G}$ is of the form $\tilde{G}(z) = \tilde{N}(z)[\tilde{D}(z)]^{-1}$, where $N(\cdot)$, $D(\cdot) \in l^1_{n\times n}$;

33 (iv) all singularities of $\tilde{G}$ in the region $\{z\colon 1 < |z| < r\}$ are isolated poles;

34 (v) $$\inf_{|z|=1} |\det[I + \tilde{F}(z)\tilde{G}(z)]| > 0.$$ ∎

35 **Remarks** (i) Note that Theorem (29) is significantly more comprehensive than its continuous-time analogue, namely, Theorem (4.5), because there is no assumption in the present case corresponding to "G is a distribution of order at most zero in some neighborhood of the origin," as in Theorem (4.5). The only assumptions on G in the present case are linearity and time invariance, and nothing else.

(ii) In Theorem (4.5), we conclude that all singularities of $\hat{G}$ must be in some *half plane*, while in the present case we conclude that all singularities of $\tilde{G}$ must lie in some *disk* in $\mathbb{C}$. As shown later, the fact that all singularities of $\tilde{G}$ lie in a compact set has the effect of making the pseudo-right-coprime factorization technique much more pertinent and valuable to the discrete-time case than the continuous-time case.

We now state the discrete analogue of Theorem (4.14).

36 **Theorem** Consider the feedback system characterized by (19a) and (19b). Suppose G is z transformable, and that $F \in l^1_{n\times n}$. Then $H \in l^1_{n\times n}$ if and only if

37 (i) There exist $\tilde{N}$, $\tilde{D}$ in $\tilde{l}^1_{n\times n}$ such that

(a) $\det D_0 \neq 0$

(b) $\det [\tilde{D}(z) + \tilde{F}(z)\tilde{N}(z)] \neq 0$ whenever $|z| \geq 1$ and $\det \tilde{D}(z) = 0$, and
(c) $\tilde{G}(z) = \tilde{N}(z)[\tilde{D}(z)]^{-1}$, and

38 (ii)
$$\inf_{|z| \geq 1} |\det[I + \tilde{F}(z)\tilde{G}(z)]| > 0$$

39 **Remark** It is easy to verify that (i) (a) and (i)(b) merely ensure that the pair ($\det \tilde{D}$, $\det(\tilde{D} + \tilde{F}\tilde{N})$) satisfies the no-cancellation condition (N) in the region $\{z: |z| \geq 1\}$. In the present case, we have exploited the fact that $\tilde{D}(z)$, $\tilde{N}(z)$, and $\tilde{F}(z)$ all have definite limits as $|z| \to \infty$, namely, D_0, N_0, and F_0, resp.

Next we turn to pseudo-right-coprime factorizations and to stability results based on them.

40 **Definition** Two elements $\tilde{\mathcal{N}}$, $\tilde{\mathcal{D}}$ in $\tilde{l}^1_{n \times n}$ are said to be *pseudo right coprime* (prc) if there exist $\tilde{\mathcal{U}}$, $\tilde{\mathcal{V}}$, $\tilde{\mathcal{W}}$ in $\tilde{l}^1_{n \times n}$ such that

(i) $\det \tilde{\mathcal{W}}(z) \neq 0$ whenever $|z| \geq 1$, $|z| < \infty$, and

41 (ii)
$$\tilde{\mathcal{U}}\tilde{\mathcal{N}} + \tilde{\mathcal{V}}\tilde{\mathcal{D}} = \tilde{\mathcal{W}} \qquad \text{for all } |z| \geq 1.$$

42 **Definition** Given a z transform $\tilde{G}$, the pair ($\tilde{\mathcal{N}}$, $\tilde{\mathcal{D}}$) is said to be a *pseudo-right-coprime factorization* (prcf) of $\tilde{G}$ if

(i) $\tilde{G} = \tilde{\mathcal{N}}\tilde{\mathcal{D}}^{-1}$,
(ii) $\tilde{\mathcal{N}}$ and $\tilde{\mathcal{D}}$ are prc, and
(iii) $\det \tilde{\mathcal{D}}_0 \neq 0$.

43 **Remark** As is the case with Laplace transforms, in order for $\tilde{G}$ to have a prcf, it is necessary that all poles of $\tilde{G}$ outside the unit disk be contained in some compact set. But in contrast with the continuous-time case, this places no real restriction on $\tilde{G}$. because if $\tilde{G}$ has poles of arbitrarily large magnitude, then we know by (29) that $H \notin l^1_{n \times n}$, and further analysis would be unnecessary.

44 **Theorem** Let $F \in l^1_{n \times n}$, and let $\tilde{G} = \tilde{\mathcal{N}}\tilde{\mathcal{D}}^{-1}$, where ($\tilde{\mathcal{N}}$, $\tilde{\mathcal{D}}$) is a prcf of $\tilde{G}$. Then $H \in l^1_{n \times n}$ if and only if

45 (i)
$$\inf_{|z| \geq 1} |\det[I + \tilde{F}(z)\tilde{G}(z)]| > 0$$

and

6a (ii) $\det[\tilde{D}(z) + \tilde{F}(z)\tilde{\mathcal{N}}(z)] \neq 0$ whenever $\det \tilde{D}(z) = 0$ and $|z| \geq 1$

46b **Theorem** Let $F \in l^1_{n\times n}$, and let $\tilde{G} = \tilde{\mathcal{N}}\tilde{\mathcal{D}}^{-1}$, where $(\tilde{\mathcal{N}}, \tilde{\mathcal{D}})$ is a prcf of $\tilde{G}$. Then $H \in l^1_{n\times n}$ if and only if

47a
$$\inf_{|z|\geq 1} |\det[\tilde{\mathcal{D}}(z) + \tilde{F}(z)\tilde{\mathcal{N}}(z)]| > 0$$

Finally, we turn to the case where $\tilde{G}(z)$ has a finite number of poles in the region $\{z \in \mathbb{C}: |z| \geq 1\}$.

47b **Theorem** Let $F \in l^1_{n\times n}$, and suppose $\tilde{G}(z)$ is of the form

48
$$\tilde{G}(z) = \sum_{i=1}^{k} \sum_{j=1}^{m_i} R_{ij}/(z - p_i)^j + \tilde{G}_b(z) = \tilde{G}_u(z) + \tilde{G}_b(z)$$

where $G_b \in l^1_{n\times n}$,

49
$$\tilde{G}_u(z) = \tilde{N}(z)[\tilde{D}(z)]^{-1}$$

where $\tilde{N}$ and $\tilde{D}$ are right-coprime-polynomial matrices, and further $\tilde{D}$ is column proper. Then $H \in l^1_{n\times n}$ if and only if

50 (i)
$$\inf_{|z|\geq 1} |\det[I + \tilde{F}(z)\tilde{G}(z)]| > 0$$

and

(ii) $\det[\tilde{D}(p_i) + \tilde{F}(p_i)\tilde{N}(p_i) + \tilde{F}(p_i)\tilde{G}_b(p_i)\tilde{D}(p_i)] \neq 0 \quad$ for $\quad i = 1, \ldots, k$

51 **Corollary** Suppose $n = 1$, that

52
$$\hat{g}(z) = \sum_{i=1}^{k} \sum_{j=1}^{m_i} r_{ij}/(z - p_i)^j + \tilde{g}_b(z)$$

and suppose $f, g_b \in l^1$. Then $h \in l^1$ if and only if

53 (i)
$$\inf_{|z|\geq 1} |1 + \tilde{f}(z)\tilde{g}(z)| > 0$$

and

54 (ii) $\quad \tilde{f}(p_i) \neq 0, \qquad$ for $\quad i = 1, \ldots, k$

We conclude with a note on the graphical test for discrete-time systems Let $\hat{G}(z)$ be of the form (48), and let $F \in l^1_{n\times n}$. The objective is to derive a means of verifying the condition (50) by examining $\tilde{G}(e^{i\theta})$, $\theta \in [0, 2\pi]$. For this purpose, define

55
$$1 + \tilde{g}(z) = \det[I + \tilde{F}(z)\tilde{G}(z)]$$

Note that $\tilde{g}(z)$ is of the form (52).

The graphical test is applicable to the image of the set $D = \{z = e^{i\theta}, \theta \in [0, 2\pi]\}$ under the map $z \mapsto 1 + \tilde{g}(z)$. In case $\tilde{g}(z)$ has a pole at some point $e^{i\theta_0}$, we indent D by "removing" from it the set $\{z = e^{i\theta}, \theta = [\theta_0 - \delta, \theta_0 + \delta]\}$, and "adding" the set $\{z = [1 + \eta(\theta - \theta_0)]e^{i\theta}, \theta \in [\theta_0 - \delta, \theta_0 + \delta]\}$, where $\eta: \mathbb{R} \to \mathbb{R}$ is the "triangular pulse" function

56
$$\eta(x) = \begin{cases} 0 & \text{if } |x| > \delta \\ x + \delta & \text{if } x \in [-\delta, 0) \\ \delta - x & \text{if } x \in [0, \delta] \end{cases}$$

Furthermore, we choose $\delta > 0$ sufficiently small so that

$$\inf_{z \in S_{\theta_0}} |1 + \tilde{g}(z)| > 0$$

where S_{θ_0} is the set $\{z = re^{i\theta}, 1 \leq r \leq 1 + \eta(\theta - \theta_0), \theta \in [\theta_0 - \delta, \theta_0 + \delta]\}$ and such that S_{θ_0} contains no poles of $\tilde{g}$ other than $\exp(i\theta_0)$. Let us again refer to the simple closed curve that results from these indentations as D. Then with each $\theta \in [0, 2\pi]$ we can associate a unique element of D, which we denote by $z(\theta)$. Now define

57
$$\tilde{g}_1(\theta) = \tilde{g}[z(\theta)]$$

It remains to define the argument of $1 + \tilde{g}_1(\theta)$. It is clear that as θ varies from 0 to 2π, the function $\tilde{g}_1(\theta)$ is uniformly continuous in θ. Moreover, we can assume without loss of generality that $1 + \tilde{g}_1(0) \neq 0$, because if $1 + \tilde{g}_1(0) = 0$, the condition (50) is automatically violated, and further analysis is unnecessary. So we define

58
$$\phi(\theta) = \text{Im} \log [1 + \tilde{g}_1(\theta)]$$

where the particular branch of the logarithm function is so chosen that $\phi(0) = 0$ (resp., π) if $1 + \tilde{g}_1(0) > 0$ [resp, $1 + \tilde{g}_1(0) < 0$].

With these definitions and conventions, we are ready to state the graphical test for discrete-time systems.

59 **Theorem** Under the above conditions,

60
$$\inf_{|z| \geq 1} |1 + \tilde{g}(z)| > 0$$

if and only if

61 (i)
$$1 + g_0 \neq 0$$

62 (ii)
$$\inf_{\theta \in [0, 2\pi]} |1 + \tilde{g}_1(\theta)| > 0$$

63 (iii)
$$\phi(2\pi) - \phi(0) = 2\pi \cdot m_p$$

where m_p is the number of poles of $\tilde{g}(z)$ outside the closed unit disk.

Exercise 2 (a) Show that (60) holds if and only if (i) $1 + g_0 \neq 0$, and (ii) $1 + \tilde{g}(z) \neq 0$ whenever $|z| \geq 1$.

(b) Define $\xi = z^{-1}$, $\forall z \in \mathbb{C}$, and define $\tilde{h}(\xi) = \tilde{g}(\xi^{-1})$. Show that (60) holds if and only if $1 + \tilde{h}(\xi) \neq 0$ whenever $|\xi| \leq 1$.

(c) Prove Theorem (59) by applying the principle of the argument to the function $\xi \to 1 + \tilde{h}(\xi)$.

Exercise 3 (a) Let $z = e^s$. Show that (60) holds if and only if

$$\inf_{\text{Re } s \geq 0} |1 + \tilde{g}(e^s)| > 0 \tag{64}$$

(b) Let

$$\tilde{g}(z) = \sum_{l=0}^{\infty} g_l z^{-l} \qquad \text{so that} \qquad \tilde{g}(e^s) = \sum_{l=0}^{\infty} g_l e^{-ls}$$

Prove Theorem (59) by applying Theorem (5.18) to the condition (64).

7 Linear time-varying systems

Linear time-varying systems have several features that distinguish them from linear time-invariant systems. To name only two:

(1) A linear time-invariant system is represented by a convolution integral, while a linear time-varying system is characterized only by an integral operator. As a result, linear time-invariant systems can be conveniently studied in the Laplace domain or in the time domain, while time-varying systems can be studied only in the time domain.

(2) Unlike a time-invariant system, a time-varying system can be L^∞ stable but not L^1 stable, or vice versa. However, a linear time-invariant system is L^∞ stable if and only if it is L^1 stable.

In many of the stability studies in this section, we do not assume that the systems under study are nonanticipative, since this assumption usually does not affect the development one way or the other.

7.1 L^∞ Stability

Consider a system whose zero-state response is given by

$$y(t) = \sum_{i=-\infty}^{\infty} w_i(t)u(t - t_i) + \int_{-\infty}^{\infty} w(t, \tau)u(\tau)\, d\tau = (Wu)(t) \tag{1}$$

where $u, y: \mathbb{R} \to \mathbb{R}$. We assume that

(i) the $w_i(\cdot)$ and $w(\cdot, \cdot)$ are all measurable [this implies, in particular, that $w(t, \cdot)$ is measurable for almost all $t \in \mathbb{R}$];

(ii) for all $t \in \mathbb{R}$, we have

2 $$\sum_{i=-\infty}^{\infty} |w_i(t)| < \infty$$

3 $$\int_{-\infty}^{\infty} |w(t, \tau)| \, d\tau < \infty$$

Throughout this section $\|\cdot\|$ will denote the L^∞ norm, e.g., $\|u\|$. Let $\mathscr{U}$, the input space, be $L^\infty(\mathbb{R})$, and let $\mathscr{Y}$, the output space, be the set of all measurable functions from $\mathbb{R}$ into $\mathbb{R}$. Then the conditions (2) and (3) ensure that W maps $\mathscr{U}$ into $\mathscr{Y}$, and clearly W is a linear map. Moreover, the domain of W is all of $\mathscr{U}$; given any $u(\cdot)$ such that $\|u\| < \infty$, the quantity $y(t)$ is well defined by (1), and $|y(t)| < \infty$, $\forall t \in \mathbb{R}$. Our objective is to derive conditions under which a system whose zero-state or input–output response is characterized by (1) is L^∞ stable.

There are two possible ways of interpreting the sentence, "The system is L^∞ stable"; namely,

(I) an input $u \in L^\infty$ produces an output $y = Wu \in L^\infty$;

(II) there exists a constant $c < \infty$ such that $\|y\| = \|Wu\| \leq c\|u\|$ whenever $u \in L^\infty$.

The first statement simply states that a bounded input produces a bounded output. Statement (II) is more restrictive; it includes statement (I) as well as the added assertion that there is a maximum possible finite ratio between the norm of the input u and that of the output $y = Wu$.

Now let us define the quantity

4 $$c_\infty = \sup_{t \in \mathbb{R}} \left(\sum_{i=-\infty}^{\infty} |w_i(t)| + \int_{-\infty}^{\infty} |w(t, \tau)| \, d\tau \right)$$

With these definitions, we can state the following theorem.

5 **Theorem** Statements (I), (II), and

6 (III) $c_\infty < \infty$

are all equivalent.

Proof We proceed in the following order: (III) $\Rightarrow$ (II) $\Rightarrow$ (I) $\Rightarrow$ (III)

(III) $\Rightarrow$ (II) Given $u \in L^\infty$, we have

7 $$|y(t)| \leq \left[\sum_{i=-\infty}^{\infty} |w_i(t)| + \int_{-\infty}^{\infty} |w(t, \tau)| \, d\tau \right] \cdot \|u\| \leq c_\infty \|u\|$$

But since the extreme right side of (7) is independent of t, it follows that $y \in L^\infty$, and that $\|y\| \leq c_\infty \|u\|$. Thus, statement (II) holds with $c = c_\infty$.

(II) $\Rightarrow$ (I) Obvious

(I) $\Rightarrow$ (III) The proof is based on the principle of uniform boundedness, which states: Let A be an arbitrary index set, and let $(\eta_t, t \in A)$ be a family of continuous linear functionals mapping a Banach space X into a normed linear space Y. If for each $x \in X$ the set $\{\eta_t(x), t \in A\}$ is a bounded subset of Y, then $\{\|\eta_t\|, t \in A\}$ is a bounded subset of $\mathbb{R}$. To apply this principle for our present purposes, we let $X = \mathscr{U} = L^\infty$, $Y = \mathbb{R}$, and define a family of linear functionals $(\eta_t, t \in \mathbb{R})$, as follows. For each $t \in \mathbb{R}$, η_t is the map $\mathscr{U} \to \mathbb{R}$ defined by

8 $$\eta_t(u) = \sum_{i=-\infty}^{\infty} w_i(t) u(t - t_i) + \int_{-\infty}^{\infty} w(t, \tau)\, u(\tau)\, d\tau$$

Clearly η_t is linear, and it is continuous by virtue of the assumptions (2) and (3).

Next, let us determine $\|\eta_t\|$. On the one hand, we have

$$|\eta_t(u)| \leq \left[\sum_{i=-\infty}^{\infty} |w_i(t)| + \int_{-\infty}^{\infty} |w(t, \tau)|\, d\tau \right] \cdot \|u\|$$

so that

9 $$\|\eta_t\| = \sup_{\|u\| \leq 1} |\eta_t(u)| \leq \sum_{i=-\infty}^{\infty} |w_i(t)| + \int_{-\infty}^{\infty} |w(t, \tau)|\, d\tau = b_t$$

We show now that the inequality in (9) is, in fact, an equality by showing that for any $\varepsilon > 0$, we can find a function $u \in L^\infty$ such that $\|u\| = 1$ and $\eta_t(u) \geq b_t - \varepsilon$, where b_t is the right-hand side of (11). So given ε, pick an open interval I_i containing $t - t_i$ such that

10 $$\int_{I_i} |w(t, \tau)|\, d\tau \leq (\varepsilon/6) 2^{-|i|}$$

Let u be the element of L^∞ defined by

11 $$u(\tau) = \begin{cases} \operatorname{sgn} w_i(t), & \text{if } \tau \in I_i \\ \operatorname{sgn} w(t, \tau), & \text{if } t \notin I_i \end{cases}$$

Then $\|u\| = 1$, and

$$\begin{aligned} \eta_t(u) &= \sum_{i=-\infty}^{\infty} |w_i(t)| + \int_{\mathbb{R} - \bigcup_i I_i} |w(t, \tau)|\, d\tau + \int_{\bigcup_i I_i} |w(t, \tau)|\; |u(\tau)|\, d\tau \\ &\geq \sum_{i=-\infty}^{\infty} |w_i(t)| + \int_{\mathbb{R}} |w(t, \tau)|\, d\tau - 2 \int_{\bigcup_i I_i} |w(t, \tau)|\, d\tau \\ &\geq b_t - 2 \sum_{i=-\infty}^{\infty} (\varepsilon 6) 2^{-|i|} = b_t - \varepsilon \end{aligned}$$

Hence $\|\eta_t\| = b_t$.

Now suppose statement (I) holds; i.e., suppose that for all $u \in L^\infty$, the set $\{\eta_t(u), t \in \mathbb{R}\}$ is bounded. Then by the principle of uniform boundedness, the set $\{\|\eta_t\|, t \in \mathbb{R}\}$ is bounded. But by (11), this means that

12 $$\sup_t \sum_{i=-\infty}^{\infty} |w_i(t)| + \int_{-\infty}^{\infty} |w(t, \tau)|\, d\tau = c_\infty < \infty$$

which is precisely statement (III). ∎

13 **Remarks** (a) Notice that W is *not* required to be nonanticipative.

(b) If $u: \mathbb{R} \to \mathbb{R}^n$ and $y: \mathbb{R} \to \mathbb{R}^m$, then $w_i(\cdot)$ and $w(\cdot, \cdot)$ would all be $m \times n$ matrices, and (12) would stand as is, except that $|\cdot|$ would have to be interpreted as any norm on $R^{m \times n}$.

(c) The number c_∞ is, in fact, the induced norm of the linear map W from L^∞ into L^∞.

Exercise 1 Consider a feedback system where $u_1, e_1, y_1: \mathbb{R}_+ \to \mathbb{R}$; H_1, H_2 map L^∞ into itself; and u_2 is identically zero. Suppose that

$$(H_1 e_1)(t) = \int_{-\infty}^{t} w(t, \tau) e_1(\tau)\, d\tau$$

where $w(\cdot, \cdot)$ satisfies (3) above; suppose also that

$$(H_2 e_2)(t) = \phi[e_2(t), t]$$

where $\phi: \mathbb{R} \times \mathbb{R}_+ \to \mathbb{R}$ is continuous and belongs to the sector $[0, k)$.

(a) Obtain conditions on the constants c_∞ and k such that $u_1 \in L^\infty$ implies $y_1 \in L^\infty$.

(b) Show that if $w(\cdot, \cdot)$ satisfies (3) above and ϕ is saturating [i.e., for each $\gamma > 0$, γ arbitrarily small, there exists a $\beta < \infty$ such that $|\phi(\sigma, t)| \leq \gamma|\sigma| + \beta$, $\forall \sigma \in \mathbb{R}$, $\forall t \in \mathbb{R}_+$], then $u_1 \in L^\infty$ implies $y_1 \in L^\infty$, regardless of the value of c_∞.

In the case of discrete systems, we have a similar characterization.

14 **Theorem** Consider a system whose input u and output y map $\mathbb{Z}_+$ into $\mathbb{R}^n$. Let

15 $$y(k) = \sum_{i=0}^{\infty} w(k, i) u(i) = (Wu)(k)$$

where $w(k, i) \in \mathbb{R}^{n \times n}$ and satisfies

16 $$\sum_{i=0}^{\infty} |w(k, i)| < \infty, \qquad \forall k \in \mathbb{Z}_+$$

U.t.c., the following three statements are equivalent:

(i) $u \in l^\infty \Rightarrow y \in l^\infty$.

17 (ii) $\exists c < \infty$ s.t. $\forall u \in l^\infty$, we have $\|y\| \leq c\|u\|$.

(iii) $\sum_{i=0}^{\infty} |w(k, i)| \leq c < \infty, \quad \forall k \in \mathbb{Z}_+$.

The proof is entirely similar to that of Theorem (7) and is, therefore, omitted.

Exercise 2 Show that (16) is automatically satisfied if W is nonanticipative; i.e., $w(k, i) = 0$ if $k < i$.

7.2 L^p Stability

Consider a system represented by

18
$$y(t) = \int_{-\infty}^{\infty} w(t, \tau)u(\tau)\, d\tau, \qquad \forall t \in \mathbb{R}$$

where $u(\cdot), y(\cdot)\colon \mathbb{R} \to \mathbb{R}$. Suppose $u \in L^1$ and that $w(t, \cdot)$ is bounded for all $t \in \mathbb{R}$. Then $y(t)$ is unambiguously defined by (18) for each $t \in \mathbb{R}$. We now derive conditions for the L^1 stability of the system represented by (18).

19 **Theorem** Let $y(\cdot)$ and $u(\cdot)$ be related by (18). U.t.c.,

(I) $u \in L^1 \Rightarrow y \in L^1$, and moreover, there exists a constant $c < \infty$ such that $\|y\|_1 \leq c\|u\|_1$ if and only if

20 (II)
$$\sup_{\tau \in \mathbb{R}} \int_{-\infty}^{\infty} |w(t, \tau)|\, dt = c_1 < \infty$$

Proof $\Leftarrow$ Suppose (20) holds, and let $u(\cdot) \in L^1$. Then for $y(\cdot)$ defined by (18), we have

$$\int_{-\infty}^{\infty} |y(t)|\, dt \leq \int_{-\infty}^{\infty} \int_{-\infty}^{\infty} |w(t, \tau)|\, |u(\tau)|\, d\tau\, dt$$

$$= \int_{-\infty}^{\infty} \left\{ \int_{-\infty}^{\infty} |w(t, \tau)|\, dt \right\} |u(\tau)|\, d\tau \leq c_1 \|u\|$$

where we use Fubini's theorem to justify interchanging the order of integration. Thus (I) follows, with $c = c_1$.

$\Rightarrow$ Let $u(\tau) = \delta(\tau - \lambda)$. Then the corresponding $y(\cdot)$ is given by

$$y(t) = w(t, \lambda)$$

If (I) holds, then this $y(\cdot)$ must belong to L^1. [Note that even though $\delta(\tau - \lambda)$ does not belong to L^1, it can be approximated arbitrarily closely in the weak * sense by an L^1 function.] In other words.

$$\int_{-\infty}^{\infty} |w(t, \lambda)| \, dt < \infty$$

Now let λ vary over $\mathbb{R}$, and let $u(\tau) = \delta(\tau - \lambda)$ as before. Then (I) implies that the corresponding functions $w(t, \lambda)$ must belong to L^1 for each $\lambda \in \mathbb{R}$, and moreover that the family of functions $[w(t, \lambda), \lambda \in \mathbb{R}]$ must be uniformly bounded. Hence, we must have

$$\sup_{\lambda \in \mathbb{R}} \int_{-\infty}^{\infty} |w(t, \lambda)| \, d\lambda < \infty$$

which is clearly equivalent to (20). ∎

21 **Remark** Note that c_1 is the induced norm of the operator W when viewed as a mapping from L^1 into itself.

To study L^p stability for $p \in (1, \infty)$, we consider once again a system represented by (18), where $w(t, \cdot)$ and $u(\cdot)$ are locally integrable.

22 **Theorem** Under these conditions, if

(a) for some constant c_∞

$$\int_{-\infty}^{+\infty} |w(t, \tau)| \, d\tau \le c_\infty < \infty, \qquad \forall t \in \mathbb{R} \tag{23}$$

(b) for some constant c_1

$$\int_{-\infty}^{+\infty} |w(t, \tau) \, dt \le c_1 < \infty, \qquad \forall \tau \in \mathbb{R} \tag{24}$$

Then, for any fixed $p \in [1, \infty]$,

$$u \in L^p(-\infty, \infty) \Rightarrow y \in L^p(-\infty, \infty)$$

In fact,

$$\|y\|_p \le c_1^{1/p} c_\infty^{1/q} \|u\|_p, \qquad \text{where} \quad 1/p + 1/q = 1 \tag{25}$$

26 **Remarks** I. Assumption (23) is the necessary and sufficient condition for L^∞ stability, while (24) is the necessary and sufficient condition for L^1 stability.

II. Assumptions (23) and (24) can be rewritten as $\exists$ constants c_∞ and c_1 s.t.

$$\|w(t, \cdot)\|_1 \le c_\infty < \infty, \qquad \forall t \in \mathbb{R}$$

$$\|w(\cdot, \tau)\|_1 \le c_1 < \infty, \qquad \forall \tau \in \mathbb{R}$$

For the time-invariant case, $w(t, \tau) = f(t - \tau)$, the two conditions are equivalent and reduce to $f(\cdot) \in L^1$.

III. (23) does not imply (24), or vice versa. To see this, consider

$$w(t, \tau) = 1(t - \tau) \cdot e^{-\tau^2}(1 + |t|)^{-1}$$

Then (23) holds, but not (24).

IV. The results still hold if u takes values in $\mathbb{R}^n$, y takes values in $\mathbb{R}^m$, and $w(t, \tau)$ is an $m \times n$ matrix. Then $|w(t, \tau)|$ should be read as the induced norm of the matrix $w(t, \tau)$.

Proof In view of Theorem (19), we need only consider the case where $1 < p < \infty$. For all $t \in \mathbb{R}$, we have

$$\begin{aligned} |y(t)| &\leq \int_{-\infty}^{+\infty} |w(t, \tau)| \; |u(\tau)| \, d\tau \\ &\leq \int_{-\infty}^{+\infty} [|w(t, \tau)|^{1/p} |u(\tau)|][|w(t, \tau)|^{1/q}] \, d\tau \\ &\leq \left[\int_{-\infty}^{+\infty} |w(t, \tau)| \; |u(\tau)|^p \, d\tau\right]^{1/p} \left[\int_{-\infty}^{+\infty} |w(t, \tau)| \, d\tau\right]^{1/q} \end{aligned}$$

(by Hölder)

$$|y(t)| \leq c_\infty^{1/q} \left[\int_{-\infty}^{\infty} |w(t, \tau)| \; |u(\tau)|^p \, d\tau\right]^{1/p} \qquad \text{(by 23)}$$

$$\begin{aligned} \|y\|_p^p &\leq c_\infty^{p/q} \int_{-\infty}^{+\infty} \left[\int_{\infty}^{+\infty} |w(t, \tau)| \; |u(\tau)|^p \, d\tau\right] dt \\ &\leq c_\infty^{p/q} \int_{-\infty}^{+\infty} |u(\tau)|^p \, d\tau \int_{-\infty}^{\infty} |w(t, \tau)| \, dt \\ &\leq c_\infty^{p/q} \, c_1 \|u\|_p^p \qquad \text{by (24)} \end{aligned}$$

Hence

$$\|y\|_p \leq c_1^{1/p} c_\infty^{1/p} \|u\|_p$$

■

Exercise 3 Give an example of a function $w(\cdot, \cdot)$ that satisfies (24) but not (23).

Exercise 4 Prove the following stronger version of Theorem (22); consider a system of the form (18). U.t.c., this system is L^p stable for all $p \in [1, \infty]$ if and only if it is L^1 stable and L^∞ stable.

27 **Application** Consider the linear time-varying system where u_1, e_1, e_2, y_1, y_2: $\mathbb{R}_+ \to \mathbb{R}$ and

28 $$y_1 = g * e_1, \qquad g \in \mathscr{A}$$

29 $$y_2(t) = k(t)e_2(t), \qquad k(\cdot) \text{ continuous on } \mathbb{R}.$$

Assume $u_2 \equiv 0$ for simplicity. The equations for the systems can be written as

30 $$e_1(t) = u_1(t) - k(t)(g * e_1)(t)$$

31 $$e_2(t) = (g * u_1)(t) - (g * ke_2)(t)$$

Since (28) and (29) are linear, we may apply the incremental small gain theorem; then, in addition to bounds, we have existence, uniqueness, and continuous dependence.

(a) L^∞ *Stability* We have immediately

$$u_1 \in L^\infty \quad \Rightarrow \quad e_1 \text{ and } e_2 \in L^\infty$$

if either

33a $$\sup_{t \geq 0} |k(t)| \int_0^t |g(\tau)\, d\tau < 1$$

or

33b $$\sup_{t \geq 0} \int_0^\infty |g(t-\tau)k(\tau)|\, d\tau = c_\infty' < 1$$

(b) L^1 *Stability* We have immediately

$$u_1 \in L^1 \quad \Rightarrow \quad e_1, e_2 \in L^1$$

if either

34a $$\sup_{\tau \geq 0} \int_\tau^\infty |k(t)g(t-\tau)|\, dt = c_1' < 1$$

or

34b $$\sup_{\tau \geq 0} |k(\tau)| \int_0^\infty |g(t)|\, dt < 1$$

(c) L^p *Stability* If (33a) and (34a) hold, or if (33b) and (34b) hold, then for any $p \in (1, \infty)$, $u_1 \in L^p \Rightarrow e_1, e_2 \in L^p$.

Exercise 5 Consider a linear time-varying system described by (30) and (31). Suppose that $g \in L^1$ and that

$$k(t) = k_0 + 2k_1 \cos \omega_0 t, \qquad \forall t \in \mathbb{R}_+$$

where k_0, k_1, and ω_0 are real constants. Apply the loop shifting theorem (II.6.8) (with the linear map $K = k_0 I$) so that the feedback is $2k_1 \cos \omega_0 t$, and the forward loop is $y_1 = g_l * e_1$. Suppose that $\hat{g}_l(j\omega)$ is of low-pass character, say, for $\omega > \omega_c$, $|\hat{g}_l(j\omega)| < |\hat{g}_l(j\omega_c)|(\omega_c/\omega)^2$. Discuss the L^2 stability of the system and show that as ω_0 becomes much larger than ω_c, then k_1 can take very large values.

7.3 A perturbational result

Consider the feedback system shown in Fig. IV.1. Our ultimate objective is to show that if the time-varying feedback gain $k(\cdot) \in L^1[0, \infty)$, then the open-loop system is L^p stable if and only if the closed-loop system is L^p stable, under quite broad conditions.

We begin with a few preliminary results. Since all of our main results are based on an integral equation relating the closed-loop and open-loop impulse responses, we first show that the closed-loop system is uniquely solvable and that its input–output relation is of the form (18). The two lemmas that follow immediately are in the nature of "dogwork," and the reader may skip to Theorem (50) without loss of continuity.

37 **Lemma** Consider the feedback system shown in Fig. IV.1, and suppose $u, e, y\colon \mathbb{R}_+ \to \mathbb{R}^n$. Suppose $G(t, \tau)$ is bounded over every compact subset of $\mathbb{R}^2$, and that $K(\cdot) \in L^1_{n\times ne}(\mathbb{R}_+)$. U.t.c., for each $u \in L^1_{ne}(\mathbb{R}_+)$, there exists a unique $e \in L^1_{ne}(\mathbb{R}_+)$ satisfying the equation

38
$$e(t) = u(t) - K(t)\int_0^t G(t, \tau)u(\tau)\, d\tau$$

Moreover, $\forall T < \infty$, $\exists c_T < \infty$ such that $\|e_T\|_1 \le c_T \|u_T\|_1$.

Remark Lemma (37) is stated for u belonging to L_e^1, since L_e^1 is the largest of the extended spaces, in the sense that L_e^1 contains L_e^2, L_e^∞, and indeed all L_e^p for $1 \le p \le \infty$.

Proof Equation (38) is of the form

39
$$e(t) = u(t) - (KGe)(t)$$

where $KG\colon L^1_{ne}(\mathbb{R}_+) \to L^1_{ne}(\mathbb{R}_+)$. Taking truncations of (38) over $[0, T]$, we get an equation of the form

40
$$e_T(t) = u_T(t) - (Fe_T)(t)$$

where $F\colon L_n^1[0, T] \to L_n^1[0, T]$ is defined by

41
$$(Fx)(t) = \int_0^t K(t)G(t, \tau)x(\tau)\, d\tau, \qquad \forall t \in [0, T]$$

Note that F can be interpreted as the operator $P_T KGP_T$, restricted to the space $L_n^1[0, T]$, where P_T is the projection operator defined by Eqs. (III.1.4).

We know from Eq. (II.7.4) that (40) has a unique solution $e_T \in L_n^1[0, T]$ corresponding to each $u_T \in L_n^1[0, T]$ if the spectral radius of the operator F_T is less than 1. Now define a family of operators $(R_T, T \in \mathbb{R}_+)$, with $R_T: L^1[0, T] \to L^1[0, T]$, by

$$(R_T x)(t) = \int_0^t |K(t)|\ g_T x(\tau)\, d\tau$$

where

42 $$g_T = \sup_{0 \le t, \tau \le T} |G(t, \tau)|$$

We show that $\rho(R_T)$, the spectral radius of R_T when viewed as a mapping from $L^1[0, T]$ into itself, is zero. It is left as an exercise to the reader to verify that, for $m \in \mathbb{Z}_+$ and $m \ge 1$, the operator $R_T{}^m$: $L^1[0, T]$ is given by

43 $$(R_T{}^m x)(t) = |K(t)| \int_0^t \left[\int_\tau^t |K(s)|\, g_T\, ds\right]^{m-1} \cdot g_T x(\tau)\, d\tau/(m-1)!$$

Now by slight modifications of Theorem (19) and Remark (21), we have

44 $$\begin{aligned}\|R_T{}^m\| &= \sup_{0 \le \tau \le T} \int_\tau^T |K(t)| \left[\int_\tau^t |K(s)|\, g_T\, ds\right]^{m-1} \cdot g_T\, dt/(m-1)! \\ &\le \left[\int_0^T |K(t)|\, \mathrm{dt}\right]^m g_T{}^m/(m-1)! = (b_T g_T)^m/(m-1)!\end{aligned}$$

where

45 $$b_T = \int_0^T |K(t)|\ dt < \infty$$

So clearly $\|R_T{}^m\|^{1/m} \to 0$ as $m \to \infty$, so that $\rho(R_T) = \lim_{m\to\infty} \|R_T{}^m\|^{1/m} = 0$. At this point, one can show by routine majorization arguments that $\rho(F_T) \le \rho(R_T) = 0$. Hence $(I + F_T)^{-1}$ is a well-defined operator on $L_n^1[0, T]$, and $\|(I + F_T)^{-1}\| \le \sum_{i=0}^{\infty} \|F_T{}^i\| = c_T$, say. Thus, (38) has a unique solution $e(\cdot) \in L_{ne}^1(\mathbb{R}_+)$ corresponding to each $u(\cdot) \in L_{ne}^1(\mathbb{R}_+)$, and moreover $\|e_T\|_1 \le c_T \|u_T\|_1$. ∎

Exercise 6 Show that $R_T{}^m$ is given by (43). (*Hint*: See Vidyasagar [Vid. 3].)

Exercise 7 Using methods entirely analogous to those in the proof of Lemma (37), show that if $G(t, \tau)$ is bounded over every compact subset of

$\mathbb{R}^2$ and $K(\cdot) \in L^1_{ne}[0, \infty)$, then for each $u(\cdot) \in L^\infty_{ne}[0, \infty)$, there exists a unique $y \in L^\infty_{ne}[0, \infty)$ satisfying the equation

46
$$y(t) = \int_0^t G(t, \tau)u(\tau)\, d\tau - \int_0^t G(t, \tau)K(\tau)y(\tau)\, d\tau$$

Moreover, $\forall T < \infty$, $\exists d_T < \infty$ such that $\|y_T\|_\infty < d_T \|u_T\|_\infty$.

Exercise 8 Prove Lemma (37) and do Exercise 7 by using Corollary (III.5.8).

47 **Lemma** Let $G(t, \tau)$ be bounded over every compact subset of $\mathbb{R}^2$, and suppose $K(\cdot) \in L^1_{n \times ne}(\mathbb{R}_+)$. U.t.c., there exists a unique solution $H(\cdot, \cdot)$ of the equation

48
$$H(t, \tau) = G(t, \tau) - \int_\tau^t G(t, v)K(v)H(v, \tau)\, dv, \qquad 0 \le \tau \le t < \infty$$

Moreover, $H(t, \tau)$ is bounded over every compact subset of $\mathbb{R}^2$.

Proof Fix $\tau \in \mathbb{R}_+$, and consider (48) to be an equation in the unknown function $H(\cdot, \tau)$. Then by Exercise 7, we see that $H(\cdot, \tau)$ is uniquely determined from (48), and that for each $T < \infty$, there exists a finite constant d_T such that

49
$$\|H(t, \tau)\| \le d_T \sup_{\tau \le t \le T} \|G(t, \tau)\|, \qquad \forall t \in [\tau, T]$$

It is clear from (49) that since $G(t, \tau)$ is bounded over every compact subset of $\mathbb{R}^2$, so is $H(t, \tau)$. ∎

We are now in a position to state our main result concerning the nature of the input–output relation of the closed-loop system in Fig. IV.1.

50 **Theorem** Consider the system shown in Fig. IV.1, where u, e, y: $\mathbb{R}_+ \to \mathbb{R}^n$. Suppose $G(t, \tau)$ is bounded over every compact set in $\mathbb{R}^2$ and that $K(\cdot) \in L^1_{n \times ne}(\mathbb{R}_+)$. U.t.c., for each $u \in L^p_{ne}(\mathbb{R}_+)$, the equations

51
$$y(t) = \int_0^t G(t, \tau)e(\tau)\, d\tau, \qquad e(t) = u(t) - K(t)y(t)$$

have a unique solution $y \in L^p_{ne}(\mathbb{R}_+)$ given by

$$y(t) = \int_0^t H(t, \tau)u(\tau)\, d\tau = (Hu)(t)$$

where $H(\cdot, \cdot)$ is the unique solution of (48).

Proof Suppose $u \in L^p_{ne}(\mathbb{R}_+)$ for some $p \in [1, \infty]$; then $u \in L^1_{ne}(\mathbb{R}_+)$. Hence the system of equations (51) has a unique solution for e (and hence y) in

$L^1_{ne}(\mathbb{R}_+)$. Now consider the function $z = Hu$. Clearly, $z \in L^p_{ne}(\mathbb{R}_+)$ and hence $z \in L^1_{ne}(\mathbb{R}_+)$, and moreover (51) is satisfied with $y = z$. Since (51) has a unique solution, this implies that $y = Hu$. ∎

52 **Remark** The thrust of Theorem (50) is in showing that

(i) the feedback system in Fig. IV.1 is solvable;
(ii) the input–output relation of the closed-loop system is of the form (18); and
(iii) the open-loop impulse response and the close-loop impulse response are related by (48).

The next three theorems relate some properties of the open-loop impulse response with the corresponding properties of the closed-loop impulse response.

53 **Definition** Let $F\colon \mathbb{R}_+{}^2 \to \mathbb{R}^{n \times n}$ be measurable and locally integrable, and suppose further that $F(t, \tau) = 0$ whenever $\tau > t$. Define

54a $$f_b = \|F\|_b = \sup_{t, \tau \in \mathbb{R}_+} |F(t, \tau)|$$

54b $$f_1 = \|F\|_1 = \sup_{\tau \in \mathbb{R}_+} \int_\tau^\infty |F(t, \tau)|\, dt$$

54c $$f_\infty = \|F\|_\infty = \sup_{t \in \mathbb{R}_+} \int_0^t |F(t, \tau)|\, d\tau$$

With these definitions, let S_b be the normed linear space

55 $$S_b = \{F\colon \|F\|_b < \infty\}$$

The normed linear spaces S_1 and S_∞ are defined similarly.

56 **Remark** Consider a system whose input–output relation is

57 $$y(t) = \int_0^\infty F(t, \tau) u(\tau)\, d\tau = \int_0^t F(t, \tau) u(\tau)\, d\tau$$

Then

(i) $F \in S_b$ if and only if $u \in L^1 \Rightarrow y \in L^\infty$, and moreover, there exists a finite constant c_b such that $\|y\|_\infty \leq c_b \|u\|_1$;
(ii) $F \in S_1$ if and only if the system (57) is L^1 stable;
(iii) $F \in S_\infty$ if and only if the system (57) is L^∞ stable.

58 **Theorem** Suppose $K\colon \mathbb{R}_+ \to \mathbb{R}^{n \times n}$ and that $K \in L^1(\mathbb{R}_+)$, and suppose $G\colon \mathbb{R}_+{}^2 \to \mathbb{R}^{n \times n}$ and $H\colon \mathbb{R}_+{}^2 \to \mathbb{R}^{n \times n}$ are related by (48). U.t.c., $H \in S_b$ iff $G \in S_b$.

Proof $\Leftarrow$ By hypothesis, G and H are related by (48), and $G \in S_b$. Let $g_b = \|G\|_b$ be defined as in (54a). Then, from (48), we have

59
$$|H(t, \tau)| \leq g_b + g_b \int_\tau^t |K(v)| \, |H(v, \tau)| \, dv$$

Let $\tau \in \mathbb{R}_+$ be fixed for the moment. Applying the Bellman–Gronwall inequality to (59), we get

60
$$|H(t, \tau)| \leq g_b \exp[g_b \int_\tau^t |K(v)| \, dv] \leq g_b \exp[g_b \cdot \|K\|_1]$$

where

61
$$\|K\|_1 = \int_0^\infty |K(v)| \, dv$$

Since the bound in (60) is independent of both t and τ, it follows that $H \in S_b$.

$\Rightarrow$ Equation (48) can be equivalently expressed as

62
$$G(t, \tau) = H(t, \tau) + \int_\tau^t H(t, v)K(v)G(v, \tau) \, dv$$

The equivalence of (48) and (62) is most easily seen by observing that if H is obtained from G by applying a feedback of K, then G is obtained from H by applying a feedback of $-K$. Now (62) is of the same type as (48), except that the roles of G and H are interchanged and K is replaced by $-K$. However, if $K \in L^1(\mathbb{R}_+)$, then so does $-K$. Thus, if $H \in S_b$, then so does G, by the same reasoning as above. ∎

63 **Theorem** Under the conditions of Theorem (58), $H \in S_b \cap S_\infty$ if and only if $G \in S_b \cap S_\infty$.

Proof $\Leftarrow$ Suppose $G \in S_b \cap S_\infty$. Then by Theorem (58), $H \in S_b$, and it only remains to show that $H \in S_\infty$. From (48), we have

64
$$\int_0^t |H(t, \tau)| \, d\tau \leq \int_0^t |G(t, \tau)| \, d\tau + \int_0^t \int_\tau^t |G(t, v)| \, |K(v)| \, |H(v, \tau)| \, dv \, d\tau$$
$$\leq g_\infty + g_b \int_0^t \int_\tau^t |K(v)| \, |H(v, \tau)| \, dv \, d\tau$$
$$= g_\infty + g_b \int_0^t |K(v)| \int_0^t |H(v, \tau) \, d\tau \, dv$$

after changing the order of integration. Now define

$$m(t) = \int_0^t |H(t, \tau)| \, d\tau$$

Then (64) becomes

65
$$m(t) \le g_\infty + g_b \int_0^t |K(v)| m(v)\, dv$$

Applying the Bellman–Gronwall inequality to (65), we get

68
$$m(t) \le g_\infty \exp[g_b \int_0^t |K(v)|\, dv] \le g_\infty \exp(g_b \cdot \|K\|_1)$$

Hence $m(\cdot)$ is bounded, and so $H \in S_\infty$.

$\Rightarrow$ This implication follows by symmetry from the proof of $\Leftarrow$, as in Theorem (58). ∎

69a **Theorem** Under the conditions of Theorem (58), $H \in S_b \cap S_1$ if and only if $G \in S_b \cap S_1$.

The proof is left as an exercise.

Exercise 9 Interpret Theorems (58), (63), and (69a) in terms of the stability of the closed-loop system versus the stability of the open-loop system.

Now we state the main result of this section.

69b **Theorem** Consider a system of the type shown in Fig. IV.1, where u, e, y: $\mathbb{R}_+ \to \mathbb{R}^n$; the forward path contains a linear time-invariant element with a transfer function

70
$$\hat{G}(s) = \hat{G}_b(s) + \sum_{i=1}^{k} \sum_{j=1}^{m_i} R_{ij}/(s - p_i)^j = \hat{G}_b(s) + \hat{G}_u(s)$$

where $G_b \in L^1_{n\times n} \cap L^\infty_{n\times n}$, $\text{Re}\, p_i \ge 0$ for $i = 1, \ldots, k$ and $m_i = 1$ if $\text{Re}\, p_i = 0$, and the feedback element is a memoryless time-varying gain multiplier with gain

71
$$F(t) = F_0 + F_v(t)$$

where $F_0 \in \mathbb{R}^{n\times n}$ and $F_v(\cdot) \in L^1_{n\times n}$. U.t.c., the following three statements are equivalent:

(I) The closed-loop system is L^∞ stable, and $W(\cdot, \cdot)$ (the closed-loop impulse response) is bounded on $\mathbb{R}^2$.

(II) The closed-loop system is L^p stable for all $p \in [1, \infty]$, and $W(\cdot, \cdot)$ is bounded on $\mathbb{R}^2$.

72 (III) (i)
$$\inf_{\text{Re}\, s \ge 0} |\det[I + F_0 \hat{G}(s)]| > 0$$

and

73 (ii)
$$\det[\hat{D}(p_i) + F_0 \hat{N}(p_i) + F_0 \hat{G}_b(p_i) \hat{D}(p_i)] \ne 0, \qquad \text{for} \quad i = 1, \ldots, k$$

where $\hat{G}_u(s) = \hat{N}(s)\hat{D}(s)^{-1}$, $\hat{N}$ and $\hat{D}$ are right coprime, and $\hat{D}$ is column proper.

Proof We proceed in the following order: (II) $\Rightarrow$ (I), (I) $\Rightarrow$ (III), (III) $\Rightarrow$ (II).

(II) $\Rightarrow$ (I) Obvious.

(I) $\Rightarrow$ (III) Suppose (I) holds. Then $W(\cdot, \cdot)$, the closed-loop impulse response, belongs to $S_b \cap S_\infty$. So by Theorem (63), it follows that the function $H_1: (t, \tau) \mapsto H(t - \tau)$, where H is the inverse Laplace transform of $\hat{G}(I + F_0\hat{G})^{-1}$, also belongs to $S_b \cap S_\infty$. By Remark (26II), this means that $H(\cdot) \in L^1(\mathbb{R}_+)$. But by Theorem (4.36), this implies (III), namely, (72) and (73).

(III) $\Rightarrow$ (II) Let $\hat{H} = \hat{G}(I + F_0\hat{G})^{-1}$. By Theorem (4.36), (III) implies that $H \in \hat{\mathscr{A}}^{n \times n}$. In fact, H contains no impulses and hence belongs to $L^1_{n \times n}$. So the function $H_1: (t, \tau) \mapsto H(t - \tau)$ belongs to $S_\infty \cap S_1$. Now if $H \in L^\infty$, then $H_1 \in S_b \cap S_\infty \cap S_1$, and this fact, together with Theorems (63) and (69a), implies (II). So the proof is completed, if we show that $H \in L^\infty$.

Since $\hat{H}$ satisfies $\hat{H} + \hat{H}F_0\hat{G} = \hat{G}$, we have from (70) that

$$\hat{H} + \hat{H}F_0\hat{G}_b + \hat{H}F_0\hat{G}_u = \hat{G}_b + \hat{G}_u$$

or

74 $$\hat{H} + \hat{H}F_0\hat{G}_b = \hat{G}_b + (I - \hat{H}F_0)\hat{G}_u$$

Since $H \in L^1_{n \times n}$ and $G_b \in L^1_{n \times n} \cap L^\infty_{n \times n}$, the first three terms in (74) are analytic for Re $s > 0$ and are bounded and uniformly continuous on Re $s = 0$. Hence so is the last term, namely, $(I - \hat{H}F_0)\hat{G}_u$. In order to show that $(I - \hat{H}F_0)\hat{G}_u$ has an inverse transform in $L^\infty_{n \times n}$, we consider an arbitrary element of $(I - \hat{H}F_0)\hat{G}_u$, which is of the form $\hat{r}(s)\hat{\phi}(s)$, where $\hat{r}$ is a partial fraction expansion at p_i, $i = 1, \ldots, k$, and $\hat{\phi} \in \hat{\mathscr{A}}$. Thus, we can consider one pole of $r(\cdot)$ at a time. Now we claim that if $\phi \in \mathscr{A}$ and if $[m!/(s - \alpha)^{m+1}]\hat{\phi}(s)$ is analytic at α, with $m \in \mathbb{Z}_+$ and Re $\alpha > 0$, then

$$f \triangleq \mathscr{L}^{-1}[m!\hat{\phi}(s)/(s - \alpha)^{m+1}] \in L^\infty$$

and that if Re $\alpha = 0$ and $\hat{\phi}(\alpha) = 0$, then $f \in L^\infty$ provided $m = 0$.

We note that

75 $$f(t) = \int_0^t (t - \tau)^m e^{\alpha(t-\tau)}\phi(\tau)\, d\tau$$

$$= \int_0^\infty (t - \tau)^m e^{\alpha(t-\tau)}\phi(\tau)\, d\tau - \int_t^\infty (t - \tau)^m e^{\alpha(t-\tau)}\phi(\tau)\, d\tau$$

using the binomial expansion, we express the first integral as

$$\sum_{i=0}^m \binom{m}{i} t^{m-i} e^{\alpha t} \int_0^\infty (-\tau)^i e^{-\alpha\tau}\phi(\tau)\, d\tau = \sum_{i=0}^m \binom{m}{i} t^{m-i} e^{\alpha t}\hat{\phi}^{(i)}(\alpha) = 0$$

where the last equality is a consequence of the fact that $\hat{\phi}(s)/(s-\alpha)^{m+1}$ is analytic at α if and only if $\hat{\phi}^{(i)}(\alpha)=0$ for $i=0,\ldots,m$. Furthermore, if either $\operatorname{Re}\alpha>0$ and $m\in\mathbb{Z}_+$, or $\operatorname{Re}\alpha=0$ and $m=0$, then the function $\tau\mapsto(t-\tau)^m e^{\alpha(t-\tau)}$ is bounded for $0\le t\le\tau$, say, by γ. Consequently, for all $t\ge 0$, we have

$$|f(t)|\le\gamma\|\phi\|_{\mathscr{A}}$$

Hence $f\in L^\infty$, and so $H\in L^\infty_{n\times n}$. ∎

76 **Corollary** Under the conditions of Theorem (69b), suppose (72) and (73) hold. Let η and y be the solutions, respectively, of the equations

77a $$y=Gu-GF_0y-GF_vy$$

77b $$\eta=Gu-GF_0\eta$$

Then, whenever $u\in L^\infty$, we have $\eta(t)-y(t)\to 0$ as $t\to\infty$.

Proof Let $\hat{H}=(I+\hat{G}F_0)^{-1}\hat{G}$. Then $H\in L^1_{n\times n}\cap L^\infty_{n\times n}$. Moreover, by Theorem (69b), $y\in L_n{}^\infty$. Now (77a) and (77b) can be rewritten as

78a $$y=H*u-H*F_vy$$

78b $$\eta=H*u$$

Subtracting (78a) from (78b), we get

$$\eta-y=H*F_vy$$

Since $y\in L_n{}^\infty$ and $F_v\in L^1_{n\times n}$, it follows that $F_vy\in L_n{}^1$. Since $H\in L^1_{n\times n}\cap L^\infty_{n\times n}$, we finally have that $(\eta-y)(t)=(H*F_vy)(t)\to 0$ as $t\to\infty$. ∎

Exercise 10 Suppose $F_v(\cdot)\in L^\infty_{n\times n}$, but not necessarily $L^1_{n\times n}$. Using the small gain theorem, obtain a bound on $\|F(\cdot)\|_\infty$ that ensures closed-loop L^∞ stability.

79 **Remarks** 1. With regard to Theorem (69b), note that the conditions (72) and (73) are sufficient for the closed-loop system to be L^∞ stable, but are not necessary, strictly speaking. If (72) and (73) are violated, in which case $\hat{H}=\hat{G}(I+F_0\hat{G})^{-1}\notin\hat{\mathscr{A}}^{n\times n}$, we can only conclude that either the closed-loop system is not L_∞ stable, or that closed-loop impulse response [equivalently $H(\cdot)$] is unbounded.

2. Theorem (69b) and Exercise 10 show that the feedback can be perturbed by an arbitrarily large $L^1_{n\times n}$ gain without affecting the stability status of the system, but that there is, in general, a limit on how large an $L^\infty_{n\times n}$ perturbation can be made in the feedback without affecting stability.

Now consider the discrete-time analogues of the preceding results. The theory in the discrete-time case is made much simpler by the fact that any sequence in l_n^1 necessarily belongs to l_n^∞. We state only the theorems and leave the proofs as exercises.

80 **Theorem** Consider the feedback system shown in Fig. IV.1, where u, e, y: $\mathbb{Z}_+ \to \mathbb{R}^n$; the elements G and F are represented by the relations

$$(Ge)(k) = \sum_{i=0}^{k-1} G(k, i)e(i) \tag{81}$$

$$(Fy)(k) = F(k)y(k) \tag{82}$$

Then the system of equations

$$e = u - Fy \tag{83a}$$

$$y = Ge \tag{83b}$$

has a unique solution of the form

$$y(k) = \sum_{i=0}^{k-1} H(k, i)u(i) \tag{85}$$

where $H(\cdot, \cdot)$ is the unique solution of the equation

$$H(k, i) = G(k, i) - \sum_{l=i}^{k-1} G(k, l)F(l)H(l, i) \tag{86}$$

87 **Remarks** 1. As is common practice, we take empty summations to equal zero.

2. The element G is not only nonanticipative [which is equivalent to requiring that $G(k, i) = 0$ for $i > k$], it has the additional property that $G(k, k) = 0$ for all $k \in \mathbb{Z}_+$. Physically, this means that there is a delay of one sampling instant before the effect of the input is felt on the output. This is the case, for example, if the subsystem G has a state representation of the form

$$x_{k+1} = A_k x_k + B_k u_k, \qquad y_k = C_k x_k$$

where x: $\mathbb{Z}_+ \to R^m$, and A, B, C map $\mathbb{Z}_+$ into an appropriate space.

In analogy with the sets S_b, S_1, and S_∞, we define

$$\mathscr{S}_b = \{G: \mathbb{Z}_+ \to \mathbb{R}^{n\times n}: \sup_{i, j \in \mathbb{Z}_+} |G(i,j)| < \infty\} \tag{88a}$$

$$\mathscr{S}_1 = \{G: \mathbb{Z}_+ \to \mathbb{R}^{n\times n}: \sup_{j \in \mathbb{Z}_+} \sum_{i=0}^{\infty} |G(i,j)| < \infty\} \tag{88b}$$

$$\mathscr{S}_\infty = \{G: \mathbb{Z}_+ \to \mathbb{R}^{n\times n}: \sup_{i \in \mathbb{Z}_+} \sum_{j=0}^{\infty} |G(i,j)| < \infty\} \tag{88c}$$

Exercise 11 Show that $\mathscr{S}_1$ and $\mathscr{S}_\infty$ are subsets of $\mathscr{S}_b$. Give a physical interpretation for each of the sets $\mathscr{S}_b$, $\mathscr{S}_1$, $\mathscr{S}_\infty$.

89 **Theorem** Suppose $G, H\colon \mathbb{Z}_+ \to \mathbb{R}^{n\times n}$, that $G(k,i) = H(k,i) = 0$ for $k \geq i$, and that G and H are related by (86). Suppose $F\colon \mathbb{Z}_+ \to \mathbb{R}^{n\times n}$ belongs to $l^1_{n\times n}$. U.t.c., $H \in \mathscr{S}_b$ (resp. $\mathscr{S}_1$, $\mathscr{S}_\infty$) if and only if $G \in \mathscr{S}_b$ (resp., $\mathscr{S}_1$, $\mathscr{S}_\infty$).

90 **Theorem** Consider the system of the type shown in Fig. IV.1, where $u, e, y\colon \mathbb{Z}_+ \to \mathbb{R}^n$; the forward element is linear and time invariant with a transfer function.

$$\tilde{G}(z) = z^{-1}\{\tilde{G}_b(z) + \sum_{i=1}^{k} \sum_{j=1}^{m_i} R_{ij}/(z - p_i)^j\} = z^{-1}\tilde{G}_b(z) + \tilde{G}_u(z) \tag{91}$$

where $G_b \in l^1_{n\times n}$, $|p_i| \geq 1$ for $i = 1, \ldots, k$, and the feedback element is a memoryless time-varying gain multiplier with gain $F\colon \mathbb{Z}_+ \to \mathbb{R}^{n\times n}$ of the form

$$F(k) = F_0 + F_v(k)$$

where $F_0 \in \mathbb{R}^{n\times n}$ and $F_v \in l^1_{n\times n}$. U.t.c., the following three statements are equivalent:

(I) The closed-loop system is l^∞ stable.

(II) The closed-loop system is l^p stable for all $p \in [1, \infty]$.

(III) (i)
$$\inf_{|z|\geq 1} |\det[I + F_0 \tilde{G}(z)]| > 0 \tag{92}$$

and

$$\text{(ii)}\quad \det[\tilde{D}(p_i) + F_0 \tilde{N}(p_i) + F_0 p_i^{-1} \tilde{G}_b(p_i)\tilde{D}(p_i)] \neq 0, \quad \text{for} \quad i = 1, \ldots, k \tag{93}$$

where $\tilde{G}_u(z) = \tilde{N}(z)\tilde{D}(z)^{-1}$, $\tilde{N}$ and $\tilde{D}$ are right coprime, and $\tilde{D}$ is column proper.

94 **Remark** In contrast with the continuous-time case, (92) and (93) are necessary and sufficient for closed-loop l^∞ stability.

8 Slowly varying systems

It frequently happens in engineering that some system parameters vary slowly. Then a typical question arises: Given that the system is stable (in some sense) when its parameters are constant, to what extent is it true that the system will still be stable when its parameters vary slowly? In this section we consider differential systems; furthermore, since there is only a small increase in difficulty to consider the nonlinear case rather than only the linear case, we shall treat the nonlinear case. The approach is due to J. Barman [Bar. 1]. Suppose that the system is represented by

1 $$\dot{x} = f(x, \varepsilon t)$$

where ε is a positive number. We denote by $|x|$ the l^2 norm of $x \in \mathbb{R}^n$. We assume throughout

(A1) $f\colon \mathbb{R}^n \times \mathbb{R}_+ \to \mathbb{R}^n$ is in C^1 and $f(0, p) = 0$, for all $p \geq 0$;
(A2) f is globally Lipschitz—there is a constant $l > 0$ such that

$$|f(x, p) - f(x', p)| \leq l|x - x'|, \qquad \forall p \geq 0, \quad \forall x, x' \in \mathbb{R}^n;$$

(A3) there is a positive constant η such that

$$|D_2 f(x, p)| \leq \eta |x|, \qquad \forall (x, p) \in \mathbb{R}^n \times \mathbb{R}_+$$

Since $D_2 f(n, p)$ denotes the derivative of f with respect to its second argument, a small η means that the vector field $x \mapsto f(x, t)$ varies slowly in time. For fixed η, by choosing ε small, we can make the system (1) be as *slowly* varying as we wish. If the parameters of (1) were held constant, the equation would become

2 $$\dot{x} = f(x, p)$$

where $p \in \mathbb{R}_+$ is fixed. We think of (2) as describing the "frozen" system or, more precisely, the system frozen at $t = p/\varepsilon$.

To describe stability, we introduce two definitions.

3 The zero solution of (1) is said to be **global uniform exponentially stable** iff there are positive constants c and α such that

4 $$|\phi(t; t_0, x)| \leq c|x|e^{-\alpha(t - t_0)}, \qquad \text{for all} \quad t \geq t_0 \geq 0, \qquad \forall x \in \mathbb{R}^n$$

where $\phi(t; t_0, x)$ is the solution of (1) at time t, starting from x at t_0.

5 The zero solution of (2) is **global uniform exponentially stable uniformly in** p iff there are positive constants k and σ such that

6 $$|\phi_f(t, x; p)| \leq k|x|e^{-\sigma t}, \qquad \forall t \geq 0, \qquad \forall (x, p) \in \mathbb{R}^n \times \mathbb{R}_+$$

where $\phi_f(t, x; p)$ is the solution of the frozen system (2) at time t, starting from x at $t = 0$.

7 **Theorem** Consider the systems (1) and (2), where $f(\cdot, \cdot)$ satisfies assumptions (A1) to (A3). U.t.c., if the zero solution of (2) is global uniform exponentially stable uniformly in p, then for ε sufficiently small, (1) is global uniform exponentially stable.

In the linear case, (1) would read $\dot{x} = A(t)x$ and (2) would read $\dot{x} = A(p)x$. Condition (6) is equivalent to requiring that all eigenvalues of $A(p)$ are in $\operatorname{Re} s < -\sigma$ for all $p \geq 0$. (A1) is automatically satisfied provided $t \mapsto A(t)$ is C^1; (A2) is equivalent to $t \mapsto A(t)$ bounded on $\mathbb{R}_+$; (A3) is equivalent to $|DA(t)| \leq \eta, \ \forall t \geq 0$.

Proof The solution of the frozen system (2) satisfies the integral equation

8
$$\phi_f(\tau, x; p) = x + \int_0^\tau f[\phi_f(t', x; p), p]\, dt'$$

Differentiating with respect to the real variable p, we have $\forall \tau,\ p \in \mathbb{R}_+$, $\forall x \in \mathbb{R}^n$

9
$$D_3\phi_f(\tau, x; p) = \int_0^\tau \{D_1 f[\phi_f(t', x; p), p]\, D_3\phi_f(t', x; p) + D_2 f[\phi_f(t', x; p), p]\}\, dt'$$

Using (6) and (A2) in (8), we obtain

10
$$\phi_f(\tau, x; p) \geq \tfrac{1}{2}|x|, \qquad \text{for} \quad 0 \leq \tau \leq 1/2kl \triangleq T, \qquad \forall (x, p) \in \mathbb{R}^n \times \mathbb{R}_+$$

Using (6), (A2), (A3), into (9), and invoking Bellman's lemma, we see that for some positive constants m and m',

11
$$|D_3 \phi_f(\tau, x; p)| \leq m'|x|e^{m\tau} \qquad \text{for all} \quad (\tau, x, p) \in \mathbb{R}_+ \times \mathbb{R}^n \times \mathbb{R}_+$$

Now choose $\beta \geq (m + \sigma)/2\sigma$ and choose

12
$$V(x, p) = \int_0^\infty |\phi_f(\tau, x; p)|^{2\beta}\, d\tau$$

as a possible Lyapunov function for the frozen system (2). Clearly, $V \in C^1$ and $V(0, p) = 0$, $\forall p \geq 0$. From (6) and (10), there are constants k_1 and k_2 such that

13
$$k_1|x|^{2\beta} \leq V(x, p) \leq k_2|x|^{2\beta}, \qquad \forall (x, p) \in \mathbb{R}^n \times \mathbb{R}_+$$

Finally, from (12),

14
$$\dot{V}_{(2)}(x, p) = \lim_{h \downarrow 0} \frac{V[\phi(h, x; p), p] - V(x, p)}{h} = -|x|^{2\beta}$$

Thus V is a Lyapunov function for the frozen system (2). We are going to show that the Lyapunov function V of (2) is also a Lyapunov function of (1), provided ε is small enough. Consider the time derivative of $V(x, \varepsilon t) = \int_0^\infty |\phi_f(\tau, x, \varepsilon t)|^{2\beta}\, d\tau$ *along solutions of* (1):

16
$$\begin{aligned}\dot{V}_{(1)}(x, \varepsilon t) &= D_1 V(x, \varepsilon t) \cdot f(x, \varepsilon t) + D_2 V(x, \varepsilon t) \cdot \varepsilon \\ &= -|x|^{2\beta} + D_2 V(x, \varepsilon t) \cdot \varepsilon\end{aligned}$$

Now

$$D_2 V(x, \varepsilon t) = 2\beta \int_0^\infty |\phi_f(\tau, x; \varepsilon t)|^{2(\beta-1)} \phi_f(\tau, x; \varepsilon t)' D_3 \phi(\tau, x; \varepsilon t)\, d\tau$$

Hence

$$|D_2 V(x, \varepsilon t)| \leq |x|^{2\beta} 2\beta \int_0^\infty k^{2\beta-1} e^{-(2\beta-1)\sigma\tau} m' e^{m\tau}\, d\tau \triangleq M|x|^{2\beta}$$

where M is finite in view of the choice of β. Then (16) reads

$$\dot{V}_{(1)}(x, \varepsilon t) \leq -(1 - \varepsilon M)|x|^{2\beta}$$

If $\varepsilon < 1/M$, $\dot{V}_{(1)} < 0$; using (13) and estimating $\dot{V}_{(1)}/V$, we see that the solutions of (1) are bounded by

$$|\phi(t; t_0, x_0)| \leq c|x_0|e^{-\alpha(t-t_0)} \tag{18}$$

where $c = (k_2/k_1)^{1/2\beta}$ and $\alpha = (1 - \varepsilon M)/(2\beta k_1)$. ∎

Exercise State precisely the theorem for the linear case, expressing the conditions in terms of characteristics appropriate for the linear case.

9 Linearization

One of the most important and the most frequently used method of analysis and design is that of linearization; that is, a nonlinear system is replaced by an (approximate) linear system which is tangent to the given nonlinear system. This approximation is, of course, valid only locally, in the same sense that, in $\mathbb{R}^2$, a tangent approximates a curve only locally.

9.1 Formulation

We restrict ourselves to differential systems; we wish to give conditions under which the linearized equations about a given trajectory will give valid results *on the whole of* $\mathbb{R}_+$. In the language of circuit theory or control theory, we are going to develop conditions under which the small-signal equivalent circuit or the variational equations give predictions for the state-space trajectory *which are valid for all* $t \geq 0$.

Consider the system of differential equations

$$\dot{x} = f(x, \tilde{u}, t) \tag{1}$$

where f: $\mathbb{R}^n \times \mathbb{R}^m \times \mathbb{R}_+ \to \mathbb{R}^n$

$$f(0, 0, t) = 0, \qquad \forall t \geq 0 \tag{2}$$

$$x(0) = 0 \tag{3}$$

Equation (1) relates the state trajectory $x(\cdot)$ to the input $\tilde{u}(\cdot)$. Equations (2) and (3) assume that the velocity under zero input is always zero and that the system starts from the zero state at $t = 0$; this is just a matter of convenience. This can always be achieved by a change of coordinates. First, we impose assumptions which guarantee the existence and uniqueness of solutions.

4 **Assumption** For every fixed $x \in \mathbb{R}^n$ and $\tilde{u} \in \mathbb{R}^m$, $f(x, \tilde{u}, \cdot)$: $\mathbb{R}_+ \to \mathbb{R}^n$ is *regulated*; for every fixed $\tilde{u} \in \mathbb{R}^m$, $t \in \mathbb{R}_+$, $f(\cdot, \tilde{u}, t)$ is *locally Lipschitz* in x; for every fixed $x \in \mathbb{R}^n$, $t \in \mathbb{R}_+$, $f(x, \cdot, t)$ is *continuous.*

We think of the input $\tilde{u}$ as consisting of a "reference" input u_0 and a small perturbation u; thus,

5 $$\tilde{u} = u_0 + u$$

We *assume* throughout that u_0 and u are regulated functions of t, defined on $\mathbb{R}_+$; as a consequence, for fixed $x \in \mathbb{R}^n$, $t \mapsto f[x, u(t), t]$ is regulated. Consequently, the state trajectory can similarly be thought of as a sum of two terms

6 $$x = x_0 + \xi$$

where we *assume* that x_0 is defined for all $t \geq 0$ by

7 $$\dot{x}_0 = f(x_0, u_0, t), \qquad x_0(0) = 0$$

Note that ξ is defined by (6).

Consider the function $t \mapsto [x_0(t), u_0(t)]$, and in $\mathbb{R}^n \times \mathbb{R}^m \times \mathbb{R}_+$ the set $\mathscr{C}$ defined by

8 $$\mathscr{C} = \{[x_0(t) + \xi, u_0(t) + u, t] \mid \quad |\xi| \leq \xi_m, \quad |u| \leq u_m, \quad t \geq 0\}$$

where ξ_m and u_m are positive numbers. We think of $\mathscr{C}$ as a "tube" surrounding the "*reference trajectory*": $t \mapsto [x_0(t), u_0(t)]$. In order to carry out our approximations, we require an additional assumption.

9 **Assumption** For some $\xi_m > 0$ and $u_m > 0$, f has in $\mathscr{C}$ well-defined, continuous, second partial derivatives with respect to x and $\tilde{u}$,and

$$\sup_{\mathscr{C}} \left| \frac{\partial^2 f_i}{\partial x_k \, \partial x_l} \right|, \qquad \sup_{\mathscr{C}} \left| \frac{\partial^2 f_i}{\partial x_k \, \partial u_j} \right|, \qquad \sup_{\mathscr{C}} \left| \frac{\partial^2 f_i}{\partial u_j \, \partial u_h} \right|$$

are *finite* for all appropriate values of i, k, l, j, and h.

Let us expand f about the reference trajectory:

0 $$\begin{aligned} f[x_0(t) + \xi(t), u_0(t) + u(t), t] &= f[x_0(t), u_0(t), t] + D_1 f[x_0(t), u_0(t), t] \cdot \xi(t) \\ &\quad + D_2 f[x_0(t), u_0(t), t] \cdot u(t) + \mathscr{g}[\xi(t), u(t), t] \end{aligned}$$

where $D_i f$ denotes the derivative of f with respect to its ith argument. Observe that $D_1 f[x_0(t), u_0(t), t]$ is the Jacobian matrix of f evaluated along the reference trajectory; therefore, it is a known function of time mapping $\mathbb{R}_+$ into

$\mathbb{R}^{n \times n}$. Similarly, $D_2 f[x_0(t), u_0(t), t]$ is the $n \times m$ matrix of partial derivatives with respect to the u_i's; therefore, it is a known function of time mapping $\mathbb{R}_+$ into $\mathbb{R}^{n \times m}$.

By the standard expression for the remainder of a Taylor series [Die.1, p.190]

$$g(\xi, u, t) = \int_0^1 (1 - \lambda) f^{(2)} \Big|_{[x_0(t), u_0(t)) + \lambda(\xi(t), u(t))]} \begin{bmatrix} \xi(t) \\ u(t) \end{bmatrix}^{(2)} d\lambda$$

assumption (9) implies that
$\exists S < \infty$ such that

11 $$|g(\xi, u, t)| \le S(|\xi| + |u|)^2, \qquad \forall [x_0(t) + \xi, u_0(t) + u, t] \in \mathscr{C}$$

In other words, g is of second order *uniformly in* t since S does *not* depend on t. Calling $A(t)$ and $B(t)$ the derivatives in (10), we rewrite (1) as

12 $$\dot{\xi} = A(t)\xi + B(t)u + g(\xi, u, t), \qquad \xi(0) = 0$$

If we drop the second-order term $g(\xi, u, t)$, we have

13 $$\dot{\xi}_0 = A(t)\xi_0 + B(t)u, \qquad \xi_0(0) = 0$$

Equation (12) is an *exact* nonlinear equation equivalent to (1). Equation (13) is an *approximate linear equation*; it is the linearized equation about the reference trajectory $[x_0(\cdot), u_0(\cdot)]$.

Intuitively, we would expect that if the linearized equation (13) is "stable," then for "small" u, Eq. (13) will give valid results. The theorem that follows will make this basic idea precise. From (13), using standard notation, we obtain

14 $$\xi_0(t) = \int_0^t \Phi(t, \tau) B(\tau) u(\tau)\, d\tau$$

where $\Phi(t, \tau)$ denotes the state transition matrix of (13).

Exercise 1 Give an example to show that if for some finite K, $|\Phi(t, 0)| < K$, $\forall t \in \mathbb{R}_+$, a small $u(\cdot)$ does not necessarily produce a small $x(\cdot)$ (small, in the sense of sup norms).

Exercise 2 Ditto for $|\Phi(t, \tau)| \to 0$ as $t - \tau \to \infty$ $(t \ge 0, \tau \ge 0)$.

Exercise 3 Show that (9) implies that $\forall \varepsilon > 0$, $\exists \delta(\varepsilon)$ s.t.

15 $$(|\xi| + |u|) < 2\delta \Rightarrow |g(\xi, u, t)| < \varepsilon(|\xi| + |u|), \qquad \forall t \ge 0$$

9.2 Main result

In terms of the above formulation, we state the following theorem.

20 **Theorem** Consider the system (1) subject to Assumptions (4) and (9). Let $u_0\colon \mathbb{R}_+ \to \mathbb{R}^m$ be regulated and $x_0(\cdot)$ be defined on $\mathbb{R}_+$ by (7). Let $\xi(\cdot)$ and $\xi_0(\cdot)$be defined by (12) and (13), respectively. Assume further that

(A1) $\exists M < \infty$ s.t. $\forall t \geq 0$

$$\int_0^t |\Phi(t, \tau)|\, d\tau \leq M \tag{21}$$

(A2) $\exists N < \infty$ s.t. $\forall t \geq 0$

$$\int_0^t |\Phi(t, \tau)B(\tau)|\, d\tau \leq N \tag{22}$$

(A3) $\forall \varepsilon > 0,\ \exists \delta(\varepsilon)$ s.t.

$$(|\xi| + |u|) < 2\delta \Rightarrow |g(\xi, u, t)| < \varepsilon(|\xi| + |u|), \qquad \forall t \geq 0 \tag{23}$$

U.t.c., if, for some $\varepsilon \in (0, 1/M)$ and a δ corresponding to it according to (23),

$$\|u\| \leq \frac{1 - \varepsilon M}{N + \varepsilon M}\delta \tag{24}$$

then, using sup norms throughout,

$$\|\xi_0\| \leq N\|u\| \leq (1 - \varepsilon M)\delta \leq \delta \tag{25}$$

$$\|\xi\| \leq \delta \tag{26}$$

$$\|\xi - \xi_0\|/\|u\| \leq [\varepsilon M(1 + N)]/(1 - \varepsilon M) \tag{27}$$

28 **Comment** Let us discuss the meaning of Theorem (20). Assumption (21) together with (22) are the necessary and sufficient conditions for the approximate linearized equation (13) to be bounded input and bounded state stable [Des.14]. Assumption (23) requires g to be of the second order (in $|\xi|$ and $|u|$) *uniformly in* t. Turning now to the conclusions: Conclusions (25) and (26) say that if the perturbational input u is bounded according to (24), then both ξ_0 and ξ, the state of the approximate linearized system and the state of the exact nonlinear system, will remain within a distance δ of the reference trajectory. Conclusion (27) says that the ratio of the "peak" difference between $\xi(t)$ and $\xi_0(t)$ to the peak input $\|u\|$ can be made arbitrarily small; i.e., for small inputs the response $t \mapsto \xi(t)$ of the *exact nonlinear* system is arbitrarily close to the response $t \mapsto \xi_0(t)$ of the *approximate linearized* system *over the whole half-line* $\mathbb{R}_+$. If the right-hand side of (1) depends linearly in u, then this last conclusion can be made even sharper [see (34), in the following].

30 **Corollary** Consider the special case where the right-hand side of (1) is linear in $\tilde{u}$; i.e.,

$$\dot{x} = f(x, t) + B(t)\tilde{u} \tag{31}$$

Equation (12) becomes

$$\dot{\xi} = A(t)\xi + B(t)u + g(\xi, t) \tag{32}$$

Consequently, assumption (23) can be simplified to read

(A3′) $\forall\, \varepsilon > 0,\ \exists\, \delta > 0$ s.t.

$$|\xi| < \delta \Rightarrow |g(\xi, t)| < \varepsilon|\xi|, \qquad \forall\, t \geq 0 \tag{33}$$

U.t.c., if (24) holds, then (25) and (26) hold, and we also have

$$\|\xi - \xi_0\|/\|\xi_0\| \leq \varepsilon M/(1 - \varepsilon M) \tag{34}$$

35 **Comment** In this case, the conclusion is much sharper because it says that by taking $\|u\|$ small, (i.e., δ small), ε can be taken arbitrarily small; hence by (34), $\|\xi - \xi_0\|/\|\xi_0\|$, the ratio of the "peak" difference between $\xi(t)$ and $\xi_0(t)$ to the peak value of $\xi_0(t)$, can be made arbitrarily small. This truly shows that the *relative error* between the nonlinear and the linearized system [i.e., $\xi(t) - \xi_0(t)$] can be made arbitrarily small. This fact has been verified computationally [Des.5].

Proof of Theorem (20) If necessary, increase N [from (22)] so that $1 - \varepsilon M < N + \varepsilon M$. For purposes of the proof, assume *temporarily* that

$$\forall\, (\xi, u, t) \in \mathbb{R}^n \times \mathbb{R}^m \times \mathbb{R}_+, \qquad |g(\xi, u, t)| \leq \varepsilon(|\xi| + |u|) \tag{36}$$

The solution of (12) is given by

$$\xi(t) = \int_0^t \Phi(t, t')[B(t')u(t') + g(\xi, u, t')]\, dt' \tag{37}$$

or, by virtue of (13),

$$\xi(t) = \xi_0(t) + \int_0^t \Phi(t, t')g(\xi, u, t')\, dt' \tag{38}$$

From (14), taking sup norms of both sides, we obtain

$$\|\xi_0\| \leq N\|u\|$$

from which (25) follows. Using the temporary assumption (36) in (38), we get

$$|\xi(t)| \leq |\xi_0(t)| + \varepsilon \int_0^t |\Phi(t, t')|\, (|\xi| + |u|)\, dt' \tag{40}$$

Pick a time T in $(0, \infty)$ and consider (40) for $t \in [0, T]$. Since $A(\cdot)$ is regulated (hence bounded on $[0, T]$), $\Phi(t, t')$ is bounded on $[0, T] \times [0, T]$; thus, the Bellman–Gronwall lemma applied in (40) implies that *for any finite* T $\|\xi_T\| < \infty$. Hence, for any T in $(0, \infty)$, we obtain from (40)

$$\|\xi_T\| \leq N\|u\| + \varepsilon M\|\xi_T\| + \varepsilon M\|u\|$$

Thus, using $\varepsilon M < 1$,

$$\|\xi_T\| \leq \frac{N + \varepsilon M}{1 - \varepsilon M}\|u\|, \qquad \forall T \quad \text{in } (0, \infty)$$

Since the right-hand side is independent of T, if we let $T \to \infty$, we see that the function $T \mapsto \|\xi_T\|$ is monotonically increasing and bounded; hence,

$$\|\xi\| \leq \frac{N + \varepsilon M}{1 - \varepsilon M}\|u\| \leq \delta \tag{42}$$

i.e., (26) has been established under the temporary assumption (36). Looking back over the derivation, we see that since, over $[0, \infty)$, $|\xi(t)| \leq \delta$ and $|u(t)| \leq \delta$, we need only require that (36) holds for all (ξ, u, t) in $\mathscr{C} = \{[x_0(t) + \xi, u_0(t) + u, t] \,\big|\, |\xi| \leq \delta, |u| \leq \delta \text{ and } t \geq 0\}$. Hence conclusions (25) and (26) hold under the assumptions of the theorem. From (38)

$$\begin{aligned}|\xi(t) - \xi_0(t)| &\leq \varepsilon \int_0^t |\Phi(t, t')|[|u(t')| + |\xi(t')|]\, dt' \\ &\leq \varepsilon M(\|\xi\| + \|u\|) \leq \varepsilon M(\|\xi - \xi_0\| + \|\xi_0\| + \|u\|)\end{aligned}$$

$$\|\xi - \xi_0\| \leq \frac{1}{1 - \varepsilon M}\varepsilon M(\|\xi_0\| + \|u\|) \leq \frac{\varepsilon M(1 + N)}{1 - \varepsilon M}\|u\|$$

Hence (27) is established.

Proof of Corollary (30) Conclusions (25) and (26) follow as before. Start with (38), where now g depends only on ξ and t, so that by (33) we have successively

$$|\xi(t) - \xi_0(t)| \leq \varepsilon \int_0^t |\Phi(t, t')|\, |\xi(t')|\, dt' \leq \varepsilon M\|\xi\| \leq \varepsilon M(\|\xi - \xi_0\| + \|\xi_0\|)$$

from which (34) follows. ∎

9.3 Discrete time case

The linearization for the discrete case follows the same pattern as the continuous case. The system is specified by the difference equation

$$x(k + 1) = f[x(k), \tilde{u}(k), k] \qquad \forall k \in \mathbb{Z}_+ \tag{50}$$

where f: $\mathbb{R}^n \times \mathbb{R}^m \times \mathbb{Z}_+ \to \mathbb{R}^n$. We assume throughout that

51 $$x(0) = 0$$

As before, we split the input $\tilde{u}$ and the response x in two parts:

52 $$\tilde{u}(k) = u_0(k) + u(k), \qquad x(k) = x_0(k) + \xi(k)$$

where $x_0(\cdot)$ is defined by

53 $$x_0(k+1) = f[x_0(k), u_0(k), k] \qquad x_0(0) = 0$$

As before, let $\xi_m > 0$ and $u_m > 0$ and define

54 $$\mathscr{C} \triangleq \{[x_0(k) + \xi(k), u_0(k) + u(k), k] \mid |\xi(k)| \leq \xi_m, |u(k)| \leq u_m, \forall k \in \mathbb{Z}_+\}$$

We further assume that

55 (a) for some $\xi_m > 0$, $u_m > 0$, f has continuous second partial derivatives with respect to x and $\tilde{u}$ in $\mathscr{C}$;

56 (b) for all appropriate values of i, k, l, j, and h,

$$\sup_{\mathscr{C}} \left| \frac{\partial^2 f_i}{\partial x_k \, \partial x_l} \right|, \qquad \sup_{\mathscr{C}} \left| \frac{\partial^2 f_i}{\partial x_k \, \partial \tilde{u}_j} \right|, \qquad \sup_{\mathscr{C}} \left| \frac{\partial^2 f_i}{\partial \tilde{u}_j \, \partial \tilde{u}_h} \right|$$

are finite.

[The sups arc taken over all $(x, \tilde{u}, k) \in \mathscr{C}$.] From Taylor's expansion theorem applied to (50) about $[x_0(k), u_0(k)]$, we obtain the *exact nonlinear* difference equation

57 $$\xi(k+1) = A(k)\xi(k) + B(k)u(k) + g[\xi(k), u(k), k], \qquad \xi(0) = 0$$

The *approximate linearized* equation is

58 $$\xi_0(k+1) = A(k)\xi_0(k) + B(k)u(k), \qquad \xi_0(0) = 0$$

Note that (55) and (56) imply that the remainder term g in (57) satisfies the following condition:

59 For any $\varepsilon > 0$, there is a $\delta(\varepsilon) > 0$ (independent of k) s.t.

60 $$|g(\xi, u, k)| < \varepsilon(|\xi| + |u|), \qquad \forall k \in \mathbb{Z}_+$$

whenever $|\xi| + |u| < 2\delta$.

61 **Theorem** Consider the system (50) and (51). Suppose that (55) and (56) hold. Suppose also that

(AI) there is an $M < \infty$ such that

62 $$\sum_{j=0}^{k-1} |\Phi(k, j+1)| \leq M, \qquad \forall k \in \mathbb{Z}_+$$

(A2) there is a $K < \infty$ such that

63
$$\sum_{j=0}^{k-1} |\Phi(k, j+1)B(j)| \leq K$$

and let $\varepsilon \in (0, 1/M)$ and $\delta(\varepsilon)$ be picked according to (59), U.t.c., if

64
$$\|u\|_\infty \leq [(1 - \varepsilon M)/(K + \varepsilon M)]\delta$$

then, using $\|\cdot\|$ to denote l^∞ norms,

65
$$\|\xi_0\| \leq K\|u\|_\infty \leq (1 - \varepsilon M)\delta \leq \delta$$

66
$$\|\xi\| \leq \delta$$

67
$$\|\xi - \xi_0\|/\|u\| \leq [\varepsilon M(1 + K)]/(1 - \varepsilon M)$$

Corollary If f in (50) is linear in $\tilde{u}$, i.e.,

68
$$x(k+1) = f[x(k), k] + B(k)\tilde{u}(k)$$

then (67) can be sharpened to

$$\|\xi - \xi_0\|/\|\xi_0\| \leq \varepsilon M/(1 - \varepsilon M)$$

Notes and references

The difficulties associated with "pole–zero" cancellations in the multivariable case can be treated by state-variable techniques using the concepts of controllability and observability. The purely algebraic approach developed in Sections 1 to 3 is due to several researchers [Pop. 1, Ros. 1, Wan. 1, Wol. 1, Des. 12]. The material in section 4 has been developed in stages by several researchers. Desoer [Des. 2] gave a general formulation of the Nyquist criterion, and this was extended by Desoer and Wu [Des. 6] and Desoer and Callier [Des. 12, Cal. 2]. The method of pseudoright-coprime factorizations is due to Vidyasagar. The graphical test of Section 5 was developed for the case of periodically spaced impulses by Willems [Wil. 1, 5], and for the general case by Callier and Desoer [Cal. 1]. Davis [Dav. 1, 2] has obtained related results. A thorough treatment of the discrete-time case, which contains the elements of the discussion of Section 6, can be found in [Des. 9] and [Wu 2]. The calculations of norms in Section 7 appear to have a long history in the mathematical literature [Edw. 1]; for the engineering literature see for example [San. 12, Wil. 2, Wu. 1]. The idea of using the principle of uniform boundedness to prove the equivalence of the two types of L^∞ stability is found in Desoer and Thomasian [Des. 1]. The spectral radius calculations in Section 7 are taken from [Vid. 3], and earlier versions of the perturbational results can be found in [Che. 1] and [Vid. 2]. The method employed in Section 8 is due to Barman [Bar. 1]. Finally, the results of Section 9 are updated versions of those found in [Des. 4].

V APPLICATIONS OF THE SMALL GAIN THEOREM

The purpose of this chapter is to illustrate the concept that once the small gain theorem [(III.2.1) and (III.3.1)] is understood and the techniques of Chapter II, Chapter IV, and the Appendices are available, it is easy to establish a large number of input–output stability results. Our emphasis is more on displaying the flexibility of the method rather than giving an exhaustive account of known results.

In Section 1, we obtain an L^p stability result based on the results of Chapter IV and the small gain theorem. Section 2 contains a sufficient condition for L^2 stability that differs in two important respects from that of Section 1: (i) The condition of Section 2 can be verified in the frequency domain, in contrast with that of Section 1. (ii) The condition of Section 2 is less conservative than that of Section 1. In Section 3, the important concept of exponential weighting is discussed, and a criterion for L^∞ stability, which can be verified directly in the frequency domain, is derived. Discrete-time analogues of some of the results of the first two sections are given in Section 4. In Section 5, we study slowly varying linear systems and obtain a condition that ensure L^p stability when each "frozen" system is stable. Section 6 presents a nonlinear circuit example that illustrates the application of the small gain theorem. In Section 7, we show how small gain techniques can be used to prove the existence of periodic solutions to a nonautonomous nonlinear differential equation. Section 8 contains a proof of the well-known Popov criterion using the small gain approach. Finally, in Section 9 we study two approaches for obtaining conditions that ensure the instability of a nonlinear feedback system.

1 Continuous-time systems—L^p stability

We consider feedback systems of the form shown in Fig. III.1, where H_1 is a linear convolution operator and H_2 is a memoryless time-varying nonlinearity. The general idea is to assume that H_2 can be approximated by a time-invariant linear map $y_2(t) = Ke_2(t)$ and to use the small gain theorem to show that if the linear time-invariant system with H_1 in the forward path and K in the feedback path is stable, then so is the original nonlinear system, provided H_2 does not deviate too much from K. We consider first an L^p stability result where $p \in [1, \infty]$.

1 **Theorem** Consider a multivariable feedback system of the form shown in Fig. III.1, where $u_1, u_2, e_1, e_2, y_1, y_2\colon \mathbb{R}_+ \to \mathbb{R}^n$. The subsystem H_1 is linear and time-invariant and is represented by

2 $$(H_1 e_1)(t) = \int_0^t G(t-\tau)e_1(\tau)\,d\tau$$

where $G(\cdot)$ is Laplace transformable, and furthermore,

3 $$\hat{G}(s) = \hat{\mathcal{N}}(s)\hat{\mathcal{D}}(s)^{-1}$$

where $\hat{\mathcal{N}}, \hat{\mathcal{D}} \in \hat{\mathscr{A}}^{n\times n}$ and the pair $(\hat{\mathcal{N}}, \hat{\mathcal{D}})$ constitutes a prcf of G. The subsystem H_2 is memoryless and is represented by

4 $$(H_2 e_2)(t) = \phi[e_2(t), t]$$

where $\phi\colon \mathbb{R}^n \times \mathbb{R}_+ \to \mathbb{R}^n$; ϕ is continuous in its first argument and regulated in its second. Suppose that

6 $$u_1, u_2 \in L_n{}^p \Rightarrow y_1, y_2 \in L_{ne}^p$$

U.t.c., if there exist a constant matrix $K \in \mathbb{R}^{n\times n}$ and real constants γ and β (with $\beta = 0$ whenever $p < \infty$) such that

7 $$|\phi(\sigma, t) - K\sigma| \le \gamma|\sigma| + \beta, \qquad \forall t \in \mathbb{R}_+, \quad \forall \sigma \in \mathbb{R}^n$$

and if

8 (a) $\inf_{\mathrm{Re}\, s \geq 0} |\det[I + K\hat{G}(s)]| > 0$

9 (b) $\det[\hat{\mathscr{D}}(s) + K\hat{\mathscr{N}}(s)] \neq 0$, whenever $\mathrm{Re}\, s \geq 0$ and $\det \hat{\mathscr{D}}(s) = 0$

10 (c) $\|H_K(\cdot)\|_{\mathscr{A}} \cdot \gamma < 1$

where

11
$$\hat{H}_K(s) \triangleq \hat{G}(s)[I + K\hat{G}(s)]^{-1} = [I + \hat{G}(s)K]^{-1}\hat{G}(s)$$

Then, for each $p \in [1, \infty]$,

12
$$u_1, u_2 \in L_n^p \Rightarrow e_1, e_2, y_1, y_2 \in L_n^p$$

and the system is L^p stable.

Proof The details of the proof are left as an exercise. Apply the loop shifting theorem (III.6.3). In view of (8) and (9) and Theorem (IV.4.27), the function $H_K(\cdot) \in \mathscr{A}^{n \times n}$. Assumption (10) and the small gain theorem lead readily to the conclusion (12). ∎

Exercise 1 Explain why it is assumed in (7) that $\beta = 0$ if $p < \infty$, while β may be nonzero if $p = \infty$.

If ϕ satisfies a global Lipschitz condition, we can invoke the incremental form of the small gain theorem (III.3.1). Thus, we state the following corollary.

13 **Corollary** If in the assumptions of Theorem (1) we replace (6) by

14
$$|[\phi(\sigma, t) - K\sigma] - [\phi(\sigma', t) - K\sigma']| \leq \gamma|\sigma - \sigma'|, \qquad \forall t \in \mathbb{R}_+, \quad \forall \sigma, \sigma' \in \mathbb{R}^n$$

then the conclusions of Theorem (1) can be strengthened to

(a) for each $u_1, u_2 \in L_n^p$, there is a unique solution $e_1, e_2, y_1, y_2 \in L_n^p$ (and it can be computed iteratively);

(b) the solution depends continuously on u_1, u_2.

Remark It is important to note that our results in no way depend on the manner in which ϕ varies with t.

Exercise 2 When $p = \infty$ (i.e., $u_1, u_2 \in L_n^\infty$), show that condition (7) of Theorem (1) and condition (14) of Corollary (13) can be relaxed so that they have to hold only for all σ in some ball whose radius depends on $\|u_1\|_\infty$ and $\|u_2\|_\infty$.

Exercise 3 Suppose ϕ satisfies (14) for some $\gamma \in \mathbb{R}$, and suppose that $G(\cdot)$ contains at most impulses in some neighborhood of the origin. Let G_0 be the "strength" of the impulse at $t = 0$. Show that, if $\det(I + KG_0) \neq 0$, then $u_1, u_2 \in L_{ne}^p \Rightarrow e_1, e_2, y_1, y_2 \in L_{ne}^p$.

2 L^2 Stability—circle criterion

The results of Section 1 are based on the inequality

$$\|H_K * e\|_p \leq \|H_K\|_{\mathscr{A}} \, \|e\|_p \tag{1}$$

which is valid for all $p \in [1, \infty]$. Theorem (1.1) and Corollary (1.13) are very powerful in that they provide a sufficient condition for L^p stability for all values of p. However, the application of Theorem (1) to practical situations is, in some instances, limited by the fact that the crucial small gain condition (10) involves $\|H_K(\cdot)\|_{\mathscr{A}}$. At the present time, there are no means available for either determining $\|H_K(\cdot)\|_{\mathscr{A}}$ or for obtaining an upper bound for $\|H_K(\cdot)\|_{\mathscr{A}}$ based solely on the knowledge of $\hat{H}_K(j\omega)$, $\omega \in \mathbb{R}_+$.† Therefore, in order to obtain an explicit value for $\|H_K(\cdot)\|_{\mathscr{A}}$, we are obliged to actually find the inverse Laplace transform of the function $H_K(\cdot)$ defined by (11), and then apply the definition of $\|\cdot\|_{\mathscr{A}}$. In applications such as distributed RC networks, this process is very cumbersome and usually involves some form of interpolation.

In this section, we use the small gain theorem to obtain a sufficient condition for L^2 stability, and we derive the so-called circle criterion. The results of this section have two main advantages over those of Section 1: (i) The small gain condition in Theorem (4) in the following is based on the induced L^2 norm of the operator H_K, and as a result (8) in the following is less conservative than (1.10). (ii) Condition (8) in the following can be readily verified by examining only $\hat{H}_K(j\omega)$.

Much of what follows is based on the following fact.

2 Fact Suppose $H \in \mathscr{A}^{n \times n}$ and $e \in L_n^{\,2}$. Then

$$\|H * e\|_2 \leq \{\sup_{\omega} \lambda_{\max}[\hat{H}(j\omega)^* \hat{H}(j\omega)]\}^{1/2} \cdot \|e\|_2 \tag{3}$$

The proof is based on Parseval's equality and is left as an exercise.

---

† We can only obtain a *lower bound* for $\|H_K(\cdot)\|_{\mathscr{A}}$, namely,

$$\|H_K(\cdot)\|_{\mathscr{A}} \geq \sup_{\omega \in \mathbb{R}} |\hat{H}_K(j\omega)|$$

We first state an L^2 stability result that brings out the main idea, and then we specialize to the circle criterion. For convenience in later formulations, we define $D[a, b]$ to be the closed disk in $\mathbb{R}^2$ whose diameter is the line segment joining the points $(a, 0)$ and $(b, 0)$.

4 **Theorem** Consider a multivariable feedback system of the form shown in Fig. III.1, where $u_1, u_2, e_1, e_2, y_1, y_2: \mathbb{R}_+ \to \mathbb{R}^n$; the subsystem H satisfies (1.2) and (1.3), and the subsystem H_2 satisfies (1.4). Suppose $u_1, u_2, \in L_n^2$ implies that $y_1, y_2 \in L_{ne}^2$. U.t.c., if there exist a matrix $K \in \mathbb{R}^{n \times n}$ and a constant $\gamma \in \mathbb{R}$ such that

$$|\phi(\sigma, t) - K\sigma| \leq \gamma |\sigma|, \qquad \forall t \in \mathbb{R}_+, \quad \forall \sigma \in \mathbb{R}^n \tag{5}$$

and if

$$\text{(a)} \quad \inf_{\operatorname{Re} s \geq 0}, \ |\det[I + K\hat{G}(s)]| > 0 \tag{6}$$

$$\text{(b)} \quad \det[\hat{\mathscr{D}}(s) + K\hat{\mathscr{N}}(s)] \neq 0, \quad \text{whenever} \quad \operatorname{Re} s \geq 0 \quad \text{and} \quad \det \hat{\mathscr{D}}(s) = 0 \tag{7}$$

$$\gamma \sup_{\omega \in \mathbb{R}} \lambda_{\max}[\hat{H}_K(j\omega)^* \hat{H}_K(j\omega)] < 1 \tag{8}$$

where $\hat{H}_K(\cdot)$ is defined by (1.11); then

$$u_1, u_2 \in L_n^2 \Rightarrow e_1, e_2, y_1, y_2 \in L_n^2 \tag{9}$$

The proof is left as an exercise.

As it stands, Theorem (4) cannot be applied to $\hat{G}(j\omega)$ alone, since the verification of (6) still requires knowledge of $\hat{G}(s)$. However, once the condition (6) has been verified, the small gain condition (8) can be applied in the frequency domain directly, and there is no need to compute the time-domain function $H_K(\cdot)$. Also recall (Section IV.5) that under certain conditions, the inequality (6) can be verified graphically by examining $\hat{G}(j\omega)$ alone.

We now state the celebrated circle criterion in a form more general than the conventional one. Because of its importance, we give both the result and its proof in full. The importance of the theorem lies in the fact that the condition is readily applicable to directly available experimental data, namely, the Nyquist diagram.

10 **Theorem** (circle criterion) Consider a scalar system of the form shown in Fig. III.1, where $u_1, u_2, e_1, e_2, y_1, y_2: \mathbb{R}_+ \to \mathbb{R}$. The subsystem H_1 is represented by

$$y_1(t) = (g * e_1)(t) \tag{11}$$

where

$$\hat{g}(s) = \sum_{i=1}^{k} \sum_{j=1}^{m_i} r_{ij}/(s - p_i)^j + \hat{g}_b(s) \tag{12}$$

Re $p_i \geq 0$ for $i = 1, \ldots, k$, and $g_b \in L^1$. The subsystem H_2 is represented by

13 $$y_2(t) = \phi[e_2(t), t]$$

with $\phi\colon \mathbb{R} \times \mathbb{R}_+ \to \mathbb{R}$ is continuous in its first argument and regulated in its second. Moreover, we assume that ϕ belongs to the sector $[\alpha, \beta]$; i.e.,

14 $$\alpha\sigma^2 \leq \sigma\phi(\sigma, t) \leq \beta\sigma^2, \qquad \forall t \in \mathbb{R}_+, \quad \forall \sigma \in \mathbb{R}$$

For convenience, let

15 $$\xi = (\alpha + \beta)/2, \qquad \rho = (\beta - \alpha)/2$$

and assume that $\xi \neq 0$. U.t.c., we have that $u_1, u_2 \in L^2 \Rightarrow e_1, e_2, y_1, y_2 \in L^2$, if the pole locations and Nyquist diagram of $\hat{g}$ [i.e., the map $\omega \mapsto \hat{g}(j\omega)$ with indentations as required] satisfy one of the following conditions, as appropriate:

(a) if $0 < \alpha < \beta$, there are no restrictions on the location of the poles of $\hat{g}$, and the Nyquist diagram of $\hat{g}$ is bounded away from the disk $D[-1/\alpha, -1/\beta]$ and encircles it in the counterclockwise direction n_p times, where n_p is the number of poles of $\hat{g}$ with positive real part;

(b) if $0 = \alpha < \beta$, $\hat{g}$ has no poles in the *open* right half-plane, and the Nyquist diagram of $\hat{g}$ must remain to the right of the vertical line of abscissa $-1/\beta$; i.e.,

$$\operatorname{Re} \hat{g}(j\omega) > -1/\beta, \qquad \forall \omega \in \mathbb{R}$$

(c) if $\alpha < 0 < \beta$, g has no poles in the *closed* right half-plane, and the Nyquist diagram of g is completely contained in the interior of the disk $D[-1/\alpha, -1/\beta]$.

Proof The result follows directly from the loop shifting theorem and the small gain theorem and can also be thought of as a corollary to Theorem (4). First of all, it is clear that whether we are in case (a), (b), or (c), the Nyquist diagram of $\hat{g}$ does not intersect the point $(-1/\xi, 0)$ and encircles it exactly n_p times in the counterclockwise direction, where n_p is the number of poles of $\hat{g}$ in the *open* right half-plane. Therefore, by the graphical test [Theorem (IV.5.5)], it follows that $\hat{h}_\xi(s) = \hat{g}(s)/[1 + \xi\hat{g}(s)] \in \hat{\mathscr{A}}$. Apply Theorem (4) with $K = \xi I$. Then the small gain condition (8) becomes

16 $$\rho \cdot \sup_\omega \left| \frac{\hat{g}(j\omega)}{1 + \xi\hat{g}(j\omega)} \right| < 1$$

It is a simple exercise to show that for $z \in \mathbb{C}$,

7a if $0 < \alpha < \beta$, then $\rho|z| < |1 + \xi z|$ is equivalent to: z is bounded away from the disk $D[-1/\alpha, -1/\beta]$;

17b if $0 = \alpha < \beta$, then $\rho|z| < |1 + \xi z|$ is equivalent to: $\text{Re } z > -1/\beta$;

17c if $\alpha < 0 < \beta$, then $\rho|z| < |1 + \xi z|$ is equivalent to: z is in the interior of the disk $D[-1/\alpha, -1/\beta]$.

Hence the conditions of Theorem (4) are satisfied, and the conclusion follows. ∎

18 **Remark** As $\beta \to \alpha > 0$, the sector condition (14) reduces ϕ to a linear characteristic of slope α; the critical disk $D[-1/\alpha, -1/\beta]$ shrinks to the critical point $(-1/\alpha, 0)$; and the circle criterion above reduces to the graphical test of Theorem (IV.5.5).

Exercise 1 In the hypothesis of Theorem (10), suppose g_b in (12) belongs to $\mathscr{A}$ and not L_1. Give an appropriately modified version of Theorem (10) and prove it.

Exercise 2 Consider an n-input–n-ouput feedback system where H_1 is specified as the zero-state response of a system whose input is e_1 and output y_1 with

$$\dot{x} = Ax + Be_1, \qquad x(0) = 0, \qquad y_1 = Cx$$

($A \in \mathbb{R}^{d \times d}$, $B \in \mathbb{R}^{d \times n}$, $C \in \mathbb{R}^{n \times d}$ are constant); all eigenvalues of A have negative real parts. Call $\hat{G}(j\omega) = C(j\omega I - A)^{-1}B$ the transfer function of H_1. Let H_2 be specified by $y_2(t) = \phi[e_2(t), t]$, where $\phi\colon \mathbb{R}^n \times \mathbb{R}_+ \to \mathbb{R}^n$ is continuous. Show that if $u_2 \equiv 0$, if $I - \hat{G}(j\omega)^* G(j\omega)$ is positive semidefinite for all $\omega \in \mathbb{R}$ and if for some $\varepsilon \in (0, 1)$

$$\phi(\sigma, t)'\phi(\sigma, t) \leq (1 - \varepsilon)\sigma'\sigma, \qquad \forall \sigma \in \mathbb{R}^n, \quad \forall t \geq 0$$

then, for any $u_1 \in L_n^{\,2}$, e_1, y_1, $y_2 \in L^2 \cap L^\infty$ and go to zero as $t \to \infty$. (*Hint*: Use l^2 norms in $\mathbb{R}^n$, and for $x \in L_n^{\,2}$, $\|x\|^2{}_{,} = \int_0^\infty \sum_1^n |x_i(t)|^2\, dt$; note that the impulse response of H_1 is $G(t) = C\exp(At)B \in L^1_{n \times n}$, and $\dot{G}(t) = CB\delta(t) + CA \exp(At)D \in \mathscr{A}^{n \times n}$.)

Exercise 3 Consider a single-input–single-ouput system with unity feedback where

$$y(t) = \int_0^t g(t - \tau)k(\tau)e(\tau)\, d\tau = (Ge)(t)$$

with $g \in L^1(0, \infty)$,

$$k(\tau) = \sum_{-\infty}^{+\infty} k_\alpha \exp(j\alpha\omega\tau)$$

where $\sum_{-\infty}^{+\infty} |k_\alpha| < \infty$. Show that

(a) for all $T > 0$, G is a continuous linear map from $P_T L_{2e}$ to $P_T L_{2e}$;
(b) $\gamma(G) \le \|g\|_1 \cdot (\sum_{-\infty}^{\infty} |k_\alpha|)$;
(c) if $\gamma(G) < 1$, then the closed-loop system is L^2 stable.

3 Exponential weighting—L^{∞} stability

The results of Section 1 are quite powerful in that they provide conditions for L^p stability for all values of p, but the price we pay for these powerful results is that the crucial small gain condition (1.10) is of a form that cannot be verified directly in the frequency domain. In Section 2, we formulated a theorem containing a small gain condition that can be directly verified in the frequency domain, but as a result we could conclude only L^2 stability. In this section, using the important technique of exponential weighting, we obtain a criterion for L^{∞} stability that is, in fact, stated in terms of the Nyquist diagram, and in return we are obliged to make a few extra assumptions.

The exponential weighting technique is predicated on two facts:

(1) If

$$y(t) = g(t) * e(t) \tag{1}$$

then, for all $a \in \mathbb{R}$,

$$y(t)\varepsilon^{at} = g(t)\varepsilon^{at} * e(t)\varepsilon^{at} \tag{2}$$

(2) If $\mathscr{L}(\cdot)$ denotes Laplace transform, then

$$\mathscr{L}[f(t)\varepsilon^{at}] = \hat{f}(s-a), \qquad \text{where} \quad \hat{f}(s) = \mathscr{L}[f(t)]$$

In the above, we use $f(t)\varepsilon^{at}$ to mean the *function* $t \mapsto f(t)\varepsilon^{at}$, but this slight notational abuse causes no confusion and saves us from unnecessary clutter. We use ε^{at} to denote $\exp(at)$, thus avoiding multiple usage of e.

3 **Theorem** Consider a scalar feedback system of the form shown in Fig. III.1. The subsystem H_1 is represented by

$$y_1(t) = (g * e_1)(t) \tag{4}$$

while the subsystem H_2 is represented by

$$y_2(t) = \phi[e_2(t), t] \tag{5}$$

we assume that $u_2(t) \equiv 0$, and that

$$\varepsilon^{at} g(t) \in L^1 \cap L^2, \qquad \text{for some} \quad a > 0 \tag{6}$$

$$\phi \in \text{sector } [\alpha, \beta], \qquad \text{with} \quad \beta > 0 \tag{7}$$

U.t.c., if the a-shifted Nyquist diagram of $\hat{g}$, namely, the image $\omega \mapsto \hat{g}(-a + j\omega)$, satisfies the circle condition of Theorem (2.10), then $u_1 \in L^\infty$ simples e_1, $y_1 \in L^\infty$, and moreover, there exist finite constants m_1 and m_2 such that

8a $$\|e_1\|_\infty \leq m_1 \|u_1\|_\infty$$

8b $$\|y_1\|_\infty \leq m_2 \|u_1\|_\infty$$

Proof The feedback system is characterized by

9 $$y(t) = \int_0^t g(t - \tau) u(\tau)\, d\tau - \int_0^t g(t - \tau) \phi[y(\tau), \tau]\, d\tau$$

10 $$= v(t) - \int_0^t g(t - \tau) \phi[y(\tau), \tau]\, d\tau$$

where we have dropped the subscript "1" for convenience, and denote $(g * u)$ by v. Clearly, by (6), $v \in L^\infty$. Now (10) can be equivalently rewritten as

11 $$\varepsilon^{at} y(t) = \varepsilon^{at} v(t) - \int_0^t \varepsilon^{a(t-\tau)} g(t - \tau) \cdot \varepsilon^{a\tau} \phi[y(\tau), \tau]\, d\tau$$

If we define

12a $$y_w(t) = \varepsilon^{at} y(t)$$

12b $$v_w(t) = \varepsilon^{at} v(t)$$

12c $$g_w(t) = \varepsilon^{at} g(t)$$

Equation (11) becomes

13 $$y_w(t) = v_w(t) - \int_0^t g_w(t - \tau) \varepsilon^{a\tau} \phi[\varepsilon^{-a\tau} y_w(\tau), \tau]\, d\tau$$

Since the map

14 $$\sigma \mapsto \varepsilon^{at} \phi(\varepsilon^{-a\tau} \sigma, \tau)$$

belongs to the sector $[\alpha, \beta]$, and since the Nyquist diagram $\omega \mapsto \hat{g}_w(j\omega) = \hat{g}(-a + j\omega)$ satisfies the circle criterion, we see by Theorem (2.10) that $y_w(\cdot) \in L_e^2$ whenever $v_w(\cdot) \in L_e^2$ and moreover that, for some finite constant ρ,

15 $$\|[y_w(\cdot)]_t\|_2 \leq \rho \|[v_w(\cdot)]_t\|_2$$

where $\|[y_w(\cdot)]_t\|_2$ denotes the L^2 norm of the truncated function $[y_w(\cdot)]_t$. However, it is easy to show that

16 $$\|[v_w(\cdot)]_t\|_2 \leq \frac{\varepsilon^{at}}{(2a)^{1/2}} \|v\|_\infty \leq \varepsilon^{at} \frac{\|g\|_1}{(2a)^{1/2}} \|u\|_\infty$$

By the sector condition on the map defined in (14), we see that

17
$$\|[\varepsilon^{a\tau}\phi[\varepsilon^{-a\tau}y_w(\tau),]\}_t\|_2 \le \beta\|[y_w]_t\|_2 \le \varepsilon^{at}\frac{\beta\rho\|g\|_1}{(2a)^{1/2}}\|u\|_\infty$$
$$= \varepsilon^{at}\rho_1\|u\|_\infty, \quad \text{say}$$

Going back now to (9), we get

18
$$|y(t)| \le |v(t)| + \int_0^t |g(t-\tau)|\,|\phi[y(\tau),\tau]|\,d\tau$$
$$\le \|g\|_1\|u\|_\infty + \varepsilon^{-at}\int_0^t \varepsilon^{a(t-\tau)}|g(t-\tau)|\,\varepsilon^{a\tau}\,|\phi[y(\tau),\tau]|\,d\tau$$
$$\le \|g\|_1\|u\|_\infty + \varepsilon^{-at}\|g(\tau)\varepsilon^{a\tau}\|_2\|\{\varepsilon^{a\tau}\,\phi[\varepsilon^{-a\tau}y_w(\tau),\tau]\}_t\|_2$$
(by Schwartz' inequality)
$$\le \|g\|_1\|u\|_\infty + \|g(\tau)\varepsilon^{a\tau}\|_2\,\rho_1\|u\|_\infty$$

Hence (8b) is established. The proof of (8a) is left as an exercise. ∎

19 **Corollary** Under the conditions of Theorem (3), if $u(\cdot)$ is bounded on $\mathbb{R}_+$ by a decaying exponential, then so are $e(\cdot)$ and $y(\cdot)$.

Proof By assumption, there exist $r, \alpha \in \mathbb{R}_+$ such that

20
$$|u(t)| \le m\varepsilon^{-\alpha t}, \qquad \forall t \ge 0$$

Without loss of generality, suppose $0 < \alpha < a$. From (9) we have

$$\varepsilon^{\alpha t}y(t) = \varepsilon^{\alpha t}u(t) - \int_0^t \varepsilon^{\alpha(t-\tau)}g(t-\tau)\varepsilon^{\alpha\tau}\phi[y(\tau),\tau]\,d\tau$$

Note that

(i) the function $t \mapsto \varepsilon^{\alpha t}u(t)$ is bounded;
(ii) the map $\sigma \mapsto \varepsilon^{\alpha\tau}\phi(\varepsilon^{-\alpha\tau}\sigma, \tau)$ belongs to the sector $[\alpha, \beta]$;
(iii) the function $t \mapsto \varepsilon^{\alpha t}g(t)$ satisfies (6), with a replaced by $(a-\alpha)/2$.

Hence by Theorem (3), $\varepsilon^{\alpha t}y(t)$ is bounded. ∎

We now present a slight generalization of Theorem (3). The generalization is based on the following lemma.

21 **Lemma** Let

22
$$\hat{G}(s) = \sum_{i=1}^{k}\sum_{j=1}^{m_i} R_{ij}/(s-p_i)^j + \hat{G}_b(s) = \hat{G}_u(s) + \hat{G}_b(s)$$

where $\operatorname{Re} p_i \geq 0$, $m_i = 1$ if $\operatorname{Re} p_i = 0$, and $G_b \in L^1_{n\times n} \cap L^2_{n\times n}$. Suppose $\hat{F} \in \hat{\mathscr{A}}^{n\times n}$. U.t.c., if $\hat{H} = \hat{G}(I + \hat{F}\hat{G})^{-1} \in \hat{\mathscr{A}}^{n\times n}$, then in fact $H \in L^1_{n\times n} \cap L^2_{n\times n}$.

Proof By hypothesis, $\hat{H} = \hat{G}(I + \hat{F}\hat{G})^{-1} \in \hat{\mathscr{A}}^{n\times n}$. Now H satisfies

23 $$\hat{H} + \hat{H}\hat{F}\hat{G}_b + \hat{H}\hat{F}\hat{G}_u = \hat{G}_b + \hat{G}_u$$

or

24 $$\hat{H} + \hat{H}\hat{F}\hat{G}_b - \hat{G}_b = (I - \hat{H}\hat{F})\hat{G}_u$$

Since $(I - \hat{H}\hat{F})\hat{G}_u$ is analytic for $\operatorname{Re} s > 0$ and bounded and uniformly continuous on $\operatorname{Re} s = 0$, we can show, as in the proof of Theorem (IV.7.69), that in fact $\mathscr{L}^{-1}[(I - \hat{H}\hat{F})\hat{G}_u] \in L^1_{n\times n} \cap L^\infty_{n\times n}$, and in particular $\mathscr{L}^{-1}[(I - \hat{H}\hat{F})\hat{G}_u] \in L^1_{n\times n} \cap L^2_{n\times n}$. Since

25 $$\hat{H} = -\hat{H}\hat{F}\hat{G}_b + \hat{G}_b + (I - \hat{H}\hat{F})\hat{G}_u$$

and all terms on the right side belong to $L^1_{n\times n} \cap L^2_{n\times n}$, the conclusion that $\hat{H} \in L^1_{n\times n} \cap L^2_{n\times n}$ follows. ∎

26 **Theorem** Consider a feedback system of the form in Fig. III.1 and suppose the subsystems H_1 and H_2 are represented by (4) and (5), respectively. Suppose that $u_2(t) \equiv 0$, and that for some $a > 0$

27 $$\hat{g}(s) = \sum_{i=1}^{k} \sum_{j=1}^{m_i} r_{ij}/(s - p_i)^j + \hat{g}_b(s)$$

28 $$\operatorname{Re} p_i \geq -a, \qquad m_i = 1, \qquad \text{if} \quad \operatorname{Re} p_i = -a$$

29 $$\varepsilon^{at} g_b(t) \in L^1 \cap L^2$$

30 $$\phi \in \text{sector } [\alpha, \beta]$$

U.t.c., if the a-shifted Nyquist diagram of $\hat{g}$ satisfies the circle conditions of Theorem (2.10) (where the right half-plane is taken as $\{s\colon \operatorname{Re} s \geq -a\}$), then $u_1 \in L^\infty$, implies $e_1, y_1 \in L^\infty$ and moreover (8a) and (8b) hold.

The proof is straightforward and is left as an exercise.

4 Discrete-time systems—L^p stability

In this brief section, we state what are essentially the discrete-time analogues of the results of Section 1. We do not explicitly state the results corresponding to those in Sections 2 and 3, since these are quite obvious.

1 **Theorem** Consider a multivariable feedback system of the form shown in Fig. III.1, where $u_1, u_2, e_1, e_2, y_1, y_2 : \mathbb{Z}_+ \to \mathbb{R}^n$. The subsystem H_1 is linear and time invariant and is represented by

$$y_1 = G * e_1 \tag{2}$$

where

$$\tilde{G}(z) = \hat{\mathcal{N}}(z)\hat{\mathcal{D}}(z)^{-1} \tag{3}$$

$\mathcal{N}, \mathcal{D} \in l^1_{n \times n}$, and $(\tilde{\mathcal{N}}, \tilde{\mathcal{D}})$ constitutes a prcf of $\tilde{G}$. The subsystem H_2 is memoryless and is represented by

$$y_2(i) = \psi[e_2(i), i], \qquad \forall i \in \mathbb{Z}_+ \tag{4}$$

U.t.c., if there exist a constant matrix $K \in \mathbb{R}^{n \times n}$ and real constants γ and ν (with $\nu = 0$ if $p < \infty$) such that

$$|\psi(\sigma, i) - K\sigma| \leq \gamma|\sigma| + \nu \tag{5}$$

$$\inf_{|z| \geq 1} |\det[I + K\tilde{G}(z)]| > 0 \tag{6}$$

$$\det[\tilde{\mathcal{D}}(z) + K\tilde{\mathcal{N}}(z)] \neq 0, \qquad \text{whenever} \quad |z| \geq 1 \quad \text{and} \quad \det \tilde{\mathcal{D}}(z) = 0 \tag{7}$$

$$\|H\|_1 \cdot \gamma < 1 \tag{8}$$

where

$$H = \mathcal{Z}^{-1}\{\tilde{G}(z)[I + K\tilde{G}(z)]^{-1}\} \tag{9}$$

then for each $p \in [1, \infty]$,

$$u_1, u_2 \in l_n^p \Rightarrow e_1, e_2, y_1, y_2 \in l_n^p \tag{10}$$

Exercise 1 Prove Theorem (1).

Exercise 2 State and prove the discrete-time analogues of Theorems (2.3) and (3.26).

5 Slowly-varying linear systems

Consider a multivariable feedback system where

$$y_1(t) = (G * e_1)(t) \tag{1}$$

$$y_2(t) = K(t)e_2(t) \tag{2}$$

If $K(\cdot)$ takes values in some subset $\mathscr{S}$ of $\mathbb{R}^{n\times n}$, and if $(I + \hat{G}M)^{-1}\hat{G} \in \hat{\mathscr{A}}^{n\times n}$ for all $M \in S$, we expect intuitively that the time-varying system characterized by (1) and (2) is also stable, provided $K(\cdot)$ varies sufficiently slowly. In what follows, we give a precise interpretation to the phrase "sufficiently slowly." Note that if $K(\cdot)$ were to be "frozen" at the value $K(\tau)$, the closed-loop transfer function of the resulting linear *time-invariant* system is

$$\hat{H}_\tau(s) = [I + \hat{G}(s)K(\tau)]^{-1}\hat{G}(s) \tag{3}$$

4 **Theorem** Consider a multivariable feedback system of the form shown in Fig. III.1, where $u_1, u_2, e_1, e_2, y_1, y_2: \mathbb{R}_+ \to \mathbb{R}^n$. Suppose the subsystem H_1 is represented by (1), and that the subsystem H_2 is represented by (2), where $K(\cdot)$ takes values in some bounded subset $\mathscr{S}$ of $\mathbb{R}^n$. Suppose that for each $M \in \mathscr{S}$, the function $[I + \hat{G}(s)M]^{-1}\hat{G}(s)$ belongs to $\mathscr{A}^{n\times n}$. U.t.c., if

$$\sup_{\tau\in\mathbb{R}_+} \int_0^\infty |H_\tau(\tau - \tau')[K(\tau) - K(\tau')]| \, d\tau' < 1 \tag{5}$$

where

$$\hat{H}_\tau(s) = [I + \hat{G}(s)K(\tau)]^{-1}\hat{G}(s) \tag{6}$$

then $u_1, u_2 \in L^\infty \Rightarrow e_1, e_2, y_1, y_2 \in L^\infty$. If

$$\sup_{\tau'\in\mathbb{R}^+} \int_{\tau'}^\infty |H_\tau(\tau - \tau')[K(\tau) - K(\tau')]| \, d\tau < 1 \tag{7}$$

then $u_1, u_2 \in L^1 \Rightarrow e_1, e_2, y_1, y_2 \in L^1$. If both (5) and (7) hold, then for each $p \in [1, \infty]$, $u_1, u_2 \in L^p \Rightarrow e_1, e_2, y_1, y_2 \in L^p$.

Proof The closed-loop system is characterized by

$$\begin{aligned} y_1(t) &= -(G * Ky_1)(t) - (G * Ku_2)(t) + (G * u_1)(t) \\ &= -(G * Ky_1)(t) + (G * u)(t) \end{aligned} \tag{8}$$

where

$$u(t) = u_1(t) - K(t)u_2(t) \tag{9}$$

Let $\tau \in \mathbb{R}_+$. Then (8) can be written as

$$y_1(t) + [G * K(\tau)y_1] = (G * u)(t) + \{G * [K(\tau) - K(t)]y_1\}(t) \tag{10}$$

Convolve both sides of (10) with the inverse Laplace transform of

$$[I + \hat{G}(s)K(\tau)]^{-1},$$

which by assumption belongs to $\hat{\mathscr{A}}^{n\times n}$; then (10) becomes

$$y_1(t) = (H_\tau * u)(t) + \int_0^t H_\tau(\tau - \tau')[K(\tau) - K(\tau')]y(\tau') \, d\tau' \tag{11}$$

In particular, for $t = \tau$, (11) becomes

12
$$y_1(\tau) = (H_\tau * u)(\tau) + \int_0^\tau H_\tau(\tau - \tau')[K(\tau) - K(\tau')]y(z')\, d\tau'$$

Now consider the mapping defined by

13
$$(Fy)(\tau) = \int_0^\tau H_\tau(\tau - \tau')[K(\tau) - K(\tau')]y(\tau')\, d\tau'$$

By the results of Section IV.7, the left side of (5) is the induced L^∞ norm of the mapping F, while the left side of (7) is the induced L^1 norm of the mapping F. The conclusions now follow from the small gain theorem. ∎

14 **Remark** By hypothesis, $H_\tau(\cdot) \in \hat{\mathscr{A}}^{n\times n}$ for each $\tau \in \mathbb{R}_+$. So both (5) and (7) are satisfied if $K(\cdot)$ varies slowly enough. The idea is to have $K(\cdot)$ remain substantially constant during the "memory time" of $H_\tau(\cdot)$, i.e., the time when $H_\tau(\cdot)$ differs appreciably from zero.

6 Nonlinear circuit example

Consider Fig. V.1. The linear time-invariant one-port $\mathscr{N}$ is connected to a nonlinear time-varying capacitor, and the parallel combination is driven by

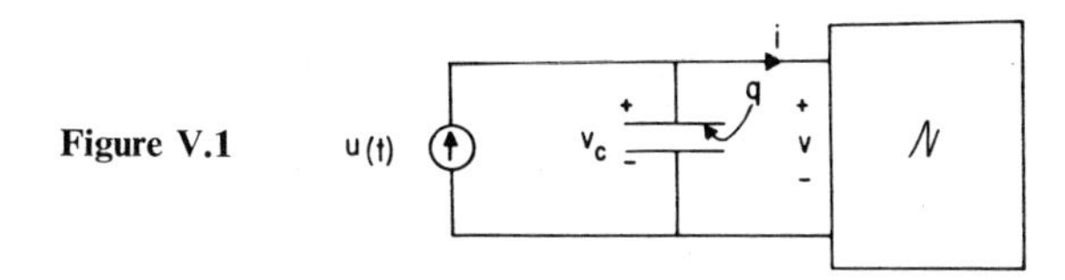

Figure V.1

a current source $u(\cdot)$. Let $g(\cdot)$ be the impulse response of $\mathscr{N}$ to a unit impulse of voltage; so $\mathscr{N}$ is characterized by

1
$$i(t) = \int_0^t g(t - \tau)v(\tau)\, d\tau, \qquad t \geq 0$$

The characteristic of the nonlinear time-varying capacitor is

2
$$v_c = \phi(q, t)$$

where q is the charge and v_c is the voltage across the plates (see Fig. V.1). The Kirchhoff laws require that $v = v_c$ and that

3
$$\dot{q}(t) = u(t) - \int_0^t g(t - \tau)\phi[q(\tau), \tau]\, d\tau$$

where $u(\cdot)$ is the current delivered by the current source.

4 **Assertion** Consider the circuit shown in Fig. V.1 and described by (3). Let

(a) $\phi: \mathbb{R} \times \mathbb{R}_+ \to \mathbb{R}$ be, for each fixed q, regulated in t;

(b) for all compact intervals $I \subset \mathbb{R}_+$, ϕ satisfy a global Lipschitz condition with Lipschitz constant $\gamma(I) < \infty$;

(c) ϕ belong to the sector $[\alpha, \beta]$ with $\beta \geq \alpha$.

Let

5 $$\bar{\alpha} \triangleq (\alpha + \beta)/2, \qquad \tilde{\alpha} = (\beta - \alpha)/2$$

Let $g \in \mathscr{A}$. U.t.c., if

6 $$s + \bar{\alpha} g(s) \neq 0, \qquad \text{for} \quad \operatorname{Re} s \geq 0$$

7 $$\sup_{\omega \geq 0} |\hat{g}(j\omega)[j\omega + \bar{\alpha} g(j\omega)]^{-1}| < 1$$

then, for any $u \in L^1 \cup L^2$, g, $\dot{q}$, $v \in L^2$, q, $v \in L^\infty$, and $q(t)$, $v(t) \to 0$ as $t \to \infty$.

8 **Comments** (a) When $u \in L^1$, the current source delivers a finite charge to the parallel connection of the one-port $\mathscr{N}$ and the nonlinear capacitor.

(b) The time variations of the nonlinear capacitor are restricted by the sector condition and the condition that $\phi(q, \cdot)$ be regulated. Note that a time-varying capacitor is an active element; i.e., it may deliver energy.

(c) Since $\hat{g}(s)$ is the input admittance of $\mathscr{N}$, (6) means that the parallel combination of $\mathscr{N}$ and a linear capacitor of $1/\bar{\alpha}$ Farad is open circuit stable.

Proof As a consequence of the global Lipschitz condition on ϕ, Theorem (III.5.2) can be used to prove that for any $u \in L^1 \cup L^2$, (3) has a unique solution $q : \mathbb{R}_+ \to \mathbb{R}$. With the sector condition in mind and the notations defined in (5), we set

9 $$\tilde{\phi}(q, t) \triangleq \phi(q, t) - \bar{\alpha} q$$

We note that both in L_e^1 and L_e^2, $\tilde{\phi}$ has a gain $\leq \tilde{\alpha}$. Thus, (3) becomes

10 $$\dot{q}(t) + \bar{\alpha}(g * q)(t) = u(t) - \int_0^t g(t - \tau)\tilde{\phi}[q(\tau), \tau]\, d\tau$$

Let

11 $$\hat{w}(s) \triangleq [s + \bar{\alpha}\hat{g}(s)]^{-1} \quad \text{and} \quad \hat{h}(s) \triangleq \hat{g}(s)\hat{w}(s) = \hat{g}(s)[s + \bar{\alpha}\hat{g}(s)]^{-1}$$

Since $g \in \mathscr{A}$ and, by (6), $s + \bar{\alpha}\hat{g}(s)$ is bounded away from zero in $\mathbb{C}_+$, $w \in \mathscr{A}$. Indeed, (11) can be rewritten as

12 $$\hat{w}(s) = \frac{1}{s+1} \cdot \left[\frac{s + \bar{\alpha}\hat{g}(s)}{s+1}\right]^{-1}$$

Thus, $\hat{w}$ is the product of two elements of $\hat{\mathscr{A}}$, hence is in $\hat{\mathscr{A}}$. For the same reason, $\hat{h} \in \hat{\mathscr{A}}$. Consider (11) and recall that $\hat{g} \in \hat{\mathscr{A}}$; then $\omega \mapsto \hat{w}(j\omega)$ and $\omega \mapsto \hat{h}(j\omega) \in L^2$ since they are both $O(1/\omega)$ as $|\omega| \mapsto \infty$. Thus, $w, h \in \mathscr{A} \cap L^2$; i.e., they have no impulses. Consequently, $w, h \in L^1 \cap L^2$.

Convolving (10) with w, we obtain

$$q(t) = (w * u)(t) - \int_0^t h(t-\tau)\tilde{\phi}[q(\tau), \tau]\, d\tau \tag{13}$$

Consider (12) as the equation of a feedback system: For any $u \in L^1 \cup L^2$, $w * u \in L^2$; furthermore, (7) is the small gain condition using L^2 norms. Hence $u \in L^1 \cup L^2$ implies $q \in L^2$. By the sector condition, $v(\cdot) = \phi[q(\cdot), \cdot]$ and $\tilde{\phi}[q(\cdot), \cdot]$ are in L^2; therefore, by (10), $\dot{q} \in L^2$. Thus, $q \in L^\infty$ and $q(t) \to 0$ as $t \to \infty$ (Exercise 1,B.2). These results, together with the sector condition, yield $v \in L^\infty$, $v(t) \to 0$ as $t \to \infty$. ∎

Exercise 1 State and prove the generalization to n-ports terminated by n nonlinear time-varying capacitors.

Exercise 2 Prove that w and h defined by (11) are elements of L^∞. [*Hint*: $\mathscr{L}(\dot{w}) = s\hat{w}(s)$.]

7 Existence of periodic solutions

In this section, we illustrate how a local form of the incremental small gain theorem can sometimes be used to demonstrate the existence of a periodic solution of a nonautonomous differential equation and to obtain bounds on the amplitude of the periodic solution.

We first formulate an existence and uniqueness result, which is in a form convenient for the present application.

1 **Lemma** Let $\mathscr{B}$ be a Banach space (i.e., a complete normed linear space), and let $f: \mathscr{B} \to \mathscr{B}$ be continuously Frechet differentiable for all $x \in \mathscr{B}$. Suppose there exist an $x_0 \in \mathscr{B}$ and a $k \in [0, 1]$ such that

$$\|f'(x)\| \le k < 1, \qquad \text{whenever} \quad x \in B[x_0; \beta/(1-k)] \tag{2}$$

where

$$B[x_0; \beta/(1-k)] = \{x \in \mathscr{B} : \|x - x_0\| \le \beta/(1-k)\} \tag{3}$$

$$\beta \ge \|f(x_0) - x_0\| \tag{4}$$

U.t.c., there exists a unique $\bar{x} \in B[x_0; \beta/(1-k)]$ such that

$$\bar{x} = f(\bar{x}) \tag{5}$$

6 **Remark** The lemma does not assert anything concerning the possible existence of fixed points of f outside the ball $B[x_0; \beta/(1-k)]$.

Proof Whenever x, y belong to $B[x_0; \beta/(1-k)]$, we have

$$\|f(x) - f(y)\| \le \sup_{\alpha \in [0,1]} \|f'[\alpha x + (1-\alpha)y]\| \cdot \|x - y\| \le k\|x - y\|$$

Since $k < 1$, f is a contraction on the complete metric space $B[x_0; \beta/(1-k)]$. Hence there exists a unique $\bar{x} \in B[x_0; \beta/(1-k)]$ such that $\bar{x} = f(\bar{x})$. ∎

Exercise 1 Prove Lemma (1) in detail. [*Hint*: Consider the sequence $(x_i)^\infty$, where $x_i = f(x_{i-1})$ for $i = 1, \ldots.$]

The best way to explain the technique is to work out an example and describe the steps so that the generality of the method becomes apparent.

7 **Example** Consider the Duffing equation

8 $$\ddot{y} + a^2 y + b y^3 = \alpha \cos \omega t, \qquad T \triangleq 2\pi/\omega$$

where a, b, α, and ω are constants. We assume throughout that $\omega \neq a$, for otherwise even with $b = 0$, (8) would not have a periodic solution. We wish to discuss the existence and local uniqueness of periodic solutions of (8) when b is small ("small" nonlinearity) and when α is small ("small" drive).

Since $\omega \neq a$, if b were zero, (8) would have a periodic solution of the form $y_0(t) = a_0 \cos \omega t$. Considering it as an approximate solution of (8) and neglecting the third harmonic term $[(\cos x)^3 = \frac{3}{4} \cos x + \frac{1}{4} \cos 3x]$, we obtain an equation for a_0:

9 $$(3b/4){a_0}^3 + (a^2 - \omega^2) a_0 = \alpha$$

Writing (8) in state form, with $x(t) = [x_1(t), x_2(t)]'$, we obtain

10 $$\dot{x} = \begin{bmatrix} 0 & 1 \\ -a^2 & 0 \end{bmatrix} x + \begin{bmatrix} 0 \\ \alpha \cos \omega t - b{x_1}^3 \end{bmatrix}$$

Considering the term $[x_1(t)]^3$ as given, (10) is of the form $\dot{x} = Ax + g[x(t)]$, so that we have

$$x(t) = \Phi(t)x(0) + \int_0^t \Phi(t - \tau) g[x(\tau)]\, d\tau$$

where $\Phi(t - \tau) = \exp A(t - \tau)$. Requiring that this solution be periodic with period T (hence, no subharmonics!), we set $x(T) = x(0)$ so

$$x(t) = \Phi(t)[I - \Phi(T)]^{-1} \int_0^T \Phi(T - \tau) g[x(\tau)]\, d\tau + \int_0^t \Phi(t - \tau) g[x(\tau)]\, d\tau$$

which is of the form

$$x(t) = \int_0^T W(t, \tau) g[x(\tau)]\, d\tau, \qquad 0 \le t \le T \tag{11}$$

Exercise 2 Give an explicit expression for the matrix $W(t, \tau)$ for $(t, \tau) \in [0, T] \times [0, T]$, for the state equations (10).

Let x_0 be the approximate solution of (10) corresponding to y_0; so we write

$$x_0(t) = [x_{10}(t), x_{20}(t)]' = (a_0 \cos \omega t, -\omega a_0 \sin \omega t)' \tag{12}$$

We are going to use Lemma (1) to show that (11) has a solution close to $x_0(\cdot)$. Note that (11) is of the form $x = f(x)$. We use the following norm

$$\|x\| = \max_{i=1,2} \sup_{0 \le t \le T} |x_i(t)| \tag{13}$$

It is well known that $\mathscr{B}$, the space of continuous functions ϕ: $[0, T] \to \mathbb{R}^2$ with the norm (13), is a Banach space. So let us obtain the constant β of (4) and a bound for $f'(x)$.

$$\begin{aligned} \|f(x_0) - x_0\| &= \max_{i=1,2} \sup_{t \in [0,T]} \left| \int_0^T w_{i2}(t, \tau)[-(b/4)a_0^3 \cos 3\tau)\, d\tau \right| \\ &\le |b| a_0^3 w_M/4 = \beta \end{aligned} \tag{14}$$

where w_M is a constant which depends on T and the resonant frequency a. Inequality (14) gives us β. Estimating $f'(x)$, we obtain

$$\begin{aligned} \|f'(x)\| &\le \max_{i=1,2} \sup_{\in [0,T]} \int_0^\tau |w_{i,2}(t, \tau) 3 b x_1^2(\tau)|\, d\tau \\ &\le 3|b| w_M \max_{0 \le t \le T} |x_1(t)|^2 \end{aligned}$$

Now

$$\max|x_1(t)| \le \max|x_{10}(t)| + \max|x_1(t) - x_{10}(t)| = a_0 + \|x - x_0\|$$

Thus,

$$\|f'(x)\| \le 3|b| w_M [a_0 + \|x - x_0\|]^2 \tag{15}$$

which is of the form of (2). Using (14) and (15) to write out condition (2), we see that we must have a $k \in [0, 1)$ such that

$$3|b| w_M \left[a_0 + \frac{|b| a_0^3 w_M}{(1-k)4} \right]^2 \le k < 1 \tag{6}$$

Thus, if such a k exists, there is a periodic solution $\bar{x}$ such that

$$\|\bar{x} - x_0\| \leq \frac{\|b\| a_0^{\,3}}{(1 - k_0)} \frac{w_M}{4} \tag{17}$$

where k_0 is the largest solution of (16). The existence of such k is immediate in certain limiting cases:

(I) If α, a, ω are given constants [and hence a_0 is determined by (9)], and if b is sufficiently small, then inequality (16) is easily satisfied for some $k < 1$. In other words, if the nonlinearity is small, a periodic solution with period T is guaranteed to exist near x_0 and satisfies the bound (17).

(II) If b, a, and ω are given, then for sufficiently small α, (16) is satisfied for some $k < 1$. Indeed, under these conditions as α decreases to zero, so does a_0, the solution of (9), and, for a_0 small, some $k < 1$ satisfying (16) always exists. So in this case a periodic solution with period T is guaranteed to exist near x_0 if the input has a small enough amplitude.

18 **Comments** (I) Unfortunately, the method does not apply to *autonomous systems*. The first difficulty is that the absence of forcing function leaves us without any hint as to the period of the periodic solution. The second difficulty is that even if that were known, in a neighborhood of the solution, the equation similar to (18) is not a contraction. Indeed suppose, that

$$\dot{x} = Ax + g(x)$$

(where $A \in \mathbb{R}^{n \times n}$) has a periodic solution $\bar{x}$ of period T. Then, as before, we obtain

$$\bar{x}(t) = \int_0^T W(t, \tau) g[\bar{x}(\tau)]\, d\tau \tag{19}$$

Now $\dot{\bar{x}}$ is also a periodic function with period T; it satisfies

$$(d/dt)\dot{\bar{x}} = A\dot{\bar{x}} + g'[\bar{x}(t)]\dot{\bar{x}}(t)$$

as can easily be seen by differentiating the equation of $\bar{x}$. Thus,

$$\dot{\bar{x}}(t) = \int_0^T W(t, \tau) g'[\bar{x}(\tau)]\dot{\bar{x}}(\tau)\, d\tau \tag{20}$$

Hence the norm of the map

$$z(\cdot) \mapsto \int_0^T W(\cdot, \tau) g'[\bar{x}(\tau)] z(\tau)\, d\tau$$

is at least 1. Thus, although (19) is of the form $\bar{x} = f(\bar{x})$, we observe that (20) implies that $\|f'(\bar{x})\| \geq 1$. Hence we cannot have a contraction. In order to establish existence, topological methods are required.

(II) In contrast to our previous work, the contraction (incremental small gain) condition is valid only *locally*; consequently, the existence and uniqueness are valid only in the ball $B[x_0; \beta/(1-k)]$.

8 Popov criterion

In this section, we prove a simple form of the Popov criterion using the small gain theorem. In Chapter VI, Section 6, we develop a more complete exposition of the Popov criterion. Here we use it as an illustration of the small gain theorem.

1 **Theorem** Consider the single-input–single-output *time-invariant* system described by

2 $$e_1 = u_1 - g * e_2$$

3 $$e_2 = \phi(e_1)$$

where $\phi : \mathbb{R} \to \mathbb{R}$ is continuous and belongs to the sector $[0, k]$, $g \in L^1$, and $\dot{g}_1 \in \mathscr{A}$. We assume that for any $u_1 \in L^2$, e_1 and e_2 are in $L_e^{\ 2}$. If for some $q \geq 0$, there is a $\delta > 0$ such that

4 $$\text{Re}\,[(1 + qj\omega)\hat{g}(j\omega)] + 1/k \geq \delta > 0, \qquad \forall\omega \geq 0$$

then whenever u_1 and $\dot{u}_1 \in L^2$, e_1, $\dot{e}_1$, $e_2 \in L^2$.

Proof Without changing e_1 and e_2, let us insert *in front* of the nonlinearity ϕ the transfer function $1/(1 + qs)$ and insert *after* the transfer function $g(s)$ the transfer function $(1 + qs)$; clearly, we need to replace u_1 by $u_1 + q\dot{u}_1$. Next, apply the loop transformation theorem and put a feedforward of $-(k/2)$ around $1/(1 + qs)$ and ϕ, and a feedback of $-(k/2)$ around $(1 + qs)\hat{g}(s)$. A compensating input of $(k/2)(u_1 + q\dot{u}_1)$ has to be inserted as shown in Fig. V.2. To apply the small gain theorem, we use L^2 norms ($\mathscr{L} = L^2$). We

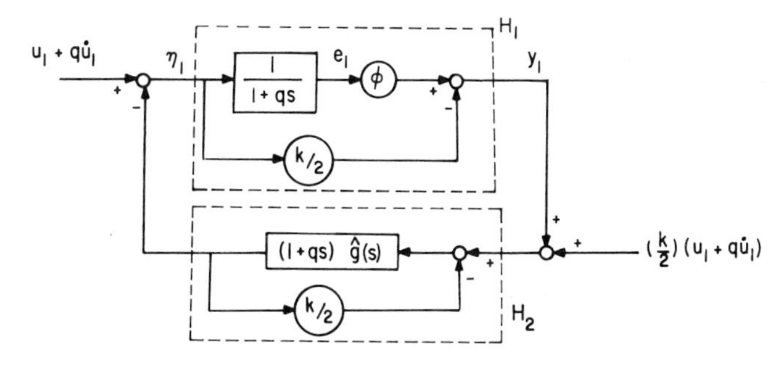

Figure V.2

claim that the gain of H_1, $\gamma(H_1)$, is smaller or equal to $k/2$. The output of H_1 is $y_1 = \phi(e_1) - k\eta_1/2$, and its input is $\eta_1 = e_1 + q\dot{e}_1$. From Fig. V.2, for any $T > 0$,

$$\begin{aligned}\|y_1\|_T{}^2 &= \int_0^T \{\phi[e_1(t)] - (k/2)[e_1(t) + q\dot{e}_1(t)]\}^2\, dt \\ &= \int_0^T \phi[e_1(t)]\{\phi[e_1(t)] - ke_1(t)\}\, dt - kq\int_0^T \phi[e_1(t)]\,\dot{e}_1(t)\, dt \\ &\quad + (k/2)^2\|\eta_1\|_T{}^2\end{aligned}$$

The first integral is nonpositive by the sector condition. If Φ is the primitive of ϕ with $\Phi(0) = 0$, we obtain

$$\begin{aligned}\|y_1\|_T{}^2 &\leq -kq\Phi[e_1(T)] + kq\Phi[e_1(0)] + (k/2)^2\|\eta_1\|_T{}^2 \\ &\leq (k/2)^2\|\eta_1\|_T{}^2 + kq\Phi[e_1(0)]\end{aligned}$$

where we noted that $\phi(\sigma) \geq 0, \quad \forall\sigma \in \mathbb{R}$ by virtue of the sector condition. Hence

$$\gamma(H_1) \leq k/2 \tag{8}$$

We claim that the gain of H_2 is smaller than $(2/k)$. For simplicity, let

$$\hat{h}(j\omega) \triangleq h_r(j\omega) + jh_i(j\omega) = (1 + qj\omega)\hat{g}(j\omega), \qquad \omega \in \mathbb{R}$$

and define

$$\beta(j\omega) = h_r(j\omega) + (1/k) \tag{9}$$

Then assumption (4) becomes

$$\beta(j\omega) \geq \delta > 0 \tag{10}$$

The gain $\gamma(H_2)$ is given by the expression

$$\begin{aligned}\gamma(H_2) &= \sup_{\omega\in\mathbb{R}}\left|\frac{\hat{h}(j\omega)}{1 + (k/2)\hat{h}(j\omega)}\right| = \frac{2}{k}\sup_{\omega\in\mathbb{R}}\left|\frac{\hat{h}(j\omega)}{(2/k) + \hat{h}(j\omega)}\right| \\ &= \frac{2}{k}\sup_{\omega\in\mathbb{R}}\left|\frac{[\beta(j\omega) - k^{-1}] + jh_i(j\omega)}{[\beta(j\omega) + k^{-1}] + jh_i(j\omega)}\right|\end{aligned} \tag{11}$$

For simplicity, let us drop the dependence of ω. Then in view of (10), we have

$$(\beta - k^{-1})^2 + h_i{}^2 = (\beta + k^{-1})^2 + h_i{}^2 - 4\beta\cdot k^{-1} \leq (\beta + k^{-1})^2 + h_i{}^2 - 4\delta\cdot k^{-1} \tag{12}$$

so that

$$\left|\frac{(\beta - k^{-1}) + jh_i}{(\beta + k^{-1}) + jh_i}\right|^2 \leq 1 - \frac{4\delta \cdot k^{-1}}{(\beta + k^{-1})^2 + h_i^2} \leq 1 - \varepsilon \tag{13}$$

where

$$\varepsilon = \inf_{\omega \in \mathbb{R}} \frac{4\delta \cdot k^{-1}}{[\beta(j\omega) + k^{-1}]^2 + [h_i(j\omega)]^2} > 0 \tag{14}$$

Substituting back in (11), we finally have that

$$\gamma(H_2) = (2/k)(1 - \varepsilon)^{1/2} < 2/k \tag{15}$$

From (8) and (15), we see that $\gamma(H_1) \cdot \gamma(H_2) \leq (1 - \varepsilon)^{1/2} < 1$; therefore $\eta_1 = e_1 + q\dot{e}_1 \in L^2$. Now the L^2 gain of the transfer function $(1 + qs)^{-1}$ is 1, so that $\|e_1\|_2 \leq \|\eta_1\|_2 < \infty$. Thus, $e_1, \dot{e}_1 \in L^2$. By the sector condition, $e_2 = \phi(e_1) \in L^2$. ∎

9 Instability

Virtually all of the foregoing sections are devoted to obtaining conditions under which a given feedback system is *stable*. In this section, we obtain conditions that ensure that a given system is *unstable*. From a mathematical point of view, obtaining sufficient conditions for instability is much more tricky than obtaining sufficient conditions for stability. In the latter case, one is required to show that *all* inputs belonging to some class produce outputs belonging to the same class. As a result, sweeping general methods can be used to achieve this purpose. In the former case, however, one is obliged to show that *some* inputs belonging to a certain class do not produce outputs belonging to that class. Thus, one is concerned not with general statements and general proofs, but with particular situations involving particular inputs. This is the major hurdle to proving instability theorems.

In this section, we give two possible interpretations to instability and derive conditions that ensure each of these types of instability. In Section 9.1, we show that under certain conditions, an L^2 input to a system does not produce an L^2 output, and moreover, we delineate the set of L^2 inputs that do not produce L^2 outputs. In Section 9.2, we study the case where an L^p input produces an L^p output, but the relationship between them is not causal.

Consider a feedback system described by the equations

$$e_1 = u_1 - H_2 e_2 \tag{1}$$

$$e_2 = u_2 + H_1 e_1 \tag{2}$$

where u_1 and u_2 are the inputs, and e_1 and e_2 are the errors. We designate $y_1 = H_1 e_1$ and $y_2 = H_2 e_2$ as the outputs. Moreover, we assume that u_1, u_2, e_1, e_2, y_1, y_2 belong to an extended Banach Space $\mathscr{L}_e$, in accordance with Chapter III.

Now suppose in the interests of simplicity that $u_2 \equiv 0$. Then (1) and (2) can be combined into the single equation

$$e_1 = u_1 - H_2 H_1 e_1 \tag{3}$$

There are several ways in which a system represented by (3) can be "unstable"

(i) For a particular $u_1 \in \mathscr{L}$, (3) may not have a solution in $\mathscr{L}_e$.

(ii) For a particular $u_1 \in \mathscr{L}$, (3) has a solution in $\mathscr{L}_e$, but this solution does not belong to $\mathscr{L}$;

(iii) For *each* $u_1 \in \mathscr{L}$, (3) has a solution $e_1 \in \mathscr{L}$, but the relation between u_1 and e_1 is noncausal. (Notice that we *do not* claim that these are all the possible ways in which instability can occur, but only some of the ways.)

With regard to these three possibilities, (i) can be ruled out under relatively mild conditions (see Section III.5). Roughly speaking, the conditions under which (iii) occurs are explored in Section 9.2, while the conditions under which (ii) occurs are the subject of Section 9.1.

9.1 Orthogonal decomposition approach

In this section, we study the case where a "bounded" input produces an "unbounded" output. The approach we present below is not inherently limited to L^2 instability, but evidently we can obtain readily verifiable conditions only in this case.

The method of this section can be briefly outlined as follows. Given a causal linear operator $G : L_e^2 \to L_e^2$, suppose G is "unstable" in the sense that the image of L^2 under G is not wholly contained in L^2, and let M denote the inverse image of L^2 under G. Then M is a subspace of L^2 and, under suitable conditions on G, is a closed subspace of L^2. With regard to the feedback system of Fig. III.1, where H_1 is represented by the operator G, we show that if a small gain type of condition is satisfied, then the output y_1 does *not* belong to L^2 whenever $u_2 \equiv 0$ and $u_1 \in M^\perp/\{0\}$, where $M^\perp$ is the orthogonal complement of M.

We begin with a lemma on the closedness of M. Throughout this section, we use $\|\cdot\|$ to denote the L^2 norm.

4 **Lemma** Let $G : L_e^2 \to L_e^2$ be linear and causal, and let M be the subspace of L^2 defined by

$$M = \{x \in L^2 : Gx \in L^2\} \tag{5}$$

If G satisfies the following two assumptions

6 $$\forall T < \infty, \quad \exists \mu_T < \infty, \quad \text{such that} \quad \|(Gx)_T\| \le \mu_T \|x_T\|, \quad \forall x \in L_e^2$$

7 $$\exists \gamma_M(G) < \infty, \quad \text{such that} \quad \|Gx\| \le \gamma_M(G)\|x\|, \qquad \forall x \in M$$

then M is a closed-loop subspace of L^2.

8 **Remarks** (1) The condition (6) essentially states that if we define a mapping $G_T : L^2[0, T] \to L^2[0, T]$ defined by

9 $$\forall f \in L^2[0, T], \qquad G_T f = (Gx)_T$$

where x is any element of L_e^2 such that $x_T = f$, then G_T is continuous. Notice, however, that the family of constants (μ_T) is not assumed to be bounded.

(2) The assumption (7) means that G has a finite gain over the elements of M.

Proof Let (x_i) be a sequence in M converging to $x_0 \in L^2$. We must show that $x_0 \in L^2$. By hypothesis, $Gx_i \in L^2$, $\forall i \in \mathbb{Z}_+$, and moreover (Gx_i) is a Cauchy sequence in L^2 in view of (7). Since L^2 is complete, this implies that (Gx_i) converges to an element of L^2, which we denote by y. By virtue of (6), we see that for each $T < \infty$, the sequence $([Gx_i]_T)$ converges to $[Gx_0]_T$. But this means that $[Gx_0]_T = y_T$, $\forall T < \infty$, i.e., that $Gx_0 = y$ and hence that $Gx_0 \in L^2$. By the definition of the set M, this implies that $x_0 \in M$. ∎

The following theorem can be thought of as an instability counterpart of Theorem (III.2.1).

10 **Theorem** Consider a feedback system of the form shown in Fig. III.1, where H_1 and H_2 map L_e^2 into itself. Suppose that corresponding to each u_1, u_2 in L_e^2 there exist e_1, e_2 in L_e^2 satisfying the system equations

11a $$e_1 = u_1 - H_2 e_2$$

11b $$e_2 = u_2 + H_1 e_1$$

Suppose there exist finite constants $\gamma(H_2)$ and β such that

12 $$\|(H_2 x)_T\| \le \gamma(H_2)\|x_T\| + \beta, \qquad \forall x \in L_e^2$$

Further, suppose $H_1 = G : L_e^2 \to L_e^2$ is linear and causal, satisfies (6) and (7), and that the subspace M defined by (5) is *not* all of L^2. U.t.c.,

(i) if $\gamma_M(G) \cdot \gamma(H_2) \le 1$ and $\beta = 0$, then $y_1 \notin L^2$ whenever $u_2 \equiv 0$, $u_1 \in M^\perp$ and $u_1 \ne 0$ where $M^\perp \triangleq$ orthogonal complement of M;

(ii) if $\gamma_M(G) \cdot \gamma(H_2) < 1$, then for each $u_2 \in L^2$, there exists a corresponding constant $m(\|u_2\|)$ such that $y_1 \notin L^2$ whenever $u_1 \in M^\perp$ and $\|u_1\| > m(\|u_2\|)$.

Proof The hypothesis on H_1 implies that M is a closed subspace of L^2. Since M is not all of L^2, it follows that $M^\perp$ is a nontrivial subspace of L^2. We first tackle the case where $\gamma_M(G) \cdot \gamma(H_2) \leq 1$, $\beta = 0$, and $u_2 \equiv 0$. Suppose by way of contradiction that $u_1 \neq 0$, $u_1 \in M^\perp$, and that $y_1 = Ge_1 \in L^2$. Then $e_1 \in M$, and

13 $$y_2 = u_1 - e_1$$

Since $u_1 \neq 0$, $u_1 \in M^\perp$, and $e_1 \in M$, we have that $\langle u_1 | e_1 \rangle = 0$, and hence

14 $$\|y_2\|^2 = \|u_1\|^2 + \|e_1\|^2 > \|e_1\|^2$$

On the other hand, we have $y_2 = H_2 H_1 e_1$, so that

15 $$\|y_2\| \leq \gamma(H_2) \cdot \gamma_M(G)\|e_1\| \leq \|e_1\|$$

which contradicts (14). Hence $y_1 \notin L^2$.

Now suppose $\gamma(H_2) \cdot \gamma_M(G) \triangleq k < 1$. The proof in this case is once again by contradiction, and we start by assuming that $u_1 \neq 0$, $u_1 \in M^\perp$, and $y_1 \in L^2$. Then combining (14) and (12), we get

16 $$\begin{aligned}\|y_2\|^2 &= \|u_1\|^2 + \|e_1\|^2 \leq \{\gamma(H_2)[\|y_1\| + \|u_2\|] + \beta\}^2 \\ &\leq \{\gamma(H_2)[\gamma_M(G)\|e_1\| + \|u_2\|] + \beta\}^2 \\ &= k^2\|e_1\|^2 + 2k[\gamma(H_2)\|u_2\| + \beta]\|e_1\| + [\gamma(H_2)\|u_2\| + \beta]^2 \\ &= k^2\|e_1\|^2 + 2kc\|e_1\| + c^2\end{aligned}$$

where

17 $$c = \gamma(H_2)\|u_2\| + \beta$$

The inequality (16) can be rearranged as follows:

18 $$\|u_1\|^2 \leq -(1 - k^2)\|e_1\|^2 + 2kc\|e_1\| + c^2$$

For $u_2 \in L^2$ fixed, k and c are fixed constants, and it is routine algebra to verify that the maximum value of the right-hand side of (18) with respect to $\|e_1\|$ is $c^2/(1-k)^2$. Therefore, if $\|u_1\| > c^2/(1-k^2) \triangleq m(\|u_2\|)$, then (18) can never be satisfied, and this contradiction establishes that $u_1 \notin L^2$. ∎

We close the section with an instability counterpart of the circle criterion [Theorem (2.10)].

19 **Theorem** Consider the feedback system of Fig. III.1, where u_1, u_2, e_1, e_2, y_1, $y_2 : \mathbb{R}_+ \to \mathbb{R}$. The subsystem H_1 is represented by

20 $$(H_1 e_1)(t) = (g * e_1)(t)$$

where $g(\cdot)$ is Laplace transformable, and $\hat{g}(s)$ is of the form

21 $$\hat{g}(s) = \hat{g}_b(s) + \sum_{i=1}^{k} \sum_{j=1}^{m_i} r_{ij}/(s - p_i)^j$$

with $g_b \in L^1$, Re $p_i > 0$ for all $i = 1, \ldots, k$, and r_{ij} belongs to $\mathbb{C}$ for all i, j. The subsystem H_2 is represented by

22 $$(H_2 e_2)(t) = \phi[e_2(t), t]$$

where $\phi : \mathbb{R} \times \mathbb{R}_+ \to \mathbb{R}$ is continuous in the first variable and regulated in the second variable, and furthermore,

23 $$\phi \in \text{sector } [\alpha, \beta], \qquad \beta > 0$$

Suppose that, for all compact intervals $I \subset \mathbb{R}_+$, the function $\sigma \to \phi(\sigma, t)$, where t is fixed in I, has finite incremental gain (i.e., obeys a global Lipschitz condition in $\mathbb{R}$). Let $\xi = (\alpha + \beta)/2$, $\rho = (\alpha - \beta)/2$, and suppose $\xi \neq 0$. Finally, suppose that corresponding to each u_1, u_2 in L_e^2, there exists a unique pair (e_1, e_2) in $L_e^2 \times L_e^2$ such that the system equations (11) are satisfied. U.t.c., the feedback system is L^2 unstable if the Nyquist diagram of $\hat{g}(j\omega)$ satisfies one of the following three conditions, as appropriate:

(a) If $0 < \alpha < \beta$, then Nyquist diagram of $\hat{g}$ does not intersect the disk $D[-1/\alpha, -1/\beta]$ and encircles it in the counterclockwise direction less than n_p times, where n_p is the number of right-half-plane poles of $\hat{g}(\cdot)$.

(b) If $0 = \alpha < \beta$, then $n_p > 0$, and the Nyquist diagram of $\hat{g}$ is contained in the closed half-plane $\{z \in \mathbb{C} : \text{Re } z \geq -1/\beta\}$.

(c) If $\alpha < 0 < \beta$, then $n_p > 0$, and the Nyquist diagram of $\hat{g}$ is contained in the disk $D[-1/\alpha, -1/\beta]$.

Proof The theorem is proved using the loop transformation theorem. Define mappings $H_{1\xi}$, $H_{2\xi} : L_e^2 \to L_e^2$ by

24 $$(H_{1\xi} e_1)(t) = (g_\xi * e_1)(t)$$

25 $$\hat{g}_\xi(s) = \hat{g}(s)/[1 + \xi \hat{g}(s)]$$

26 $$(H_{2\xi} e_2)(t) = \phi[e_2(t), t] - \xi e_2(t) \triangleq \phi_\xi[e(t), t]$$

We show that the hypotheses of Theorem (10) are satisfied with H_1 and H_2 replaced by $H_{1\xi}$ and $H_{2\xi}$. First, since the mapping $\phi_\xi \in$ sector $[-\rho, \rho]$, $H_{2\xi}$. satisfies (12) with $\gamma(H_{2\xi}) = \rho$ and $\beta = 0$. Next, the conditions on the Nyquist diagram of $\hat{g}(j\omega)$ imply that $\hat{g}_\xi(j\omega)$ is bounded as ω varies over $\mathbb{R}$, but that $\hat{g}_\xi(s)$ has one or more poles in the open right half-plane. It is easy to verify that since $g_\xi(\cdot) \in L_e^1$, the mapping $H_{1\xi}$ satisfies (6), and it only remains to verify (7). It is clear that in the present case, the subspace M consists of functions in L^2 whose Laplace transforms have zeros at the points where $\hat{g}_\xi(\cdot)$ has poles. Suppose $f(\cdot) \in M$; then $\hat{g}_\xi(s)$ is analytic in Re $s > 0$ and $\hat{g}_\xi(j\omega)\hat{f}(j\omega) \in L^2(\mathbb{R})$. Moreover, for all $f \in M$, we have by Parseval's equality that

27
$$\|g_\xi * f\| = (1/2\pi)\|\hat{g}_\xi(\cdot)\hat{f}(\cdot)\| \leq \sup_{\omega \in \mathbb{R}} |\hat{g}_\xi(j\omega)| \cdot (1/2\pi)\|\hat{f}(\cdot)\|$$
$$= \sup_{\omega \in \mathbb{R}} |\hat{g}_\xi(j\omega)| \cdot \|f(\cdot)\|$$

Therefore, H_1 satisfies (7) with

28
$$\gamma_M(G_\xi) = \sup_{\omega \in \mathbb{R}} |\hat{g}(j\omega)|$$

The present conclusion now follows from Theorem (10), since the circle criterion on the Nyquist diagram of $\hat{g}(j\omega)$ ensures [see Theorem (2.10)] that

$$\gamma_M(G_\xi) \cdot \gamma(H_{2\xi}) = \sup_{\omega \in \mathbb{R}} |\hat{g}_\xi(j\omega)| \cdot \rho \leq 1$$ ∎

Another approach to L^2 instability based on orthogonal decomposition is found in Section VI.12.

9.2 Noncausality approach

In this subsection, we study a very special kind of "instability," namely, the case where a "bounded" input does produce a "bounded" output, but the map relating the input to the output is not causal.

We first prove a general result, which we then specialize to obtain instability conditions.

29 **Theorem** Let $\mathscr{B}$ be a Banach algebra with unit element I, and let $\mathscr{B}^+$ be a subalgebra of $\mathscr{B}$ containing I (i.e., $x \in \mathscr{B}^+$, $y \in \mathscr{B}^+ \Rightarrow xy \in \mathscr{B}^+$, $yx \in \mathscr{B}^+$). Let x, $y \in \mathscr{B}^+$ and let $\mathscr{S}$ be a bounded connected subset of $\mathbb{C}$ or $\mathbb{R}$, as appropriate. Suppose that for each $\alpha \in \mathscr{S}$, the element $x + \alpha y$ is invertible [i.e., $(x + \alpha y)^{-1} \in \mathscr{B}$], and that the collection of these inverses is bounded; that is, there exists a finite constant m such that

30
$$\|(x + \alpha y)^{-1}\| \leq m < \infty, \qquad \forall \alpha \in \mathscr{S}$$

U.t.c., $(x + \alpha y)^{-1} \in \mathscr{B}^+$, $\forall \alpha \in \mathscr{S}$, if and only if $(x + \alpha y)^{-1} \in \mathscr{B}^+$ for some $\alpha \in \mathscr{S}$.

Proof $\Rightarrow$ Obvious

$\Leftarrow$ The statement is clearly true if $y = 0$; so suppose $y \neq 0$, and suppose $(x + \alpha_0 y)^{-1} \in \mathscr{B}^+$ where $\alpha_0 \in \mathscr{S}$. First of all, note that if $\alpha \in \mathscr{S}$, $(x + \alpha y)^{-1} \in \mathscr{B}^+$, and $|\alpha - \alpha'| < (\|y\| \cdot m)^{-1}$, then $(x + \alpha' y)^{-1}$ exists and belongs to $\mathscr{B}^+$ (whether or not α' belongs to $\mathscr{S}$). This is immediate from the observation that

$$x + \alpha' y = x + \alpha y + (\alpha' - \alpha)y = [I + (\alpha' - \alpha)y(x + \alpha y)^{-1}](x + \alpha y)$$

and the contraction mapping principle for Banach algebras.

Given that $(x + \alpha_0 y)^{-1} \in \mathscr{B}^+$, let $\alpha \in \mathscr{S}$. Since $\mathscr{S}$ is connected, there exists a finite sequence of points $\alpha_1, \alpha_2, \ldots, \alpha_{N+1} = \alpha$ such that $|\alpha_i - \alpha_{i+1}| < (\|y\| \cdot m)^{-1}$ for $i = 0, \ldots, N$. Now since $|\alpha_1 - \alpha_0| < (\|y\|m)^{-1}$ and $(x + \alpha_0 y)^{-1} \in \mathscr{B}^+$, it follows that $(x + \alpha_1 y)^{-1} \in \mathscr{B}^+$; since $|\alpha_2 - \alpha_1| < (\|y\| \cdot m)^{-1}$ and $(x + \alpha_1 y)^{-1} \in \mathscr{B}^+$, it follows that $(x + \alpha_2 y)^{-1} \in \mathscr{B}^+$. Repeating this reasoning N times, we see that $(x + \alpha_{N+1} y)^{-1} = (x + \alpha y)^{-1} \in \mathscr{B}^+$. Since $\alpha \in \mathscr{S}$ is arbitrary, this completes the proof. ∎

31 **Remark** The basic idea of the proof is a follows. Given that $(x + \alpha_0 y)^{-1} \in \mathscr{B}^+$, it can be shown that $(x + \alpha_1 y)^{-1} \in \mathscr{B}^+$, provided $|\alpha_1 - \alpha_0|$ is sufficiently small. The assumption (30) that the collection of inverses $(x + \alpha y)^{-1}$ is bounded really means that the upper bound on $|\alpha_1 - \alpha_0|$ is independent of α_0. Now given that $(x + \alpha_0 y)^{-1} \in \mathscr{B}^+$, in order to show that $(x + \alpha y)^{-1} \in \mathscr{B}^+$ where $|\alpha - \alpha_0|$ exceeds the aforementioned upper bound, we construct a "chain" of numbers $\alpha_1, \ldots, \alpha_{N+1} = \alpha$ in $\mathscr{S}$ such that $|\alpha_i - \alpha_{i+1}|$ is suitably small.

Exercise 1 Under the conditions of Theorem (29), suppose $(x + \alpha_0 y)^{-1} \in \mathscr{B}^+$. Show that $(x + \alpha y)^{-1} \in \mathscr{B}^+$ whenever

$$\inf_{\alpha' \in \mathscr{S}} |\alpha - \alpha'| < (\|y\| \cdot m)^{-1} \tag{32}$$

Exercise 2 Prove the following stronger version of Theorem (29). Let $\mathscr{B}$ be a Banach algebra with unit element I; let $\mathscr{B}^+$ be a subalgebra containing I; and let $x, y \in \mathscr{B}^+$. Let $(\alpha_j)_{j \in J}$ be a finite or countable collection of points in $\mathbb{C}$ or $\mathbb{R}$ (as appropriate), such that

(i) $(x + \alpha_j y)^{-1} \in \mathscr{B}^+ \qquad \forall j \in J$
(ii) $\|(x + \alpha_j y)^{-1}\| \leq m, \qquad \forall j \in J$
(iii) $\sup_{j \in J} \inf_{i \neq j} |\alpha_i - \alpha_j| \leq \delta$
(iv) $\|y\| \cdot m \cdot \delta < 1$

U.t.c., if $(x + \alpha_j y)^{-1} \in \mathscr{B}^+$ for some $j \in J$, then $(x + \alpha y)^{-1} \in \mathscr{B}^+$ whenever

$$\inf_{j \in J} |\alpha - \alpha_j| < (\|y\| m)^{-1} \tag{33}$$

The significance of the above results to the stability question is now illustrated.

34 **Fact** Let $1 \leq p \leq \infty$, and let $\mathscr{B}(L^p)$ denote the set of continuous linear operators mapping L^p into itself, and $\mathscr{B}^+(L^p)$ denote the subset of $\mathscr{B}(L^p)$ consisting of all causal operators in $\mathscr{B}(L^p)$. Then $\mathscr{B}(L^p)$ is a Banach algebra with

a unit element; $\mathscr{B}^+(L^p)$ is a subalgebra of $\mathscr{B}(L^p)$; and $\mathscr{B}^+(L^p)$ contains the unit element.

We are now in a position to state a small gain theorem for instability in the sense of noncausality.

35 **Theorem** Consider a system represented by (1) and (2). Suppose H_1 and H_2 are extensions to $\mathscr{L}_e$ of continuous linear mappings on $\mathscr{L}$ (we denote the restrictions of H_1 and H_2 to $\mathscr{L}$ also by H_1 and H_2). Suppose there exists a continuous linear map K on $\mathscr{L}$, which can be extended to $\mathscr{L}_e$, such that the operator $(I + KH_1)^{-1}$ is well defined on $\mathscr{L}_e$ and continuous on $\mathscr{L}$. U.t.c., if

$$\|H_1(I + KH_1)^{-1}\| \cdot \|H_2 - K\| \triangleq \rho < 1 \tag{36}$$

then

(i) $(I + H_2 H_1)^{-1}$ is well defined on $\mathscr{L}_e$ and continuous on $\mathscr{L}$;
(ii) $(I + H_2 H_1)^{-1}$ is causal $\Leftrightarrow$ $(I + KH_1)^{-1}$ is causal;
(iii) Equations (1) and (2) have unique solutions for e_1 and e_2 given by

$$e_1 = (I + H_2 H_1)^{-1}(u_1 - H_2 u_2) \tag{37a}$$

$$e_2 = (I + H_1 H_2)^{-1}(u_2 + H_1 u_2) \tag{37b}$$

Comment In view of the linearity of H_1 and H_2, e_2 can also be expressed as

$$e_2 = u_2 + H_1(I + H_2 H_1)^{-1}(u_1 - H_2 u_2) \tag{38}$$

Proof Conclusions (i) and (iii) are proved by the familiar methods of the small gain theorem. To prove conclusion (ii), consider the family of elements in $\mathscr{B}(x)$ defined by

$$F_\alpha = I + KH_1 + \alpha(H_2 - K), \qquad \alpha \in [0, 1] \tag{39}$$

By virtue of the assumption that $(I + KH_1)^{-1}$ exists, and in view of condition (36), we see that $F^{-1} \in \mathscr{B}(x)$ exists for all $\alpha \in [0, 1]$. Moreover, the collection of these inverses is bounded, since

$$\|F_\alpha^{-1}\| \le \|(I + KH_1)^{-1}\|/(1 - \rho) \tag{40}$$

Hence by Theorem (29), F_α^{-1} is causal for all $\alpha \in [0, 1]$ if and only if F_α^{-1} is causal for some $\alpha \in [0, 1]$. In particular, $F_1^{-1} = (I + H_2 H_1)^{-1}$ is causal if and only if $F_0^{-1} = (I + KH_1)^{-1}$ is causal. ∎

Let us now turn to convolution feedback systems. We give only a few results, and we do not always state the strongest possible results, in the interests of simplicity.

41 **Definition** The set $\mathscr{A}_2$ consists, by definition, of all generalized functions $f(\cdot)$ of the form

42 $$f(t) = \sum_{i=-\infty}^{\infty} f_i \delta(t - t_i) + f_a(t)$$

where $t_i, f_i \in \mathbb{R}, f_a : \mathbb{R} \to \mathbb{R}$, and

43a $$\sum_{i=-\infty}^{\infty} |f_i| < \infty$$

43b $$\int_{-\infty}^{\infty} |f_a(t)| \, dt < \infty$$

The set $\mathscr{A}_2$ can be made into a linear space in the obvious way. If we define

44 $$\|f\|_{\mathscr{A}_2} = \sum_{i=-\infty}^{\infty} |f_i| + \int_{-\infty}^{\infty} |f_a(t)| \, dt$$

and if we let the product of two elements f and g of $\mathscr{A}_2$ be their convolution, then $\mathscr{A}_2$ becomes a Banach algebra. One can think of $\mathscr{A}_2$ as a two-sided version of the Banach algebra $\mathscr{A}$ defined in Appendix D. In fact, if we define

45 $$\mathscr{A} = \{f(\cdot) \in \mathscr{A}_2 : f(t) = 0, \quad \forall t < 0\}$$

then $\mathscr{A}$ is a subalgebra of $\mathscr{A}_2$.

Let $\hat{\mathscr{A}}_2$ denote the set of Laplace transforms of all elements of $\mathscr{A}_2$. The conditions under which an element of $\hat{\mathscr{A}}_2$ is invertible are discussed in the following theorem.

46 **Theorem** Suppose $\hat{f} \in \hat{\mathscr{A}}_2$. Then $1/\hat{f} \in \hat{\mathscr{A}}_2$ if and only if

47 $$\inf_{\text{Re}\, s=0} |\hat{f}(s)| > 0$$

Suppose $\hat{f} \in \hat{\mathscr{A}}$. Then $1/\hat{f} \in \hat{\mathscr{A}}_2$ if and only if (47) holds, and $1/\hat{f} \in \hat{\mathscr{A}}$ if and only if

48 $$\inf_{\text{Re}\, s \geq 0} |\hat{f}(s)| > 0$$

Now we turn to the question of feedback stability.

49 **Theorem** Suppose $\hat{G}, \hat{F} \in \hat{\mathscr{A}}_2^{n \times n}$. Then $\hat{H} = \hat{G}(I + \hat{F}\hat{G})^{-1} \in \hat{\mathscr{A}}_2^{n \times n}$ if and only if

50 $$\inf_{\text{Re}\, s=0} |\det[I + \hat{F}(s)\hat{G}(s)]| > 0$$

With the above results in hand, we can state the instability results.

51 **Theorem** Consider a multivariable feedback system of the form shown in Fig. III.1. Suppose the subsystem H_1 is represented by

$$y_1(t) = (G * e_1)(t) \tag{52}$$

where $G \in \mathscr{A}^{n \times n}$ and that the subsystem H_2 is represented by

$$y_2(t) = \phi[e_2(t), t] \tag{53}$$

where $\phi : \mathbb{R}^n \times \mathbb{R} \to \mathbb{R}^n$ is continuous in the first argument and regulated in the second argument. Suppose further that $e_1, e_2, y_1, y_2 \in L_{ne}{}^p(\mathbb{R})$ whenever $u_1, u_2 \in L_n{}^p(\mathbb{R})$. U.t.c., if there exist a matrix $K \in \mathbb{R}^{n \times n}$ and real constants γ and β with $\beta = 0$ whenever $p < \infty$ such that

$$|\phi(\sigma, t) - K\sigma| \leq \gamma|\sigma| + \beta \qquad \forall \sigma \in \mathbb{R}^n, \forall t \in \mathbb{R}_+ \tag{54}$$

$$\inf_{\text{Re } s = 0} |\det[I + K\hat{G}(s)]| > 0 \tag{55}$$

$$\|H_K\|_{\mathscr{A}_2} \cdot \gamma < 1 \tag{56}$$

where

$$\hat{H}_K \triangleq \hat{G}(I + K\hat{G})^{-1} \tag{57}$$

then

$$u_1, u_2 \in L_n{}^p(\mathbf{R}) \Rightarrow e_1, e_2, y_1, y_2 \in L_n{}^p(\mathbf{R}) \tag{58}$$

Moreover, the map $(u_1, u_2) \to (e_1, e_2)$ is causal if and only if

$$\inf_{\text{Re } s \geq 0} |\det[I + K\hat{G}(s)]| > 0 \tag{59}$$

The proof is immediate from Theorem (35).

60 **Corollary** Under the assumptions and conditions of Theorem (51), suppose (56) is replaced by

$$\sup_{\omega \in \mathbb{R}} |\hat{H}_K(j\omega)| \cdot \gamma < 1 \tag{61}$$

Then the conclusions of Theorem (51) hold for $p = 2$.

62 **Theorem** Consider a scalar feedback system of the form shown in Fig. III.1, where the subsystem H_1 is represented by

$$y_1(t) = (g * e_1)(t)$$

with $g \in L^1(\mathbb{R})$, and the subsystem H_2 is represented by

$$y_2(t) = \phi[e_2(t), t]$$

with $\phi \in$ sector $[\alpha, \beta]$, $0 < \alpha < \beta$. Let $D[-1/\alpha, -1/\beta]$ be the disk in $\mathbb{C}$ whose diameter is the line segment connecting the points $-1/\alpha + j0$ and $-1/\beta + j0$. U.t.c., if the Nyquist diagram of $\hat{g}(j\omega)$ does not intersect the disk $D[-1/\alpha, -1/\beta]$ and encircles it in the clockwise direction at least once, then

$$u_1, u_2 \in L^2(\mathbb{R}) \Rightarrow e_1, e_2, y_1, y_2 \in L^2(\mathbb{R})$$

and the map $(u_1, u_2) \to (e_1, e_2)$ is noncausal.

Notes and references

Early versions of the small gain theorem and circle criterion were given by Sandberg [San. 4] and Zames [Zam. 3], both of whom also explored the technique of exponential weighting [San. 8], [Zam. 2]. Exponential weighting techniques are also utilized in [Ber. 1]. Stability results involving a circle criterion based on a Liapunov approach were derived by Brockett [Bro. 1, 2], and by Narendra and Goldwyn [Nar. 1]. The theorem on slowly varying linear systems is a generalization of an idea due to Sandberg [San. 12], while those on the existence of periodic solutions are due to Holtzman [Hol. 1, 3]. The nonlinear circuit example is in the spirit of [San. 7]. Takeda and Bergen [Tak. 1] were the first to study the orthogonal decomposition approach to L^2 instability, while the noncausality approach is due to Willems [Wil. 1]. Instability results have also been obtained by Brockett [Bro. 5], who used Liapunov theory, and by Davis [Dav. 1, 2], who used the concept of Fredholm operators. Finally, an application of small gain techniques to pulse-width modulated systems can be found in [Sko. 1].

VI PASSIVITY

0 Introduction

The thrust of this chapter is the systematic use of the concept of passivity, which plays an essential role in circuit theory and, more generally, in physics. The first section uses a very simple circuit example to motivate the formalism. The technical properties of scalar products are presented in Section 2. Then, as in Chapter III, a section is devoted to the general framework. This abstract section serves an important unifying role in that it allows us to see many problems as special cases of a general problem. The main difference is that now we work in inner-product spaces rather than normed spaces. Section 4 defines passive operators and presents many examples of passive operators which are used later. The reader need not study every example and work out every exercise because whenever one of these examples is used in later developments, a specific reference is made to it. The passivity theorems of Section 5 correspond to the small gain theorem of Chapter III. They constitute the main results of this chapter. Several forms of the Popov criterion are developed in Sections 6 and 7 for the scalar case, the multivariable case, the continuous-time case, and the discrete-time case. The logarithmic variation criterion is the subject of Section 8. The interesting feature of that criterion is that if the *average* rate of variation of a feedback gain is small enough, then the stability of the frozen system implies that of the time-varying system. This complements the results of Chapter V, Section 5. The technique of noncausal multipliers with applications is the subject of Section 9: The general pattern of the technique is presented, and two methods of factorization are given. In the next section, it is shown that under rather general conditions, the passivity theorem and the small gain theorem are equivalent; that is to say, that if we are given a feedback system whose stability can be established by the passivity theorem, then, under some general conditions, this system can be transformed into another equivalent one whose stability can be established by the small gain theorem, and vice versa. The problem of invertibility of an operator of the form $I + H$ is fundamental to the study of feedback systems. Passivity is used in Section 11 to obtain sufficient conditions for $I + H$ to be a bijection. The final section presents a general instability theorem based on passivity. The technique is then applied to obtain an instability counterpart to Popov's criterion.

1 Motivation from circuit theory

Consider a one-port whose port voltage (current) is $v(\cdot)$ [$i(\cdot)$, resp.]. The power delivered to the one-port at time t is $v(t)i(t)$, provided of course that the usual reference directions are used (see Fig. VI.1). If $\mathscr{E}(t_0)$ denotes the energy stored in the one-port at time t_0, then it is natural to say that the one-port is **passive** iff

1
$$\mathscr{E}(t_0) + \int_{t_0}^{t} v(t)i(t)\,dt \geq 0, \qquad \forall v(\cdot), i(\cdot), \quad \forall t \geq t_0$$

This is a natural definition since the integral evaluates the energy delivered to the one-port during the time interval $[t_0, t]$.

More generally, an *n-port* $\mathscr{N}$ is viewed as a relation in $\mathscr{F} \times \mathscr{F}$, where $\mathscr{F} = \{f: \mathbb{R} \to \mathbb{R}^n\}$; more precisely, $\mathscr{N}$ is defined by all the pairs $(v(\cdot), i(\cdot)) \in \mathscr{F} \times \mathscr{F}$, which are its possible port voltages and port currents. Taking the view that the n-port $\mathscr{N}$ had zero stored energy at $t = -\infty$ when it was put together, we say that $\mathscr{N}$ **is passive iff**

2
$$\operatorname{Re} \int_{-\infty}^{t} v(t)^* i(t)\,dt \geq 0, \qquad \forall (v, i) \in \mathscr{N}, \quad \forall t \in \mathbb{R}$$

(Here the superscript asterisk (*) denotes, as usual, the complex conjugate transpose.) Of course, in the present case taking the complex conjugate is vacuous; however, it becomes important when voltages and currents are represented in terms of phasors.

One of the earliest connections between passivity and stability is due to Youla who considered the linear case. The technique, however, carries over to the nonlinear case. We state it as a theorem.

3 **Theorem** Let the (possibly nonlinear) n-port $\mathcal{N}$ have the property that v, $i \in L_{ne}^2(\mathbb{R})$, $\forall (v, i) \in \mathcal{N}$. Assume that for the connection shown in Fig. VI.1 and for any input $e \in L_{ne}^2(\mathbb{R})$, there is a response v, $i \in L_{ne}^2$. U.t.c., if $\mathcal{N}$ is passive, then $e \in L_n^2$ implies that $\|v\|_2 \leq \|e\|_2$ and $\|i\|_2 \leq \|e\|_2$.

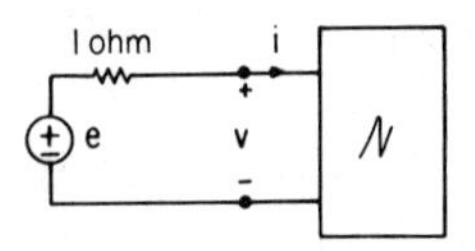

Figure VI.1

Proof By definition, let

$$\langle v | i \rangle_T = \int_{-\infty}^{T} v(t)^* i(t)\, dt$$

Hence the passivity assumption is equivalent to

$$\langle v | i \rangle_T \geq 0, \qquad \forall (v, i) \in \mathcal{N}, \forall T \tag{4}$$

Now from Kirchhoff's voltage law, $e = v + i$ and since $e \in L^2$,

$$\begin{aligned} \infty > \langle e | e \rangle \geq \langle e | e \rangle_T, &\qquad \forall T \in \mathbb{R} \\ = \langle v + i | v + i \rangle_T & \\ = \langle v | v \rangle_T + \langle v | i \rangle_T + \langle i | v \rangle_T + \langle i | i \rangle_T & \\ \geq \langle v | v \rangle_T + \langle i | i \rangle_T & \end{aligned} \tag{5}$$

where in the last step we used passivity. The conclusion follows immediately; indeed, inequality (5) holds for all T, hence, in particular, for $T \to \infty$. ∎

6 **Comment** We had to make the assumption that for any $e \in L^2$ there is at least one response. So existence is assumed, and passivity is used to prove stability. No assumption nor conclusion can be made concerning uniqueness and/or continuous dependence.

2 Scalar products

Any function (denoted below by $\langle \cdot | \cdot \rangle$) mapping $\mathscr{H} \times \mathscr{H}$ into $\mathbb{C}$, where $\mathscr{H}$ is a linear space over the field $\mathbb{C}$, is called a scalar product iff it satisfies the following axioms (we use the superscript asterisk (*) to denote the complex conjugate):

$$\left.\begin{array}{ll} \text{SI.} & \langle x | y + y' \rangle = \langle x | y \rangle + \langle x | y' \rangle \\ \text{SII.} & \langle x | y \rangle = \langle y | x \rangle^* \\ \text{SIII.} & \langle x | \lambda y \rangle = \lambda \langle x | y \rangle \\ \text{SIV.} & \langle x | x \rangle > 0 \Leftrightarrow x \neq \theta \end{array}\right\}, \qquad \begin{array}{l} \forall x, y, y' \in \mathscr{H} \\ \forall \lambda \in \mathbb{C} \end{array}$$

where θ denotes the zero vector in $\mathscr{H}$.

Exercise 1 Prove the following consequences of the axioms:

(a) The function $x \mapsto \langle x | x \rangle^{1/2}$ is a norm on $\mathscr{H}$. It will be denoted below by $\|x\|$; so, by definition,

1 $$\|x\|^2 \triangleq \langle x | x \rangle$$

This norm and this scalar product are related by *Schwarz's* inequality:

2 $$|\langle x | y \rangle| \geq \|x\| \, \|y\|, \qquad \forall x, y \in \mathscr{H}$$

and equality holds if and only if (x, y) are linearly dependent or one or both are zero.

3 (b) $$\langle x + x' | y \rangle = \langle x | y \rangle + \langle x' | y \rangle$$

4 (c) $$\langle \lambda x | y \rangle = \lambda^* \langle x | y \rangle$$

5 **Comments** (a) For fixed $x \in \mathscr{H}$, $y \mapsto \langle x | y \rangle$ is a *linear* functional on $\mathscr{H}$.

(b) In most of our applications, the linear space $\mathscr{H}$ is over the field $\mathbb{R}$, and the scalar product $\langle \cdot | \cdot \rangle$ takes real values. Then by Axiom SII, $\langle x | y \rangle = \langle y | x \rangle$, for all $x, y \in \mathscr{H}$. Furthermore, the function mapping the ordered pair $(x, y) \in \mathscr{H} \times \mathscr{H}$ into $\langle x | y \rangle \in \mathbb{R}$ is *bilinear*; that is, $\forall x \in \mathscr{H}$, $y \mapsto \langle x | y \rangle$ is linear, and $\forall y \in \mathscr{H}$, $x \mapsto \langle x | y \rangle$ is linear.

6 **Examples**

(I) Let $x, y \in \mathbb{R}$ or $\mathbb{C}$, then $\langle x | y \rangle \triangleq x^* y$, the usual multiplication and where * denotes the conjugate.

(II) Let $x, y \in \mathbb{C}^n$ with $x = (\xi_1, \xi_2, \ldots, \xi_n)$, $y = (\eta_1, \eta_2, \ldots, \eta_n)$, then $\langle x | y \rangle = \sum_1^n \xi_i^* \eta_i$.

(III) Let $x, y: \mathbb{R}_+ \to \mathbb{R}$ with $x, y \in L^2$, then $\langle x \mid y \rangle = \int_0^\infty x(t)y(t)\,dt$. [If x and y are complex valued, the integrand is changed to $x(t)^*y(t)$.]

(IV) Let $x, y: \mathbb{R}_+ \to \mathbb{C}^n$ with $x, y \in L_n^2$ and use * to denote the conjugate transpose, then $\langle x \mid y \rangle = \int_0^\infty x(t)^*y(t)\,dt$.

(V) In the previous cases, we can also use a weighting factor and write $\int_0^\infty w(t)x(t)^*y(t)\,dt$, where $w(\cdot)$ is bounded, continuous, and $w(t) > 0$ for all t. Typically, $w(t) = \varepsilon^{-2\alpha t}$ $(\alpha > 0)$.

(VI) Let $x, y \in l_n^2$, with $x(i) \triangleq [x_1(i), x_2(i), \ldots, x_n(i)]$ and each $x_k(i) \in \mathbb{R}$

$$\langle x \mid y \rangle = \sum_{i=0}^{\infty} \left[\sum_{k=1}^{n} x_k(i) y_k(i) \right]$$

3 Formal framework

Let $\mathscr{T}$ be the set of instants of time of interest. (Typically, $\mathscr{T} = \mathbb{R}_+$, $\mathbb{R}$, $\mathbb{Z}$, or $\mathbb{Z}_+ = \{0, 1, 2, \ldots\}$.)

Let $\mathscr{V}$ be a linear space with scalar product $(\cdot, \cdot)$.

Let $\mathscr{F}$ be a class of functions $x: \mathscr{T} \to \mathscr{V}$. Let a scalar product $\langle \cdot \mid \cdot \rangle$ be defined on a subset of $\mathscr{F}$. If $\mathscr{T} = \mathbb{R}^+$, $\mathscr{V} = \mathbb{R}^n$, and $(\cdot, \cdot)$ is the usual scalar product in $\mathbb{R}^n$, we might have

1 $$\langle x \mid y \rangle = \int_0^\infty (x(t), y(t))\,dt$$

similarly, with $\mathscr{T} = \mathbb{Z}_+$,

2 $$\langle x \mid y \rangle = \sum_{i=0}^{\infty} (x(i), y(i))$$

For any $t \in \mathscr{T}$, let P_T denote as before the *linear* operator defined on $\mathscr{F}$ by the condition that for any $x \in \mathscr{F}$, $T \in \mathscr{T}$,

3 $$(P_T x)(t) = \begin{cases} x(t), & t \leq T, \quad t \in \mathscr{T} \\ \theta, & t > T \end{cases}$$

where θ denotes the zero vector in $\mathscr{V}$. Clearly, $P_T^2 = P_T$; hence P_T is, for each T, a *projection*. We shall often use the notation

$$x_T \triangleq P_T x$$

The projections P_T identify linear subspaces of $\mathscr{F}$, namely,

$$P_T \mathscr{F} = \{g \in \mathscr{F} \mid g = P_T f \text{ for some } f \in \mathscr{F}\} = \{g \in \mathscr{F} \mid g(t) = \theta \text{ for } t > T\}$$

Let

5 $$\mathscr{H}_e \triangleq \{x \in \mathscr{F} \mid \forall T \in \mathscr{T},\ \|x_T\|^2 = \langle x_T \mid x_T \rangle < \infty\}$$

Thus, $\mathcal{H}_e$ is the space of all x with the property that for all $T \in \mathcal{T}$, x_T has finite norm. From Schwarz's inequality it follows that if

$$x, y \in \mathcal{H}_e, \qquad \text{then} \quad \forall T \in \mathcal{T}, \quad |\langle x_T | y_T \rangle| < \infty$$

Similarly, let

6 $$\mathcal{H} \triangleq \{x \in \mathcal{F} \mid \|x\|^2 = \langle x | x \rangle < \infty\}$$

The scalar product is required to fulfill the following conditions:

8 HI. For all $x \in \mathcal{H}_e$, the function $T \to \|x_T\|$ is monotonically increasing.

9 HII. For all $x \in \mathcal{H}$, $\lim_{T \to \infty} \|x_T\| = \|x\|$.

10 HIII. For all $x, y \in \mathcal{H}_e$, $\forall T \in \mathcal{T}$,

$$\langle x_T | y_T \rangle = \langle x_T | y \rangle = \langle x | y_T \rangle \triangleq \langle x | y \rangle_T$$

Note that the six examples of scalar products given in Section 2 satisfy these three conditions.

4 Passive systems: definition and examples

We use in this section the framework just developed to define passive systems. We give several examples and exercises, which are important instances of passive systems.

Let $H : \mathcal{H}_e \to \mathcal{H}_e$. We say that H is **passive** iff $\exists$ some *constant* β s.t.

1 $$\langle Hx | x \rangle_T \geq \beta, \qquad \forall x \in \mathcal{H}_e, \quad \forall T \in \mathcal{T}$$

We say that $H : \mathcal{H}_e \to \mathcal{H}_e$ is **strictly passive** iff $\exists \delta > 0$ and $\exists \beta$ s.t.

2 $$\langle Hx | x \rangle_T \geq \delta \|x_T\|^2 + \beta, \qquad \forall x \in \mathcal{H}_e, \quad \forall T \in \mathcal{T}$$

We say that $H : \mathcal{H}_e \to \mathcal{H}_e$ is **incrementally passive** iff

3 $$\langle Hx - Hx' | x - x' \rangle_T \geq 0, \qquad \forall x, x' \in \mathcal{H}_e, \quad \forall T \in \mathcal{T}$$

We say that $H : \mathcal{H}_e \to \mathcal{H}_e$ is **incrementally strictly passive** iff $\exists \tilde{\delta} > 0$ s.t.

4 $$\langle Hx - Hx' | x - x' \rangle_T \geq \tilde{\delta} \|x - x'\|_T{}^2, \qquad \forall x, x' \in \mathcal{H}_e, \quad \forall T \in \mathcal{T}$$

5 **Comments** (a) If H is linear, then β can be taken to be zero in (1) and (2). More importantly, when H is linear,

(i) H is passive if and only if it is incrementally passive;
(ii) H is strictly passive if and only if H is strictly incrementally passive.

(b) It is very important to distinguish between *passivity*, *strict passivity*, etc., which are notions tested on the *extended* space $\mathcal{H}_e$, and the more common notion of positivity. In Section 8 we shall define $\mathscr{H}$ *positivity* by the condition:

$$\langle Hx|x\rangle \geq 0, \qquad \forall x \in \mathscr{H}$$

where $H: \mathscr{H} \to \mathscr{H}$. When H is *causal* (nonanticipative), these two notions are identical [see Lemma (8.2)]. They are distinct when H is noncausal (see Exercise 2, Section 8).

The remainder of this section displays many classes of passive systems both by demonstration through examples and by exercises.

6 **Example 1** Let $H: L_e^2 \to L_e^2$ and be defined by

7 $$Hu = h * u, \qquad \text{where} \quad h \in \mathscr{A} \quad \text{and} \quad u \in L_e^2$$

Note that since $h \in \mathscr{A}$, H is causal. We assert that:

8 H is passive iff $\mathrm{Re}[\hat{h}(j\omega)] \geq 0$, $\forall \omega \in \mathbb{R}$;

9 H is strictly passive iff, for some $\delta > 0$,

$$\mathrm{Re}[\hat{h}(j\omega)] \geq \delta, \qquad \forall \omega \in \mathbb{R}$$

The proof is based on the following calculation:

$$\begin{aligned} \langle u|h * u\rangle_T &= \langle u_T|h * u\rangle && \text{by (3.10)} \\ &= \langle u_T|h * u_T\rangle && \text{because } H \text{ is causal} \\ &= (1/2\pi)\int_{-\infty}^{\infty} \mathrm{Re}[\hat{h}(j\omega)]\,|\hat{u}_T(j\omega)|^2\,d\omega && \text{(Parseval)} \end{aligned}$$

observing that

$$\|u_T\|^2 = (1/2\pi)\int_{-\infty}^{\infty} |\hat{u}_T(j\omega)|^2\,d\omega$$

Statements (8) and (9) follow easily.

Example 2 Let H be an $n \times n$ matrix whose elements belong to $\mathscr{A}$, and let the operator $\mathbf{H}$ be defined by $\mathbf{H}u \triangleq H * u$, for all $u \in L_{ne}^2$. Thus, $\mathbf{H}: L_{ne}^2 \to L_{ne}^2$. We assert that

10 $\mathbf{H}$ is passive iff the Hermitian matrix $\hat{H}(j\omega) + \hat{H}(j\omega)^*$ is positive semi-definite, $\forall \omega \in \mathbb{R}$.

11 $\mathbf{H}$ is strictly passive iff, for some $\delta > 0$,

$$\lambda_{\min}[\hat{H}(j\omega) + \hat{H}(j\omega)^*] \geq \delta > 0, \qquad \forall \omega \geq 0$$

i.e., for all $\omega \in \mathbb{R}$, the least eigenvalue of the Hermitian matrix $\hat{H}(j\omega) + \hat{H}(j\omega)^*$ is $\geq \delta$.

Exercise 1 Prove (10) and (11) in detail.

Exercise 2 (discrete-time case) Let $H : l_e^2 \to l_e^2$ and be defined by $Hu = h * u$, where $h = (h_0, h_1, h_2, \ldots) \in l^1$. Let $u \in l_e^2$. Show that H is passive (strictly passive) iff $\text{Re}[\tilde{h}(e^{j\theta})] \geq 0$ (for some $\delta > 0$, $\text{Re}[\tilde{h}(e^{j\theta})] \geq \delta$) for all $\theta \in [0, 2\pi]$.

Exercise 3 (discrete-time case) Let $\mathbf{H} : l_{ne}^2 \to l_{ne}^2$ and be defined by $\mathbf{H}u = H * u$, where $H = (H_0, H_1, H_2, \ldots) \in l_{n \times n}^1$. Let $u \in l_{ne}^2$. Show that $\mathbf{H}$ is passive (strictly passive) iff the Hermitian matrix $\tilde{H}(e^{j\theta}) + \tilde{H}(e^{j\theta})^*$ is positive semidefinite (for some $\delta > 0$, $\lambda_{\min}[\tilde{H}(e^{j\theta}) + \tilde{H}(e^{j\theta})^*] \geq \delta$, resp.) for all $\theta \in [0, 2\pi]$.

Example 3 Consider the system whose input is u and whose output is $y = \mathbf{H}u$, where $u, y : \mathbb{R}_+ \to \mathbb{R}^n$. The equations of the system are

$$\dot{\xi}(t) = u(t), \qquad \xi(0) = \xi_0, \quad t \geq 0 \tag{12}$$

$$y(t) = R\xi(t) \tag{13}$$

where $\xi : \mathbb{R}_+ \to \mathbb{R}^n$ and $R \in \mathbb{R}^{n \times n}$. The system can be visualized as a bank of n integrators whose input is $u(t)$ and output is $\xi(t)$ [see Eq. (12)], and the integrator outputs are combined linearly to obtain the system output $y(t)$, as required by (13). The system $\mathbf{H}$ has a well-defined response for any $u(\cdot)$ in $L_{ne}^2(\mathbb{R}_+)$. We assert that if R is a symmetric positive semidefinite matrix, then $\mathbf{H}$ is passive.

Proof For any $u \in L_{ne}^2(\mathbb{R}_+)$ and any $T \in \mathbb{R}_+$,

$$\langle u | \mathbf{H}u \rangle_T = \langle u | y \rangle_T = \langle y | u \rangle_T = \int_0^T \xi(t)' R' \dot{\xi}(t) \, dt$$

This is a line integral in $\mathbb{R}^n$ along the curve $t \mapsto \xi(t)$ for $t \in [0, T]$. Since R is symmetric, the value of the integral is independent of the path; so we can evaluate it along the line segment $\lambda \mapsto (1 - \lambda)\xi_0 + \lambda\xi(T)$, where $\xi_0 = \xi(0)$. Thus,

$$\begin{aligned}\langle u | \mathbf{H}u \rangle_T &= \int_0^1 \{\xi_0 + \lambda[\xi(T) - \xi_0]\}' R[\xi(T) - \xi_0] \, d\lambda \\ &= \xi_0' R' [\xi(T) - \xi_0] + \tfrac{1}{2}[\xi(T) - \xi_0]' R [\xi(T) - \xi_0] \\ &= \tfrac{1}{2}\xi(T)' R \xi(T) - \tfrac{1}{2}\xi_0' R \xi_0\end{aligned}$$

And passivity follows from the positive semidefiniteness of R. ∎

Exercise 4 (a) Show that even if $\xi_0 = 0$ and if R is positive definite, it still does *not* follow that the system defined by (12) and (13) is strictly passive. (Use an example.)

(b) Show that the path integral above depends only on its initial point and its final point by observing that since R is symmetric, it follows that

$$2\xi(t)'R\dot{\xi}(t) = d[\xi(t)'R\xi(t)]/dt$$

Exercise 5 Let $\mathbf{H}: \mathscr{H}_e \to \mathscr{H}_e$. Let $\mathbf{K}$ denote a time-varying gain: $\mathbf{K}: \mathscr{H}_e \to \mathscr{H}_e$ such that

$$(\mathbf{K}u)(t) = k(t)u(t)$$

where $k: \mathscr{T} \to \mathbb{R}$ and k is a bounded function on $\mathscr{T}$. Show that

(a) if $\mathbf{H}$ is passive, then $\mathbf{KHK}$ is also passive;

(b) if $\mathbf{H}$ is strictly passive and if k is bounded away from zero on $\mathscr{T}$, then $\mathbf{KHK}$ is strictly passive.

Example 4 Consider the system shown in Fig. VI.2; the input of $\mathbf{H}$ is u and

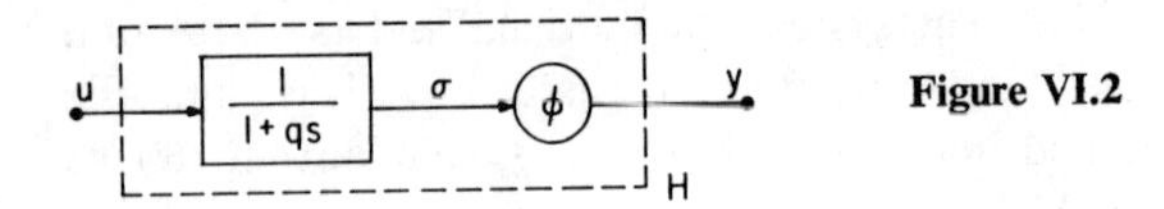

Figure VI.2

its output is y. We have

$$q\dot{\sigma}(t) + \sigma(t) = u(t), \qquad \sigma(0) = \sigma_0 \tag{14}$$

$$y(t) = \phi[\sigma(t)] \tag{15}$$

where $u, \sigma, y: \mathbb{R}_+ \to \mathbb{R}$; $\phi: \mathbb{R} \to \mathbb{R}$ and is continuous. We assert that if $q \geq 0$ and if $\phi \in$ sector $[0, \infty)$, then $\mathbf{H}$ is passive.

Proof For all $T \geq 0$ and all $u \in L_e^2$ we have

$$\langle Hu|u\rangle_T = \langle \phi(\sigma)|u\rangle_T = \langle \phi(\sigma)|q\dot{\sigma} + \sigma\rangle_T$$

$$= q\int_0^T \phi[\sigma(t)]\dot{\sigma}(t)\,dt + \int_0^T \sigma(t)\phi[\sigma(t)]\,dt$$

Since $\phi \in$ sector $[0, \infty)$, the last integral is nonnegative, and if we define $\Phi: \mathbb{R} \to \mathbb{R}$ by

$$\Phi(\sigma) = \int_0^\sigma \phi(\xi)\,d\xi \tag{16}$$

then $\Phi(\sigma) \geq 0$, $\forall \sigma \in \mathbb{R}$. Finally, using Φ to evaluate the first integral above, and noting that $q \geq 0$, we obtain

$$\langle Hu | u \rangle_T \geq -q\Phi[\sigma(0)], \qquad \forall u \in L_e^2, \quad \forall T \geq 0$$

Hence the system is passive. ∎

Exercise 6 Give an example to show that if in the system above ϕ is time varying but $\phi \in$ sector $[0, \infty)$, $\forall t \in \mathbb{R}_+$, then H is not necessarily passive.

Exercise 7 Suppose that in Fig. VI.2 we interchange the order of the blocks. Show that the resulting system is not passive for all $\phi \in$ sector $[0, k)$. [*Hint*: Consider $\phi(\sigma) = \sigma$ for $\sigma > 0$ and $\phi(\sigma) = 0$ for $\sigma < 0$.]

Exercise 8 Consider the n-input–n-output generalization of the system shown in Fig. VI.2. Let P, $Q \in \mathbb{R}^{n \times n}$; $\sigma(t), u(t)$, $y(t) \in \mathbb{R}^n$, and

$$Q\dot{\sigma}(t) + P\sigma(t) = u(t) \tag{17}$$

$$y(t) = \phi[\sigma(t)] \tag{18}$$

where ϕ: $\mathbb{R}^n \to \mathbb{R}^n$, is continuous with

$$\sigma' P \phi(\sigma) \geq 0, \qquad \forall \sigma \in \mathbb{R}^n \tag{19}$$

Assume further that

$$\phi(\sigma)' Q = [\text{grad } V(\sigma)]', \qquad \forall \sigma \in \mathbb{R}^n \tag{20}$$

where V: $\mathbb{R}^n \to \mathbb{R}$ is in C^1 and $V(\sigma) \geq 0$, $\forall \sigma \in \mathbb{R}^n$. Show that $\mathbf{H}$: $u \mapsto y$ is passive. Show that if ϕ consists of "noninteracting" nonlinearities, i.e., for $i = 1, 2, \ldots, n$, $\phi_i(\sigma) = f_i(\sigma_i)$ [i.e., the ith component of $\phi(\sigma)$ depends only on σ_i], and if each f_i is in the sector $[0, \infty)$, then (19) and (20) can be satisfied by $P = Q = I$. Give $V(\sigma)$ for such a case.

Example 5 To illustrate the use of a slightly different scalar product, consider the system shown in Fig. VI.2 with the same assumptions and notations as before: Eqs. (14), (15), (16), $q > 0$, and $\phi \in$ sector $[0, \infty)$. We assert that if $q > 0$ and for some $\alpha \geq 0$

$$\phi_0 \triangleq \inf_{\sigma} \sigma\phi(\sigma)/\Phi(\sigma) \geq 2\alpha q \tag{21}$$

then, for $\sigma(0) = 0$,

$$\int_0^T \varepsilon^{2\alpha t} u(t) \phi[\sigma(t)]\, dt \geq 0, \qquad \forall T \geq 0, \quad \forall u \in L^2 \tag{22}$$

Proof

$$\int_0^T \varepsilon^{2\alpha t} u(t)\phi[\sigma(t)]\,dt = \int_0^T \varepsilon^{2\alpha t}(q\dot{\sigma} + \sigma)\phi(\sigma)\,dt$$
$$= q\varepsilon^{2\alpha T}\Phi[\sigma(T)] - \int_0^T \varepsilon^{2\alpha t}\{2\alpha q\Phi[\sigma(t)] - \sigma(t)\phi[\sigma(t)]\}\,dt$$

where we used the fact that $\Phi[\sigma(0)] = 0$ since $\sigma(0) = 0$. The first term is nonnegative because $\phi \in$ sector $[0, \infty)$, and the second integral is nonpositive by (21). ∎

Exercise 9 (passive system with multiplier) In the system shown in Fig. VI.3, u and $y \in L_e^2$. ϕ denotes a memoryless time-varying nonlinearity whose

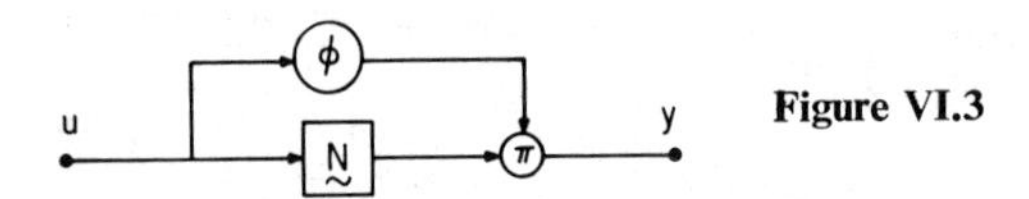

Figure VI.3

characteristic $\phi(\cdot, t) \in$ sector $(0, k)$ for some $k \in (0, \infty]$. Let $\mathbf{N}$: $L_e^2 \to L_e^2$ be arbitrary except that for some $\delta \geq 0$,

$$(\mathbf{N}u)(t) \geq \delta \geq 0, \qquad \forall u \in L_e^2, \qquad \forall t \geq 0$$

The output y is the product of the output of $\mathbf{N}$ and of ϕ. U.t.c., show that the system is passive. Give some additional restriction that will make the system strictly passive.

Example 6 Let $\mathbf{P}$ be an operator from $L_e^2 \to L_e^2$. Let $\mathbf{K}$ be a time-varying gain; i.e., $\mathbf{K}$: $L_e^2 \to L_e^2$ with

$$(\mathbf{K}x)(t) = k(t)x(t), \qquad \forall t \in \mathbb{R}_+ \tag{26}$$

where $k(\cdot)$ is absolutely continuous on $\mathbb{R}_+$ with

$$0 \leq \underline{k} \triangleq \inf_t k(t) \leq k(t) \leq \sup_t k(t) \triangleq \bar{k} < \infty$$

The class of all such operators is labeled $\mathscr{K}_0$; if $\underline{k} > 0$, it is called K. We assert that

27 if $\mathbf{P}$ is passive (strictly passive) and $k(\cdot) \in \mathscr{K}_0$ $(\mathscr{K})$ is ↘, then $\mathbf{KP}$ is passive (strictly passive) (↘ means monotone nonincreasing);

28 if $\mathbf{P}$ is passive (strictly passive) and $k(\cdot) \in \mathscr{K}$ is ↗, then $\mathbf{PK}$ is passive (strictly passive).

29 **Comment** The importance of the assumption that $k(\cdot)$ is absolutely continuous is that $k(\cdot)$ is absolutely continuous if and only if

(a) $\dot{k}(\cdot)$ is defined almost everywhere, and
(b) k is the indefinite integral of $\dot{k}(\cdot)$ [McS.1].

Proof of (27) For all $u \in L_e^2$ and for all $T \geq 0$

30
$$\langle u | \mathbf{KP}u \rangle_T = \int_0^T u(t)k(t)(\mathbf{P}u)(t)\, dt = k(T)\langle u | \mathbf{P}u \rangle_T - \int_0^T \dot{k}(t)\langle u | \mathbf{P}u \rangle_t\, dt \geq 0$$

because the first term is nonnegative and the integral is nonpositive because P is passive, $k(T) \geq 0$ for all T, and $\dot{k}(t) \leq 0$ for all t. ∎

Proof of (28) $\forall u \in L_e^2$, $\forall T \geq 0$, with $\mathbf{K}u \triangleq v$

$$\langle u | \mathbf{PK}u \rangle_T = \langle \mathbf{K}^{-1}v | \mathbf{P}v \rangle_T = \int_0^T [1/k(t)]v(t)(\mathbf{P}v)(t)\, dt$$

Note that $u \in L_e^2 \Leftrightarrow v = \mathbf{K}u \in L_e^2$ because $k(\cdot) \in \mathscr{K}$. So we have the same integral as (30) except that $k(t)$ is replaced by $1/k(t)$. Hence the same calculation shows that **PK** is passive. ∎

Exercise 10 Prove the assertions for the strictly positive case, and prove related assertions for the discrete-time case.

The following example is a variation on Example 6 in that k is not assumed to be increasing, but using exponential weighting techniques, it considers the case where $t \mapsto k(t)\exp(\sigma t)$ is nondecreasing.

Example 7 Suppose there are numbers $\underline{k}$ and $\bar{k}$ such that $0 < \underline{k} \leq k(t) \leq \bar{k} < \infty$ for all t. Let $\mathbf{k}$: $L_e^2 \to L_e^2$ and be defined by (26). Let $\mathbf{g}$: $L_e^2 \to L_e^2$ with $\mathbf{g}x \triangleq g * x$, where $g \in \mathscr{A}$. Let $\beta > 0$ and assume that $\hat{g}$ can be continued analytically up to $\text{Re}\, s = -\beta$. We assume that there is a $\delta > 0$ s.t.

31
$$\text{Re}\, \hat{g}(j\omega) \geq \delta > 0, \qquad \forall \omega \in \mathbb{R}$$

and

32
$$\text{Re}\, \hat{g}(j\omega - \beta) \geq 0, \qquad \forall \omega \in \mathbb{R}$$

U.t.c.,

(i) if for some $\sigma \in (0, 2\beta)$, $t \mapsto k(t)\exp \sigma t$ is $\nearrow$, then **gk** is strictly passive and has finite gain; with $\delta = 0$, $\beta = \sigma > 0$, **gk** is passive;

(ii) if for some $\sigma \in (0, 2\beta)$, $t \mapsto k(t)\exp(-\sigma t)$ is $\searrow$, then **kg** is strictly passive and has finite gain.

33 **Comment** If $k \in \mathscr{K}$, then, in (i), we could write the assumption as

34
$$\frac{d \log k(t)}{dt} = \frac{\dot{k}(t)}{k(t)} \geq -\sigma, \qquad \forall t \geq 0$$

Proof (i) Let $p(t) \triangleq 1/k(t)$; then for some numbers $\underline{p}$ and $\bar{p}$, we have

35
$$0 < \underline{p} \leq p(t) \leq \bar{p}$$

and $t \mapsto p(t)e^{-\sigma t}$ is $\searrow$. Now for some $\delta_1 > 0$, sufficiently small, since $2\beta > \sigma > 0$, we have that $[p(t) - \delta_1] \exp(-2\beta t)$ is $\searrow$. (Take the logarithm and differentiate !) Then, $\forall u \in L_e^2$, $\forall t \geq 0$, with $v = \mathbf{k}u$, we have

36
$$\langle u | \mathbf{gk}u \rangle_T = \int_0^T p(t)v(t)(\mathbf{g}v)(t)\, dt$$

$$= \delta_1 \int_0^T v(t)(\mathbf{g}v)(t)\, dt + \int_0^T \{[p(t) - \delta_1]e^{-2\beta t}\}v(t)e^{\beta t}(\mathbf{g}v)(t)e^{\beta t}\, dt$$

The first integral is larger than

38
$$\delta_1\, \delta(\underline{k})^2\, \|u\|_T{}^2$$

The second integral is nonnegative. Apply to it the second mean value theorem [McS.1, p. 210], noting that the bracket is positive and $\searrow$; hence it is equal to

$$[p(0) - \delta_1] \int_0^{T'} v(t)e^{\beta t} \cdot e^{\beta t}(\mathbf{g}v)(t)\, dt$$

where T' is some suitable number in $[0, T]$. Now $t \mapsto v(t) \exp \beta t$, truncated at T', is in L^2; hence if we call $\hat{v}_T$ its Laplace transform and if we note that

$$e^{\beta t}(\mathbf{g}v)(t) = e^{\beta t}(g * v)(t) = (ge^{\beta t} * ve^{\beta t})$$

we conclude, from Parseval's theorem that the second integral is equal to

40
$$(1/2\pi) \int_{-\infty}^{+\infty} \hat{g}(j\omega - \beta)\, |\hat{v}_T(j\omega)|^2\, d\omega \geq 0$$

where the last inequality follows from (32). From (36), (38), and (40), we conclude that $\mathbf{gk}$ is strictly passive. Also, $\gamma(\mathbf{gk}) = \|\mathbf{g}\|_{\mathscr{A}}\, \bar{k}$.

The proof of (ii) is immediate because

41
$$\langle u | \mathbf{kg}u \rangle_T = \langle \mathbf{k}u | \mathbf{g}u \rangle_T = \langle v | \mathbf{gk}^{-1}v \rangle_T$$

and $\exp(\sigma t)/k(t) \nearrow$ is equivalent to $k(t) \exp(-\sigma t) \searrow$. ∎

42 **Comment** The manipulation in (41) is valid under general assumptions; namely, $\mathbf{k}$ must be self-adjoint, $\gamma(\mathbf{k}) < \infty$, and $\gamma(\mathbf{k}^{-1}) < \infty$.

5 Passivity theorem

In this section, we formulate a simplified version and a generalized version of the passivity theorem. We are guided by our circuit-theoretic intuition discussed in Section 1. We use throughout the general framework of Sections 3 and 4.

We start by proving a simple version of the passivity theorem.

1 **Theorem** Consider the usual feedback system of Fig. III.1 with $u_2 \equiv 0$ so that

2 $$e_1 = u_1 - H_2 e_2$$

3 $$e_2 = H_1 e_1$$

Here H_1 and H_2 map $\mathscr{H}_e$ into $\mathscr{H}_e$. We assume that for any $u_1 \in \mathscr{H}$, there are solutions e_1, e_2 in $\mathscr{H}_e$. U.t.c., if H_1 is *passive*, H_2 is *strictly passive*, and if $u_1 \in \mathscr{H}$, then $H_1 e_1 \in \mathscr{H}$.

Proof We obtain successively by using (2) and (3)

4 $$\langle u_1 | H_1 e_1 \rangle_T = \langle e_1 | H_1 e_1 \rangle_T + \langle H_2 e_2 | e_2 \rangle_T \geq 0 + \delta_2 \|e_2\|_T^2 + \beta_2$$

where δ_2 and β_2 are constants with $\delta_2 > 0$, since H_2 is strictly passive. Hence by Schwarz, and noting that $u_1 \in \mathscr{H}$, we obtain

5 $$\|u_1\| \; \|H_1 e_1\|_T \geq \delta_2 \; \|H_1 e_1\|_T^2 + \beta_2, \qquad \forall T \in \mathscr{T}$$

from which it follows that $T \mapsto \|H_1 e_1\|_T$ is bounded; i.e., $e_2 = H_1 e_1 \in \mathscr{H}$.

∎

Exercise 1 Suppose that, in the strict passivity condition for H_2, the constant β_2 is nonnegative. Then calculate from (5) the constant k such that

$$\|H_1 e_1\|_T \leq k \|u_1\|_T, \qquad \forall u \in L_e^2, \quad \forall T \in \mathscr{T}$$

6 **Comments** (a) This form of the passivity theorem is easy to prove, easy to apply, and easy to remember. Its circuit-theoretic interpretation makes it obvious (refer to Fig. III.2): The current sources u_1 face the parallel combination of a passive n-port and a strictly passive n-port. The theorem proves that if $u_1 \in \mathscr{H}$, the port voltages $H_1 e_1 = e_2 \in \mathscr{H}$.

(b) Note that it is *not* claimed that e_1 and $H_2 e_2 \in \mathscr{H}$. Indeed, in case of one-ports, a counterexample is easily built up by taking $u_1(\cdot)$ to be a rectangular pulse of current, H_1 a 1-henry inductor, and H_2 a parallel connection of a 1-ohm resistor and a 2-henry inductor; after the pulse of current has become zero, there remains a constant current through the inductors! Thus, e_1 and $H_2 e_2$ are *not* in L^2.

(c) In order to be able to claim that both e_1 and $e_2 = H_1 e_1 \in \mathscr{H}$, one must have a finite-gain assumption on H_1 or H_2 as done in Theorem (10) in the following.

(d) Intuitively, one would expect that H_1 and H_2 need not *both* be passive; what should suffice is that any "activity" (circuit-theoretic term for nonpassivity) of one should be compensated by some "passivity" of the other so that the parallel connection is strictly passive. This is done precisely in Theorem (10).

(e) Clearly, by permutations and combinations of the examples of passive systems of Section 4, we can construct dozens of L^2-stability theorems.

We turn now to the more general version of the passivity theorem.

10 **Theorem** Consider a feedback system as shown in Fig. III.1 and described by

$$e_1 = u_1 - H_2 e_2 \tag{12}$$

$$e_2 = u_2 + H_1 e_1 \tag{13}$$

where H_1 and H_2 map $\mathscr{H}_e$ into $\mathscr{H}_e$. Assume that for any u_1 and u_2 in $\mathscr{H}$, there are solutions e_1 and e_2 in $\mathscr{H}_e$. Suppose that there are constants γ_1, β_1, δ_1, β_1', ε_2, and β_2' such that

$$\left.\begin{aligned} &\|H_1 x\|_T \le \gamma_1 \|x\|_T + \beta_1 && (14)\\ &\langle x | H_1 x\rangle_T \ge \delta_1 \|x\|_T^2 + \beta_1' && (15)\\ &\langle H_2 x | x\rangle_T \ge \varepsilon_2 \|H_2 x\|_T^2 + \beta_2' && (16)\end{aligned}\right\}, \qquad \forall x \in \mathscr{H}_e, \quad \forall T \in \mathscr{T}$$

U.t.c., if

$$\delta_1 + \varepsilon_2 > 0 \tag{17}$$

then

$$u_1, u_2 \in \mathscr{H} \text{ imply that } e_1, e_2, H_1 e_1, H_2 e_2 \in \mathscr{H}$$

18 **Comments** (a) *Generality* This theorem applies to continuous-time ($\mathscr{T} = \mathbb{R}_+$) or discrete-time ($\mathscr{T} = \mathbb{Z}_+$) systems. The systems may be single input–single output ($\mathscr{V} = \mathbb{R}$) or multiple input–multiple output ($\mathscr{V} = \mathbb{R}^n$) or have distributed inputs and outputs ($\mathscr{V}$ is an inner-product space).

(b) (14) means that H_1 has finite gain.

(c) When $\varepsilon_2 = 0$, (17) requires that $\delta_1 > 0$; then the theorem holds if H_1 is *strictly passive* with *finite gain* and H_2 is *passive*. When $\varepsilon_2 \ne 0$, if we go back to the circuit-theoretic interpretation of Fig. III.2 for the one-port case, we see that the "impedance operator" H_1 dissipates more energy than a *resistor* of δ_1 ohm, and the "admittance operator" H_2 dissipates more energy than a *resistor* of ε_2 ohm; thus, the condition (17) says that the net amount of energy dissipated must be positive.

(d) If H_2 is a bijection of $\mathscr{H}_e$ onto $\mathscr{H}_e$, (16) can be restated as

$$\langle y | H_{-1}{}^2 y\rangle_T \geq \varepsilon_2 \|y\|_T{}^2 + \beta_2', \qquad \forall y \in \mathscr{H}_e, \ \forall T$$

thus if $\varepsilon_2 > 0$ (16) means that $H_{-1}{}^2$ is strictly passive.

Proof For any $u_1, u_2 \in \mathscr{H}$, for any $T \in \mathscr{T}$,

20
$$\begin{aligned}\langle e_1 | H_1 e_1\rangle_T + \langle H_2 e_2 | e_2\rangle_T &= \langle u_1 - H_2 e_2 | H_1 e_1\rangle_T + \langle H_2 e_2 | u_2 + H_1 e_1\rangle_T \\ &= \langle u_1 | H_1 e_1\rangle_T + \langle H_2 e_2 | u_2\rangle_T\end{aligned}$$

where we used (12) and (13). In the last equality, use (14), (15), (16), and Schwarz's inequality

21
$$\begin{aligned}\delta_1 \|e_1\|_T{}^2 + \varepsilon_2 \|H_2 e_2\|_T{}^2 \leq \|u_1\|_T \gamma_1 \|e_1\|_T &+ \beta_1 \|u_1\|_T \\ &+ \|u_2\|_T \|H_2 e_2\|_T - \beta_1' - \beta_2'\end{aligned}$$

To eliminate $H_2 e_2$ in (21), note that $H_2 e_2 = u_1 - e_1$ so that

22
$$\|u_1 - e_1\|_T{}^2 \geq \|u_1\|_T{}^2 - 2\|u_1\|_T \, \|e_1\|_T + \|e_1\|_T{}^2$$

Substituting (12) in (21) and replacing ε_2 by $|\varepsilon_2|$ in the right-hand side, we obtain

23
$$\begin{aligned}(\delta_1 + \varepsilon_2)\|e_1\|_T{}^2 \leq \|e_1\|_T[(2|\varepsilon_2| + \delta_1)\|u_1\|_T &+ \|u_2\|_T] \\ + \|u_1\|_T \|u_2\|_T + \beta_1 \|u_1\|_T &+ |\varepsilon_2| \, \|u_1\|_T{}^2 - \beta_1' - \beta_2'\end{aligned}$$

Using the key assumption $\delta_1 + \varepsilon_2 > 0$, we rewrite this inequality in the form

24
$$\|e_1\|_T{}^2 \leq 2b(T)\|e_1\|_T + c(T)$$

where $b(T)$ and $c(T)$ are monotonically increasing and, as $T \to \infty$, tend to *finite* constants since $u_1, u_2 \in \mathscr{H}$. Call the constants b and c, respectively. From (24) we have

25
$$\|e_1\|_T \leq b(T) + [b(T)^2 + c(T)]^{1/2} \leq b + (b^2 + c)^{1/2}, \qquad \forall T \in \mathscr{T}$$

So $e_1 \in \mathscr{H}$. By (14) the same holds for $y_1 = H_1 e_1$. By (12) and (13) it follows that e_2 and $H_2 e_2$ are also in $\mathscr{H}$. ∎

26 **Corollary** Under the conditions of Theorem (10),

(a) if $u_1 \equiv 0$, then the map $u_2 \mapsto H_2 e_2$ is passive;
(b) if $u_2 \equiv 0$, then the map $u_1 \mapsto H_1 e_1$ is passive.

Exercise 2 Give a circuit-theoretic interpretation of Corollary (26).

Proof (a) By (20), since $u_1 \equiv 0$, we have $\forall u_2 \in \mathscr{H}_e$ and $\forall T \in \mathscr{T}$,

$$\begin{aligned}\langle u_2 | H_2 e_2 \rangle_T &= \langle e_1 | H_1 e_1 \rangle_T + \langle H_2 e_2 | e_2 \rangle_T \\ &\geq \delta_1 \|e_1\|_T^2 + \beta_1' + \varepsilon_2 \|H_2 e_2\|_T^2 + \beta_2' \\ &= (\delta_1 + \varepsilon_2)\|e_1\|_T^2 + \beta_1' + \beta_2' \geq \beta_1' + \beta_2'\end{aligned}$$

Hence $u_2 \mapsto H_2 e_2$ is passive; we cannot conclude that it is strictly passive because the assumptions do not exclude the case where H_2 sends all inputs into the zero output.

(b) The proof is similar. ∎

27 **Corollary** If in addition to the assumptions of Theorem (10), we have $\beta_1 = \beta_1' = \beta_2' = 0$, then the maps sending (u_1, u_2) into e_1, e_2, $H_1 e_1$, and $H_2 e_2$ are L^2 stable.

Proof U.t.c., the quantities b and c of Eq. (25) are *homogeneous* polynomials in $\|u_1\|$ and $\|u_2\|$ of degrees one and two, respectively. Hence from (25), there is a $k < \infty$ s.t.

$$\|e_1\| \leq k \max(\|u_1\|, \|u_2\|)$$

The remaining maps are L^2 stable as a consequence of (12), (13), and (14). ∎

In discussing the small gain theorem (III.2.1), we noted that we obtained sharper results by requiring conditions on the incremental gains rather than on the gains themselves; in fact, in the first case, we could only assert that the norms of the outputs were finite; with conditions on the incremental gains we obtained, in addition, existence, uniqueness, and continuous dependence. A similar behavior occurs when one considers incremental passivity.

30 **Theorem** Consider the usual feedback system described by (12) and (13), where H_1 and H_2 map $\mathscr{H}_e$ into $\mathscr{H}_e$. Suppose that any u_1, u_2 in $\mathscr{H}$ produce $e_1, e_2 \in \mathscr{H}_e$. Let $H_1 0 = 0$; $H_2 0 = 0$. U.t.c., if

(a) H_1 has finite incremental gain and is strictly incrementally passive, i.e., there are constants $0 < \tilde{\gamma}_1 < \infty$, $\tilde{\delta}_1 > 0$ such that

$$\left.\begin{aligned} &\|H_1 x - H_1 x'\|_T \leq \tilde{\gamma}_1 \|x - x'\|_T && (31) \\ &\langle H_1 x - H_1 x' | x - x' \rangle_T \geq \tilde{\delta}_1 \|x - x'\|_T && (32) \end{aligned}\right\}, \quad \forall x, x' \in \mathscr{H}_e, \quad \forall T \in \mathscr{T}$$

(b) H_2 is incrementally passive, i.e.,

$$\langle H_2 x - H_2 x' | x - x' \rangle_T \geq 0, \qquad \forall x, x' \in \mathscr{H}_e, \quad \forall T \in \mathscr{T} \tag{33}$$

then

(i) for any input $u_1, u_2 \in \mathscr{H}$, the outputs $e_1, e_2, y_1, y_2 \in \mathscr{H}$ and are *unique*;

(ii) the mappings $(u_1, u_2) \to e_1$, $(u_1, u_2) \to e_2$ are uniformly continuous on $\mathscr{H} \times \mathscr{H}$;

(iii) the mappings sending (u_1, u_2) into e_1, e_2, $H_1 e_1$, and $H_2 e_2$ are L^2 stable.

Proof (i) and (ii). Since by assumption $H_1 0 = 0$, $H_2 0 = 0$, by putting $x' = 0$ in (31), (32), and (33), we obtain (14), (15), and (16) with $\gamma_1 = \tilde{\gamma}_1$, $\delta_1 = \tilde{\delta}_1 > 0$, $\varepsilon_2 = 0$, and all the β's zero. Consequently, by Theorem (10), $e_1, e_2, y_1, y_2 \in \mathscr{H}$. To establish uniqueness, consider the input pairs (u_1, u_2), (u_1', u_2') and their corresponding solutions (e_1, e_2), (e_1', e_2'). Now, as in the proof of Theorem (10), we obtain that $\forall T \in \mathscr{T}$

34
$$\langle e_1 - e_1' | H_1 e_1 - H_1 e_1' \rangle_T + \langle e_2 - e_2' | H_2 e_2 - H_2 e_2' \rangle_T = \langle u_1 - u_1' | H_1 e_1 - H_1 e_1' \rangle_T + \langle u_2 - u_2' | H_2 e_2 - H_2 e_2' \rangle_T$$

Using (31), (32), (33), and Schwarz's inequality, we obtain the inequality

35
$$\tilde{\delta}_1 \|e_1 - e_1'\|_T^2 \le \|u_1 - u_1'\|_T \tilde{\gamma}_1 \|e_1 - e_1'\|_T + \|u_2 - u_2'\|_T [\|e_1 - e_1'\|_T + \|u_1 - u_1'\|_T]$$

Hence if $u_1 = u_1'$ and $u_2 = u_2'$, (35) implies that $e_1 = e_1'$; whence $e_2 = e_2'$ by (13). Therefore, uniqueness is established.

(ii) To establish uniform continuity, we rewrite the right-hand side of (35) as

36
$$\|e_1 - e_1'\|_T [\|u_2 - u_2'\|_T + \tilde{\gamma}_1 \|u_1 - u_1'\|_T] + [\|u_1 - u_1'\|_T \cdot \|u_2 - u_2'\|_T]$$

The two bracketed terms are increasing functions of T and as $T \to \infty$, they tend to two constants, say, $2b\tilde{\delta}_1$ and $c\tilde{\delta}_1$. Thus, from (35), (36), and $\tilde{\delta}_1 > 0$, we conclude that

$$\|e_1 - e_1'\|_T^2 \le 2b \|e_1 - e_1'\|_T + c, \qquad \forall T \in \mathscr{T}$$

where b and c are homogeneous polynomials in $\|u_1 - u_1'\|$ and $\|u_2 - u_2'\|$ of degrees one and two, respectively, and by elementary algebra,

38
$$\|e_1 - e_1'\|_T \le b + (b^2 + c)^{1/2}, \qquad \forall T$$

Since b and c are constants and $\| \cdot \|_T$ increases monotonically with T, we may drop the subscript T in (38).

Now if $u_1' \to u_1$ and $u_2 \to u_2'$ in $\mathscr{H}$ (i.e., $\|u_i - u_i'\| \to 0$ for $i = 1, 2$, and consequently $\|u_i - u_i'\|_T \to 0$ for any T), then by (38), $\|e_1 - e_1'\| \to 0$. The same holds for e_2 because, by (14) and (31), we have

39 $$\|e_2 - e_2'\| \leq \|u_2 - u_2'\| + \tilde{\gamma}_1 \|e_1 - e_1'\|$$

Therefore, uniqueness and uniform continuity on $\mathscr{H} \times \mathscr{H}$ is established.
(iii) L^2 stability follows from (38), (39), (31), and $H_2 e_2 = u_1 - e_1$. ∎

6 The Popov criterion

A very important application of the passivity theorem is the derivation of the Popov criterion and its extensions.

Case I $\phi \in$ sector $[0, \infty)$ [i.e., $\phi(0) = 0$ and $\sigma\phi(\sigma) \geq 0$, $\forall \sigma \in \mathbb{R}$].

1 **Theorem** Let $\phi: \mathbb{R} \to \mathbb{R}$ be continuous and be in the sector $[0, \infty)$. Let $g: \mathbb{R}_+ \to \mathbb{R}$, $g \in L^1(\mathbb{R}_+)$, and $\dot{g} \in \mathscr{A}$. For the system shown in Fig. VI.4, we

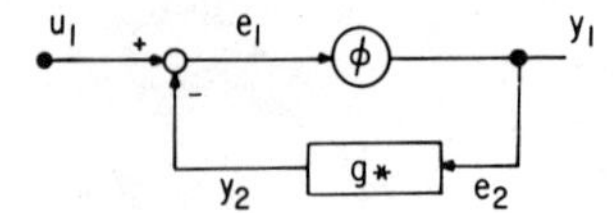

Figure VI.4

assume that for any u_1 such that $u_1, \dot{u}_1 \in L^2$, then $e_1, e_2 \in L_e^2$. U.t.c., if there is a $q \geq 0$ such that

2 $$\inf_{\omega \geq 0} \operatorname{Re}[(1 + qj\omega)\hat{g}(j\omega)] \triangleq \delta > 0$$

and if $u_1, \dot{u}_1 \in L^2$, then

(i) $e_1, \dot{e}_1, e_2, y_1, y_2$, and $\dot{y}_2 \in L^2$;
(ii) e_1, y_1, and y_2 are continuous, belong to L^∞, and go to zero as $t \to \infty$.

3 **Exercise 1** Show that $u_1, \dot{u}_1 \in L^2$ imply that $u_1 \in L^\infty$, u_1 is continuous, and $u_1(t) \to 0$ as $t \to \infty$. [*Hint*: $t \mapsto u_1(t)\dot{u}_1(t) \in L^1$; so its integral is continuous and tends to a finite constant as $t \to \infty, \ldots$.]

Exercise 2 Show that if an input u_2 were inserted at the usual location in the system of Fig. VI.4, then all the conclusions of Theorem (1) would still hold, provided that $u_2 \in L^2$. (*Hint*: Use the linearity of H_2 to replace u_2 by an equivalent input at u_1; note that if $z_2 = g * u_2$, then $\dot{z}_2 = \dot{g} * u_2$, where $\dot{g}$ is the derivative of g in the distribution sense.)

Proof Transform the system of Fig. VI.4 into the one shown in Fig. VI.5. Define H_1 and H_2 by $H_1\eta_1 = y_1$, $H_2 e_2 = y_2 + q\dot{y}_2$. By Example 4 of Section 4, H_1 is passive, and by Example 1 of Section 4, H_2 is strictly passive, as a consequence of (2). Therefore, by Corollary (5.26), u_1, $\dot{u}_1 \in L^2$ imply that

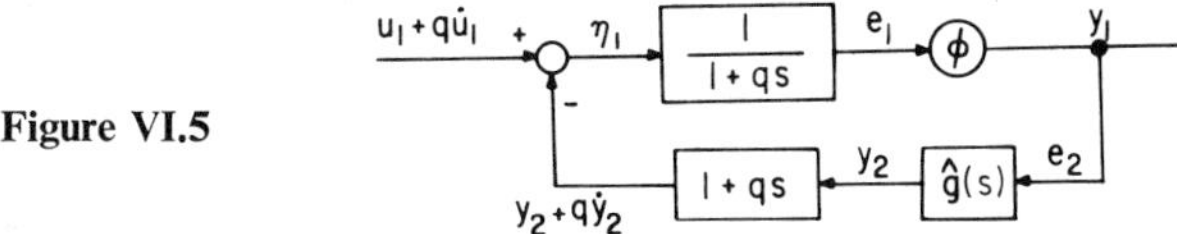

Figure VI.5

$y_1 = e_2 \in L^2$. Since $g \in L^1$ and $\dot{g} \in \mathscr{A}$, H_2 has finite gain; hence y_2, $\dot{y}_2$, and $\eta_1 \in L^2$. Going back to Fig. VI.4, we have e_1, $\dot{e}_1 \in L^2$; hence $e_1 \in L^\infty$, $e_1(\cdot)$ is continuous, and $e_1(t) \to 0$ as $t \to \infty$. The same holds for $y_1(t) = \phi[e_1(t)]$; indeed, ϕ is continuous and the continuous function ϕ maps compact sets in $\mathbb{R}$ into compact sets in $\mathbb{R}$. The same properties hold for y_2 since $y_2 = g * e_2$ and $g \in L^1$. ∎

Case II $\phi \in$ sector $[0, k]$.

5 **Theorem** Consider the system shown in Fig. VI.4, where now $\phi \in$ sector $[0, k]$. Assume that all previous assumptions hold except that (2) is replaced by: If there is a $q > 0$ and some $\delta > 0$ such that

$$\mathrm{Re}[(1 + qj\omega)\hat{g}(j\omega)] + 1/k \triangleq \delta > 0, \qquad \forall\omega \geq 0 \tag{6}$$

then the same conclusions follow.

7 **Graphical Interpretation** If we write $\hat{g}(j\omega) = \hat{g}_r(j\omega) + j\hat{g}_i(j\omega)$, then (6) will hold if and only if

$$q\omega\hat{g}_i(j\omega) \leq \hat{g}_r(j\omega) + [(1/k) - \delta], \qquad \forall\omega \in \mathbb{R}_+$$

We need only check this inequality for $\omega \geq 0$ because $\hat{g}_r(j\omega)$ and $\omega\hat{g}_i(j\omega)$ are even functions. The inequality is equivalent to the following: The complex plane curve $\omega \mapsto [\hat{g}_r(j\omega), \omega\hat{g}_i(j\omega)]$ lies below the straight line of slope $1/q$, which goes through the point $(\delta-(1/k),0)$. Since $\delta > 0$ can be arbitrarily small, this means that the curve $\omega \mapsto [\hat{g}_r(j\omega), \omega\hat{g}_i(j\omega)]$ lies below and is bounded away from the straight line of slope $1/q$, which goes through the point $(-1/k, 0)$.

Proof Consider H_1 shown in Fig. VI.5, we have for all $T \geq 0$,

$$\begin{aligned}\langle \eta_1 \mid H_1\eta_1 \rangle_T = \langle e_1 + q\dot{e}_1 \mid \phi(e_1)\rangle_T &= \langle e_1 \mid \phi(e_1)\rangle_T + q\langle \dot{e}_1 \mid \phi(e_1)\rangle_T \\ &\geq (1/k)\langle \phi(e_1) \mid \phi(e_1)\rangle_T - q\Phi[e_1(0)]\end{aligned}$$

where we used the notation of Example 4, Section 4. In other words, calling β_1 the last term, we have

$$\langle \eta_1 | H_1 \eta_1 \rangle_T \geq (1/k) \| H_1 \eta_1 \|_T^2 - \beta_1$$

Now H_2 is a linear operator with finite gain since $g \in L^1$ and $\dot{g} \in \mathscr{A}$, where

$$\langle e_2 | H_2 e_2 \rangle_T \geq \inf_{\omega \in \mathbb{R}} \operatorname{Re}[(1 + qj\omega)\hat{g}(j\omega)] \| e_2 \|_T^2$$

Therefore, H_1 and H_2 satisfy the conditions of the passivity theorem (5.10), and the map $u_1 + q\dot{u}_1 \mapsto (\eta_1, e_2)$ is L^2 stable. The remaining conclusions are obtained by the same considerations as above. ∎

8 **Comment** The proof can also be obtained by direct calculation as follows. The system equation reads (we drop the subscript 1 for simplicity)

$$u = e + g * \phi(e) \tag{9a}$$

Since $\dot{u} \in L^2$ and $\dot{g} \in \mathscr{A}$, we obtain by differentiation

$$\dot{u} = \dot{e} + \dot{g} * \phi(e) \tag{9b}$$

Since all terms in these two equations are in L_e^2, we can take truncated scalar products,

$$\begin{aligned}\langle \dot{u} + qu | \phi(e) \rangle_T = &\langle e - [\phi(e)/k] | \phi(e) \rangle_T + q\langle \dot{e} | \phi(e) \rangle_T \\ &+ \langle (g + q\dot{g}) * \phi(e) + (1/k)\phi(e) | \phi(e) \rangle_T\end{aligned}$$

Using Schwarz's inequality, the sector condition, $q \geq 0$, and (6), we obtain

$$(\|u\| + q\|\dot{u}\|) \, \|\phi(e)\|_T \geq \delta \|\phi(e)\|_T^2 - q\Phi[e(0)]$$

Hence $\phi(e) \in L^2$. Then $e \in L^2$ by (9a) and $\dot{e} \in L^2$ by (9b).

10 **Remark** It is important to note that Theorems (1), (5), and (11) assume that the memoryless nonlinearity is *time invariant*. If arbitrary time variations are introduced while still obeying the sector conditions (say, as in the circle criterion), one can show by examples that instability results for some chosen $\phi(\sigma, t)$ and some chosen inputs.

Case III g includes an integrator and $\phi \in$ sector$[\varepsilon, k + \varepsilon]$ for some small *positive* ε.

11 **Theorem** Let ϕ be continuous, $\phi: \mathbb{R} \to \mathbb{R}$, and $\phi \in$ sector$[\varepsilon, k + \varepsilon]$ for some sufficiently small *positive* ε. Let

$$g(t) = r + g_1(t)$$

with the constant $r > 0$; $\dot{g}_1 \in \mathscr{A}$, $g_1 \in L^1(\mathbb{R}_+)$. Assume that, for the system of Fig. VI.4, $u_1, \dot{u}_1 \in L_e^2$ implies $e_1, e_2 \in L_e^2$. U.t.c., if there is a $q > 0$ such that for some $\delta > 0$

12
$$\mathrm{Re}[(1 + qj\omega)\hat{g}_\varepsilon(j\omega)] + 1/k \geq \delta, \qquad \forall \omega \geq 0$$

where

$$\hat{g}_\varepsilon(j\omega) = \hat{g}(j\omega)[1 + \varepsilon\hat{g}(j\omega)]^{-1}$$

and if $u_1, \dot{u}_1 \in L^2$, then $e_1, \dot{e}_1, e_2 \in L^2$; $e_1, e_2 \in L^\infty$ and go to zero as $t \to \infty$.

Proof Since $r > 0$, for $\varepsilon > 0$ sufficiently small, $[1 + \varepsilon\hat{g}(s)]^{-1} \in \hat{\mathscr{A}}$. Consequently, $\hat{g}_\varepsilon(s)$ and $s\hat{g}_\varepsilon(s) \in \hat{\mathscr{A}}$ [Theorem (IV.4.10)]. Hence $\omega \mapsto (1 + qj\omega)\hat{g}_\varepsilon(j\omega)$ represents a continuous linear operator (finite gain). Starting with the system of Fig. VI.4 by a feedback of ε around $\hat{g}$, we change $\hat{g}$ to $\hat{g}_\varepsilon$ [see (13)] and by a feedforward of ε around ϕ we replace ϕ by

$$\phi_\varepsilon(e_1) = \phi(e_1) - \varepsilon e_1$$

Thus, ϕ_ε belongs to the sector $[0, k]$. Thus, with g_ε and ϕ_ε satisfying these properties, we are back to the previous case. ∎

14 **Remark** In Theorems (1), (5), and (11), the linearity of the subsystem $\hat{g}$ was never used in the proofs; what was used repeatedly was that the transfer function $(1 + qs)\hat{g}(s)$ represents a system with finite gain and the appropriate passivity properties [as in (2), (6), or (12)].

Extensions of the Popov criterion to multi-input multi-output systems are quite easy. The basic principle is illustrated by the following theorem.

15 **Theorem** Consider the system described by

16
$$e_1 = u_1 - He_2$$

17
$$e_2 = \phi(e_1)$$

where u_1, e_1, and e_2 map $\mathbb{R}_+$ into $\mathbb{R}^n$. Let $\phi: \mathbb{R}^n \to \mathbb{R}^n$, $\phi(0) = 0$ and be continuous. Let $P, Q \in \mathbb{R}^{n \times n}$ and s.t. the zeros of $s \mapsto \det(P + sQ)$ are in the open left half-plane. For some symmetric positive definite $K \in \mathbb{R}^{n \times n}$, let

18
$$(P\xi)'\phi(\xi) \geq \phi(\xi)'K\phi(\xi), \qquad \forall \xi \in \mathbb{R}^n$$

and let there exist a scalar function $V \in C^1$, $V: \mathbb{R}^n \to \mathbb{R}_+$ s.t.

19
$$\phi(e)'Q = \nabla V(e), \qquad \forall e \in \mathbb{R}^n$$

Let H and DH map L_{ne}^2 into L_{ne}^2.† Assume that u_1, $\dot{u}_1 \in L_n^2$ imply that e_1, $e_2 \in L_{ne}^2$. U.t.c., if there is a $\delta > 0$ s.t.

21 $$\langle (P + QD)Hx + Kx | x \rangle_T \geq \delta \|x\|_T^2, \qquad \forall x \in L_{ne}^2, \quad \forall T \in \mathbb{R}_+$$

then

$$u_1, \dot{u}_1 \in L_n^2 \qquad \text{imply that} \quad e_2 = \phi(e_1) \in L_n^2$$

If, in addition, H and DH map L_n^2 into L_n^2, then e_1, $Q\dot{e}_1 \in L_n^2$; with Q nonsingular, e_1, $e_2 \in L_n^\infty$ and go to zero as $t \to \infty$.

Proof in Outline Introduce the multipliers $P + QD$ and $(P + QD)^{-1}$ and the feedback and feedforward of gain K. The result is Fig. VI.6. The operator

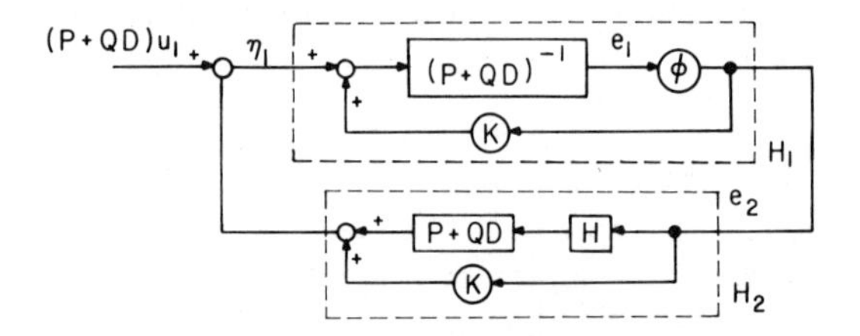

Figure VI.6

H_1 is passive since

22 $$\langle \eta_1 | H_1 \eta_1 \rangle_T = \langle Pe_1 + Q\dot{e}_1 - K\phi(e_1) | \phi(e_1) \rangle_T$$
$$= \int_0^T [Pe_1 - K\phi(e_1)]'\phi(e_1)\, dt + \int_0^T \phi(e_1)'Q\dot{e}_1\, dt$$

The first term is nonnegative by the sector condition (18). The second term can be integrated

$$\int_0^T \phi(e_1)'Q\dot{e}_1\, dt = \int_{e_1(0)}^{e_1(T)} \phi(\xi)'Q\, d\xi = V[e_1(T)] - V[e_1(0)]$$

Since $V(\xi) \geq 0$, $\forall \xi \in \mathbb{R}^n$, we conclude from (22) that H_1 is passive. Now assumption (21) simply states that H_2, shown in Fig. VI.6, is strictly passive. Hence by Theorem (5.1), u_1, $\dot{u}_1 \in L_n^2$ imply that $e_2 = \phi(e_1) \in L_n^2$. With the additional assumption that H and DH map L_n^2 into L_n^2, we have He_2 and $DHe_2 \in L_n^2$. Hence

$$\eta_1 = (P + QD)u_1 - H_2 e_2 \in L_n^2$$

† DH denotes the map that sends x into $(d/dt)[(Hx)(t)]$.

Now since $(P + sQ)^{-1}$ is an exponentially stable matrix transfer function,

$$e_1 = (P + QD)^{-1}(\eta_1 + Ke_2) \in L_n^{\ 2}$$

Finally,

$$Pe_1 + Q\dot{e}_1 = \eta_1 + Ke_2 \in L_n^{\ 2}$$

from which we obtain $Q\dot{e}_1 \in L_n^{\ 2}$. Thus, with Q nonsingular, we have e_1, $\dot{e}_1 \in L_n^{\ 2}$ so that $e_1 \in L_n^{\ \infty}$ and $|e_1(t)| \to 0$ as $t \to \infty$. The same holds for e_2 because (18) implies that

$$|e_1(t)| \, \|P\| \, |\phi[e_1(t)]| \geq |\phi[e_1(t)]|^2 \, \lambda_{\min}(K), \qquad \forall t \geq 0$$

where $\lambda_{\min}(K)$ denotes the least eigenvalue of K, which is positive since K is positive definite. ∎

Exercise Write down a formal proof of Theorem (15) in the style of Comment (8).

7 Discrete-time case

The techniques required for the discrete-time case are somewhat different. For simplicity, we consider below the single-input–single-output case. Thus, e_1, e_2, y_1, and y_2 map $\mathbb{Z}_+$ into $\mathbb{R}$ and

1
$$\|e\|_N^{\ 2} = \sum_0^N e(n)^2$$

$$\langle e \,|\, \phi(e) \rangle_N = \sum_0^N e(n)\phi[e(n)]$$

Instead of having a differential operator, we have the difference operator

2
$$(\nabla e)(n) = e(n) - e(n-1) \qquad \text{(backward difference)}$$

or

3
$$(\Delta e)(n) = e(n+1) - e(n) \qquad \text{(forward difference)}$$

Similarly,

$$(\nabla Gx)(n) = (Gx)(n) - (Gx)(n-1)$$

4 **Remark** The discrete-time problem has some features that make it much simpler than the continuous-time problem. For example, if $x = [x(0), x(1), x(2), \ldots] \in l^2$, then *necessarily* $x \in l^\infty$ and $x(n) \to 0$ as $n \to \infty$.

5 **Theorem** Consider a system where u_1, e_1, e_2, y_1, and y_2 map $\mathbb{Z}_+ \to \mathbb{R}$ and

$$e_1 = u_1 - Ge_2 \tag{6}$$

$$e_2 = \phi(e_1) \tag{7}$$

Let $\phi\colon \mathbb{R} \to \mathbb{R}$ belong to the sector $[\alpha, \beta]$ with $0 \leq \alpha \leq \beta$. Let G be causal and map $l_e^2 \to l_e^2$. Suppose that for some $q \geq 0$, there is a $\delta > 0$ such that

$$\langle (G + q\,\nabla G + 1/\beta)x \,|\, x\rangle_N \geq \delta\langle x \,|\, x\rangle_N, \qquad \forall x \in l_e^2, \quad \forall N \in \mathbb{Z}_+ \tag{8}$$

(a) U.t.c., if $\alpha > 0$ and if

$$\delta - (q\beta/4\alpha^2) > 0 \tag{9}$$

then $u_1 \in l^2$ implies that $e_1, e_2 \in l^2$.

(b) U.t.c., if $\phi \in$ sector $[0, \beta]$ and is *monotonically increasing* and if G has finite gain, i.e., $\exists\ \gamma\,(G) \in \mathbb{R}$ s.t.

$$\|Gx\|_N \leq \gamma(G)\|x\|_N, \qquad \forall x \in l_e^2, \quad \forall N \in \mathbb{Z}_+ \tag{10}$$

then $u_1 \in l^2$ implies that $e_1, e_2 \in l^2$.

Proof (a) We have

$$u_1 = e_1 + G\phi(e_1)$$

Hence

$$\nabla u_1 = \nabla e_1 + \nabla G\ \phi(e_1)$$

and, for all $N \in \mathbb{Z}_+$,

$$\langle u_1 + q\ \nabla u_1 \,|\, \phi(e_1)\rangle_N = \left\langle e_1 - \frac{\phi(e_1)}{\beta} \,\middle|\, \phi(e_1)\right\rangle_N + \left\langle \left(G + q\ \nabla G + \frac{1}{\beta}\right)\phi(e_1) \,\middle|\, \phi(e_1)\right\rangle_N + q\langle \nabla e_1 \,|\, \phi(e_1)\rangle_N \tag{15}$$

By the first sector condition, the first term is nonnegative. Now

$$\begin{aligned} \langle \nabla e_1 \,|\, \phi(e_1)\rangle_N &= \sum_0^N \phi[e_1(n)][e_1(n) - e_1(n-1)] \\ &= \sum_0^N \frac{\phi[e_1(n)]}{e_1(n)}\left[e_1(n) - \frac{1}{2}e_1(n-1)\right]^2 - \frac{1}{4}\sum_0^N \frac{\phi[e_1(n)]}{e_1(n)}\, e_1(n-1)^2 \\ &\geq -\frac{\beta}{4}\|e_1\|_N^2 \end{aligned} \tag{16}$$

Since $q \geq 0$, we obtain from (15)

17 $$|\langle u_1 + q\nabla u_1 \,|\, \phi(e_1)\rangle_N \geq \left\langle \left(G + q\nabla G + \frac{1}{\beta}\right)\phi(e_1) \,|\, \phi(e_1)\right\rangle - \frac{q\beta}{4}\|e_1\|_N{}^2$$

Noting that $\|\nabla u_1\| \leq 2\|u_1\|$ and using Schwarz's inequality, we obtain

18 $$(1 + 2q)\|u_1\| \; \|\phi(e_1)\|_N \geq \left(\delta - \frac{q\beta}{4\alpha^2}\right)\|\phi(e_1)\|_N, \qquad \forall N$$

Hence

19 $$\|\phi(e_1)\| \leq (1 + 2q)\|u_1\|\left(\delta - \frac{q\beta}{4\alpha^2}\right)^{-1}; \qquad \text{hence} \quad \phi(e_1) \in l^2$$

We also have $e_1 \in l^2$ since $\|e_1\|^2 \leq \|\phi(e_1)\|^2/\alpha^2$.

(b) Now ϕ belongs to the sector $[0, \beta]$, but ϕ is monotonically increasing (i.e., $(\sigma_1 - \sigma_2)[\phi(\sigma_1) - \phi(\sigma_2)] \geq 0$, $\forall \sigma_1, \sigma_2 \in \mathbb{R}$). As before, we have (15). The estimate in (16) is different:

22 $$\begin{aligned}\langle \nabla e_1 \,|\, \phi(e_1)\rangle_N &= \sum_0^N \phi[e_1(n)][e_1(n) - e_1(n-1)] \\ &\geq \sum_{n=0}^N \int_{e_1(n-1)}^{e_1(n)} \phi(\sigma)\, d\sigma = \int_0^{e_1(N)} \phi(\sigma)\, d\sigma \\ &= \Phi[e_1(N)] \geq 0, \qquad \forall N\end{aligned}$$

Note that we used the fact that $e_1(-1) = 0$. Thus, in this case, the last term in (17) drops out, and (18) becomes

23 $$(1 + 2q)\|u_1\| \; \|\phi(e_1)\|_N \geq \delta\|\phi(e_1)\|_N{}^2, \qquad \forall N$$

hence, letting $N \to \infty$, $\|\phi(e_1)\| \leq \|u_1\|(1 + 2q)/\delta$. Since G has finite gain,

24 $$\|e_2\| = \|G\phi(e_1)\| \leq \gamma(G)\|\phi(e_1)\| < \infty$$ ∎

26 **Remarks** (I) The theorem does not require that the subsystem G be linear or *time invariant*.

(II) The derivations could just as well have been carried out using the forward difference operator (3) rather than the backward difference operator (2). Slight modifications are required.

27 **Corollary** If the operator G is linear and time invariant and, in particular, is a convolution operator whose impulse response $(g_0, g_1, g_2, \ldots) \in \ell^2$ and has a z transform $\tilde{g}(z)$ which is bounded on the unit circle ($|z| = 1$), then

condition (8) can be checked by considering the graph of $\theta \mapsto \tilde{g}(e^{j\theta})$ in the complex plane (here θ varies from 0 to π). Indeed, condition (8) becomes

$$\mathrm{Re}[1 + q(1 - z^{-1})]\tilde{g}(z) + (1/\beta) \geq \delta, \qquad \text{for} \quad z = e^{j\theta}, \quad 0 \leq \theta \leq \pi$$

Recall that if $\tilde{e}(z) = \mathscr{Z}[e(\cdot)]$ is the z transform of the sequence $\{e(0), e(1), e(2), \ldots\}$, then $z^{-1}\tilde{e}(z)$ is the z transform of the sequence $\{0, e(0), e(1), e(2), \ldots\}$.

8 Average logarithmic variation criterion

The average logarithmic variation criterion is a general L^2-stability result concerning a linear time-varying system shown in Fig. VI.7(a). The interesting

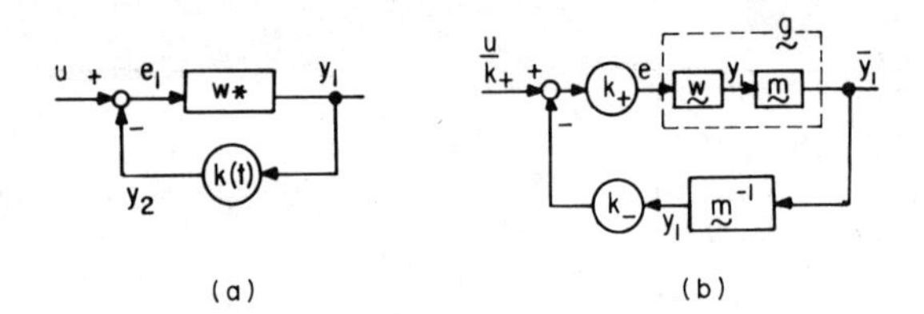

Figure VI.7

feature of this criterion is that it puts a condition on the *average* rate of *increase* of the logarithm of the feedback gain $k(t)$ and on the shifted Nyquist diagram of $\hat{w}$. Although the technique of proof requires the construction of multipliers, the L^2-stability conditions do not.

Description of the system and assumptions

The two subsystems are described by

1 $$y_1 = w * e_1 \qquad y_2(t) = k(t)y_1(t)$$
$$e_1 = u - y_2$$

where u, e_1, y_1, and y_2 map $\mathbb{R}_+$ into $\mathbb{R}$, and

2 $$w(t) = w_0\,\delta(t) + w_a(t)$$

with $w_0 \in \mathbb{R}$ and for some $\sigma_0 \in \mathbb{R}$, $t \mapsto w_a(t)\exp(\sigma_0 t) \in L^1(\mathbb{R}_+)$;

3 $$k(\cdot) \in \mathscr{K}$$

where $\mathscr{K} = \{f\colon \mathbb{R}_+ \to \mathbb{R} \mid f$ absolutely continuous and $0 < \inf_t f(t) \leq \sup_t f(t) < \infty\}$.

4 $\hat{w}(\cdot) \triangleq \mathscr{L}[w]$ can be continued analytically so that it is an analytic function in $\mathrm{Re}\, s > -\sigma_c$ for some $\sigma_c > 0$.

5 For all $u \in L^2$, e_1 and $y_1 \in L_e^{\,2}$.

6 Let $\sigma_{\text{sh}} \in (0, \sigma_c)$, then the complex-plane curve $\omega \mapsto \hat{w}(j\omega - \sigma_{\text{sh}})$, $\omega \in \mathbb{R}$, together with the point $(w_0, 0)$, is called the σ_{sh}**-shifted Nyquist diagram** of $\hat{w}$. Assume that $\omega \mapsto \hat{w}(j\omega - \sigma_{\text{sh}}) \to w_0$ as $\omega \to \infty$.

Notation The operator $e_1 \mapsto w * e_1$ is denoted by $\mathbf{w}$; thus, w is the kernel (or impulse response) of $\mathbf{w}$, and $\hat{w}$ denotes the corresponding transfer function.

Exercise 1 Assumption (5) is very mild:

(a) Suppose that for some $t' \in \mathbb{R}_+$, $1 + w_0 k(t') = 0$; what effect does it have on the existence of a solution?

(b) Give condition on w_0 and $k(\cdot)$ that guarantee the existence and uniqueness of the solution.

8 **Theorem** For the system shown in Fig. VI.7(a), let assumptions (1) to (5) hold. U.t.c., if the σ_{sh}-shifted Nyquist diagram of $\hat{w}$ does not intersect the negative real axis (i.e., $\{z \in \mathbb{C} \mid \text{Re } z \le 0, \text{ Im } z = 0\}$) and if for some $T > 0$ and some $r \ge 0$

10
$$\sup_{t \ge 0}(1/T) \int_t^{t+T} [(d/d\tau) \log k(\tau)]^+ \, d\tau \le 2r < 2\sigma_{\text{sh}}$$

(where we use the notation $[f(\tau)]^+ \triangleq \max[f(\tau), 0]$), then the system is L^2 stable.

The method of proof consists in two steps: first, a factorization of the gain $k(\cdot)$ and the introduction of a "multiplier" $\mathbf{m}$, second, the use of the passivity theorem (5.10) and of Example 7, Section 4. The multiplier $\mathbf{m}$ is a causal convolution operator on $L_e^{\,2}$ defined by its transfer function $\hat{m}(\cdot)$ with the property that $\mathbf{m}$ and $\mathbf{m}^{-1}$, restricted to L^2, have finite gains.

We start by proving a factorization lemma for $k(\cdot)$.

12 **Lemma** If $k(\cdot) \in \mathscr{K}$ and satisfies (10), then there are two functions $k_+(\cdot)$ and $k_-(\cdot)$ such that

13 (i)
$$k(t) = k_+(t)k_-(t)$$

14 (ii) k_+ and k_- are bounded away from zero and bounded on $\mathbb{R}_+$;

15 (iii)
$$k_+(t)\exp(2rt) \text{ is} \nearrow$$

16
$$k_-(t)\exp(-2rt) \text{ is} \searrow$$

The multiplier $\mathbf{m}$ is constructed by the following lemma.

18 **Lemma** Given that $\hat{w}$ satisfies assumptions (2) and (4) with $w_0 > 0$, and the shifted Nyquist diagram condition of Theorem (8), there exists a causal convolution operator **m** such that $\hat{m}$ is analytic in Re $s > -\sigma_{sh}$ with $t \mapsto m(t)\exp(\sigma_{sh} t) \in \mathscr{A}$ and $\hat{m}(s) \to 1$ as $|s| \to \infty$; furthermore, for some δ_1, $\delta_2 > 0$

$$\mathrm{Re}[\hat{m}(j\omega - \sigma_{sh})] \geq \delta_1 > 0 \tag{19}$$

$$\mathrm{Re}[\hat{m}(j\omega - \sigma_{sh})\hat{w}(j\omega - \sigma_{sh})] \geq \delta_2 > 0 \tag{20}$$

for all $\omega \in \mathbb{R}$; finally, $\hat{m}(s)^{-1}$ is analytic in Re $s > -\sigma_{sh}$ and bounded in Re $s \geq -\sigma_{sh}$.

21 **Comments** It follows from Lemma (18) that the operators **m** and $\mathbf{m}^{-1}$, when restricted to L^2, have finite gains; indeed, since $\sigma_{sh} > 0$, $\omega \mapsto \hat{m}(j\omega)$ and $\omega \mapsto [\hat{m}(j\omega)]^{-1}$ are bounded on $\mathbb{R}$.

Exercise Show that if $w_0 = 0$, by the loop transformation theorem, one can transform the system to one where $w_0 > 0$, though possibly very small.

We shall prove Lemmas (12) and (18) later. Using these lemmas, we prove now Theorem (8).

Proof of Theorem (8) Refer to Fig. VI.7(a) and (b). In view of the properties of k_+, k_-, **m**, and $\mathbf{m}^{-1}$, the system shown in (a) is L^2 stable if and only if the system shown in (b) is L^2 stable. Now the forward loop gain, $\mathbf{mwk}_+ \triangleq \mathbf{gk}_+$, is strictly passive and has finite gain. Indeed, we can show that the assumptions of Example 8, Section 4 are satisfied; consider (10), (15), and (20). Furthermore, $\hat{m}(s)\hat{w}(s)$ is analytic in Re $s > -\sigma_{sh} < 0$ and tends to $w_0 > 0$ as $|s| \to \infty$; therefore, we have $\mathrm{Re}[\hat{m}(j\omega)\hat{w}(j\omega)] \geq \delta_2 > 0$, $\forall \omega \in \mathbb{R}$, because the real part of an analytic function reaches its minimum on the boundary of its domain of analyticity.

The feedback gain $\mathbf{k}_-\mathbf{m}^{-1}$ is strictly passive. Indeed, the assumptions of Example 7, Section 4 are satisfied; see (16) and the fact that $\hat{m}(s)^{-1}$ is analytic together with (19). Thus, the L^2 stability of the system (b) follows by the passivity theorem (5.10). ∎

Proof of the Factorization Lemma (12) Let $l(t) = \log k(t)$. Since $k \in \mathscr{K}$, $l: \mathbb{R}_+ \to \mathbb{R}$ is bounded. Consider the triangular weighting function

$$\mu(t) = \begin{cases} 1 - t/T, & 0 < t \leq T \\ 0, & \text{elsewhere} \end{cases}$$

Note that $\dot{\mu}(t) = \delta(t) - [1(t) - 1(t - T)]/T$, where $1(t)$ is the unit step. Define

$$l_+(t) \triangleq \int_0^t [\dot{l}(\tau)]^+ \mu(t - \tau)\, d\tau \tag{24}$$

and

25 $$l_-(t) \triangleq l(t) - l_+(t)$$

By (10) we see that l_+ is bounded on $\mathbb{R}_+$; in fact,

26 $$0 \leq l_+(t) \leq 2rT, \qquad \forall t \geq 0$$

And, since l is bounded by assumption, l_- is also bounded. Consequently, $k_+ \triangleq \exp l_+$ and $k_- \triangleq \exp l_-$ are bounded away from zero and bounded on $\mathbb{R}_+$. Finally, by (25), $k(t) = k_+(t)k_-(t)$, $\forall t \geq 0$. This establishes (i) and (ii).

Differentiate (24) to obtain

$$\dot{l}_+(T) = [\dot{l}(t)]^+ - \int_0^t [\dot{l}(\tau)]^+(1/T)[1(t-\tau) - 1(t-\tau-T)]\, d\tau$$

Since the first term is nonnegative and since (10) bounds the integral by $2r$, we obtain

$$\dot{l}_+(t) \geq -2r, \qquad \text{equivalently} \quad k_+(t)\exp 2rt \nearrow$$

Similarly, from (25) we show that

$$\dot{l}_-(t) \leq 2r, \qquad \forall t \geq 0$$

∎

It remains to construct the causal convolution operator **m**. We first establish a technique to construct a causal convolution operator with prescribed phase.

30 **Lemma** We are given a phase characteristic $\omega \mapsto \hat{\phi}_0(j\omega)$, $\omega \in \mathbb{R}$, which is odd, i.e., differentiable, and such that $\hat{\phi}_0$ and its derivative $\hat{\phi}_0'$ are in $L^2(\mathbb{R})$. U.t.c.,

(i) there cxists a function $\lambda \in L^1(\mathbb{R})$ with $\lambda(t) = 0$ for $t < 0$ and

31 $$\text{Im } \hat{\lambda}(j\omega) = \hat{\phi}_0(j\omega)$$

(ii) there exists a function $z \in L^1(\mathbb{R})$ with $z(t) = 0$ for $t < 0$ and

32 $$1 + \hat{z}(j\omega) = \exp[\hat{\lambda}(j\omega)]$$

(iii) if, in addition, $-\pi < \hat{\phi}_0(j\omega) < \pi$, for all $\omega \in \mathbb{R}$, then

33 $$\arg[1 + \hat{z}(j\omega)] = \hat{\phi}_0(j\omega) \qquad \text{and} \qquad 1 + \hat{z}(s) \neq 0, \qquad \text{for} \quad \text{Re } s \geq 0$$

Exercise Show that $\hat{\phi}_0$, $\hat{\phi}_0' \in L^2$ imply that $\hat{\phi}_0$ is in L^∞, is uniformly continuous, and $\to 0$ as $|\omega| \to \infty$. (*Hint*: Think of Riemann–Lebesgue.)

Proof (i) Since $\hat{\phi}_0$ is in L^2, it has an inverse Fourier transform which is also in L^2:

$$\phi_0(t) \triangleq (1/2\pi) \operatorname*{l.i.m.}_{\Omega \to \infty} \int_{-\Omega}^{+\Omega} j\hat{\phi}_0(j\omega)\exp(j\omega t)\, d\omega$$

and since $\hat{\phi}_0$ and $\hat{\phi}_0{}'$ are in L^2, $\phi_0 \in L^1(\mathbb{R})$. (See Appendix B.2.5.) Since $t \to \phi_0(t)$ is odd, consider the *even* function

$$\phi_e(t) \triangleq \phi_0(t) \operatorname{sgn} t$$

ϕ_e is even, $\in L^1(\mathbb{R})$, and $\hat{\phi}_e(j\omega)$ is real for all ω. Let $\lambda(t) \triangleq \phi_e(t) + \phi_0(t)$; then $\lambda \in L^1(\mathbb{R})$, $\lambda(t) = 0$ for $t < 0$ and (31) holds. Also $\hat{\lambda}(s)$ is analytic and bounded in $\operatorname{Re} s \geq 0$.

(ii) Note that

$$\exp[\hat{\lambda}(j\omega)] = \exp[\hat{\phi}_e(j\omega)] \cdot \exp[j\hat{\phi}_0(j\omega)] \tag{36}$$

and

$$\exp[\hat{\lambda}(s)] = \sum_0^\infty [\hat{\lambda}(s)]^n/n! \triangleq 1 + \hat{z}(s) \tag{37}$$

In the time domain

$$z(t) = \lambda(t) + (\lambda * \lambda)(t) + \cdots + (\lambda * \lambda * \cdots * \lambda)(t)/n! + \cdots \tag{38}$$

Since $\lambda \in L^1(\mathbb{R})$ and since $\|\lambda * \lambda\|_1 \leq \|\lambda\|_1 \cdot \|\lambda\|_1$ it is clear that the series in (38) converges in the L^1 norm and that $\|z\|_1 \leq \exp(\|\lambda\|_1) - 1$. Since $L^1(\mathbb{R})$ is complete, $z \in L^1(\mathbb{R})$. Also, $z(t) = 0$ for $t < 0$, by (38).

(iii) If $-\pi < \hat{\phi}_0(j\omega) < \pi$, we may take the logarithm of (36) (since we avoid crossing the branch cut on the negative real axis), and

$$\arg[1 + \hat{z}(j\omega)] = \hat{\phi}_0(j\omega), \qquad \forall \omega \in \mathbb{R}$$

Since $\hat{\lambda}$ is analytic and bounded in $\operatorname{Re} s \geq 0$, by (37), $1 + \hat{z}(s)$ is bounded away from zero in $\operatorname{Re} s \geq 0$ by $\exp(-\|\lambda\|_1)$. ∎

Lemma (30) shows us how to construct, on the basis of the phase $\hat{\phi}_0$, a function $1 + \hat{z}$ such that itself and its inverse are analytic in $\operatorname{Re} s > 0$ and bounded in $\operatorname{Re} s \geq 0$. We now use this result to construct the multiplier $\mathbf{m}$.

Proof of Lemma (18) (I) By assumption (2), $\hat{w}$ is analytic in $\operatorname{Re} s \geq -\sigma_{\text{sh}} > -\sigma_c$. By assumption, $\hat{w}(j\omega - \sigma_{\text{sh}}) \neq 0$, $\forall \omega \in \mathbb{R}$; hence $\log[\hat{w}(j\omega - \sigma_{\text{sh}})]$ is analytic for all $\omega \in \mathbb{R}$. Therefore, $\arg \hat{w}(j\omega - \sigma_{\text{sh}})$ is well defined (in view of the properties of the Nyquist diagram) and is a C^∞ function of ω on $\mathbb{R}$. Also, $\arg \hat{w}(j\omega - \sigma_{\text{sh}}) \to 0$ as $|\omega| \to \infty$ since, by (6), $\hat{w}(j\omega - \sigma_{\text{sh}}) \to w_0 > 0$ as $|\omega| \to \infty$. To specify $\hat{\phi}_0$, choose a frequency Ω large enough so that $|\arg \hat{w}(j\omega - \sigma_{\text{sh}})|$ is small for all $|\omega| > \Omega$, say, smaller than $\pi/12$; then

$$\hat{\phi}_0(j\omega) \triangleq \begin{cases} -\frac{1}{2}\arg[\hat{w}(j\omega - \sigma_{\text{sh}})], & \text{for } |\omega| \leq \Omega \\ c\Omega/\omega, & \text{for } |\omega| > \Omega \end{cases} \tag{41}$$

where $c \in \mathbb{R}$ is chosen so that $\hat{\phi}_0$ is continuous. In view of the properties of the Nyquist diagram and by construction, (41), we have

$$|\hat{\phi}_0(j\omega)| < \pi/2 \qquad \text{and} \qquad |\hat{\phi}_0(j\omega) + \arg[\hat{w}(j\omega - \sigma_{sh})]| < \pi/2$$

for all $\omega \in \mathbb{R}$.

Clearly, by (41), $\hat{\phi}_0, \hat{\phi}_0' \in L^2$. ($\hat{\phi}_0'$ is well defined on $\mathbb{R}$ except at $|\omega| = \Omega$, where it may have a jump.)

By Lemma (30) there is a $\hat{z}(s)$ with the properties (33). Let

$$\hat{m}(s) = \int_0^\infty [\delta(t) + z(t)\exp(-\sigma_{sh} t)] \exp(-st)\, dt = 1 + \hat{z}(s + \sigma_{sh}) \tag{44}$$

From (41), (44), and the properties of $\hat{z}$, it follows that

(I) $\hat{m}(s)$ and $\hat{m}(s)^{-1}$ are analytic and bounded in $\operatorname{Re} s \geq 0$;

(II) the functions $\omega \mapsto \hat{m}(j\omega - \sigma_{sh})$, $\omega \mapsto \hat{m}(j\omega - \sigma_{sh})\hat{w}(j\omega - \sigma_{sh})$ are uniformly continuous on $\mathbb{R}$, have phases in $(-\pi/2, \pi/2)$, and as $|\omega| \to \infty$, they tend to 1 and $w_0 > 0$, resp. Therefore, the existence of δ_1 and δ_2 in (19) and (20) is established. ∎

This concludes the proof of the logarithmic variation criterion.

9 Multiplier theory

The basic idea behind the multiplier technique is that by multiplying certain operators by appropriately chosen "multipliers," the product can be doctored to satisfy the conditions of the passivity theorem. For example, $u \mapsto g * u$ is passive if and only if $\operatorname{Re}[\hat{g}(j\omega)] \geq 0$ for all ω; i.e., the Nyquist diagram of $\hat{g}$ lies in the right half-plane. In the Popov criterion, the multiplier $1 + qs = \hat{m}(s)$ is introduced and, consequently, $\operatorname{Re}[(1 + qj\omega)\hat{g}(j\omega)]$ is required to be nonnegative; i.e., the curve $\omega \mapsto [\hat{g}_r(j\omega), \omega\hat{g}_i(j\omega)]$ must lie below the line of slope $1/q$ through the origin. Thus, for convolution operators we can think of the multiplier as a device which makes $\hat{g}(s)$ look passive by having the phase of $\hat{m}(j\omega)\hat{g}(j\omega)$ remain in $(-\pi/2, \pi/2)$. If the multiplier $\hat{m}(s)$ is rational and causal and if $u \mapsto m * u$ maps $L^2(\mathbb{R})$ into $L^2(\mathbb{R})$, then m may not have poles in the closed right half-plane. This last requirement severely constrains the choice of the phase. If, for this reason, we let $\hat{m}(s)$ have right-half-plane poles and if we require $u \mapsto m * u$ to map $L^2(\mathbb{R})$ into $L^2(\mathbb{R})$, then in order to calculate the kernel $t \mapsto m(t)$ from $\hat{m}(\cdot)$ we have to choose the $j\omega$ axis as the path of integration in the calculation of the inverse Laplace transform. Then, as a consequence, $t \mapsto m(t)$ is not identically zero for $t < 0$; i.e., the multiplier is *noncausal*.

Since we shall allow noncausal multipliers throughout, we start by examining some of the consequences of noncausality.

9.1 Causal and anticausal operators

Throughout this section, let $\mathscr{H}$ be a Hilbert space over the field $\mathbb{R}$ with scalar product denoted by $\langle \cdot | \cdot \rangle$. Consequently, $(x, y) \mapsto \langle x | y \rangle$ is a bilinear map. Typically, $\mathscr{H}$ will be $L^2(\mathbb{R})$, $L_n^2(\mathbb{R})$, l^2, or l_n^2. Let H map either $\mathscr{H}$ into itself or $\mathscr{H}_e$ into itself. Recall that H is said to be **causal** (or, equivalently, nonanticipative) iff $P_T x = P_T y$ implies that $P_T Hx = P_T Hy$, $\forall x, y \in \mathscr{H}$ (or $\mathscr{H}_e$), $\forall T \in \mathscr{T}$. This condition can also be written $P_T H = P_T H P_T$, $\forall T \in \mathscr{T}$. Thus, for *causal* operators, *past* outputs depend only on *past* inputs. Recall also that if H is causal and if $H: \mathscr{H} \to \mathscr{H}$, then H can be extended into a map, also denoted by H, which maps $\mathscr{H}_e$ into $\mathscr{H}_e$; the extended map is defined by the relation $P_T Hx \triangleq P_T H P_T x$, $\forall x \in \mathscr{H}_e$, $\forall T \in \mathscr{T}$. Note that if $x \in \mathscr{H}_e$, $P_T x \in \mathscr{H}$ so that $HP_T x$ is well defined. Finally, as with the term nonlinear, we say *noncausal* when we mean *not necessarily causal.*

1 The map $H: \mathscr{H} \to \mathscr{H}$ is said to be **anticausal** iff $(I - P_T)x = (I - P_T)y$ implies $(I - P_T)Hx = (I - P_T)H(I - P_T)y$, $\forall x, y \in \mathscr{H}$, $\forall T \in \mathbb{R}$; equivalently, $(I - P_T)H = (I - P_T)H(I - P_T)$, $\forall T \in \mathscr{T}$. Thus, for *anticausal* maps, *future* outputs depend only on *future* inputs.

Exercise 1 Let $H: u \to h * u$, where $h \in L^1(\mathbb{R})$, $u \in L^2(\mathbb{R})$. Give conditions on h so that H is (a) causal, (b) anticausal, (c) neither causal nor anticausal.

The presence of noncausal operators (as a result of introducing noncausal multipliers) creates some difficulties in the application of Fourier techniques to demonstrate passivity. The following lemma and exercise exhibit useful facts.

2 **Lemma** Let $H: \mathscr{H} \to \mathscr{H}$ and be *causal.* U.t.c.,

3 $$\{\exists \delta \geq 0 \text{ s.t. } \langle x | Hx \rangle \geq \delta \|x\|^2, \ \forall x \in \mathscr{H}\}$$

if and only if

4 $$\{\exists \delta \geq 0 \text{ s.t. } \langle u | Hu \rangle_T \geq \delta \|u_T\|^2, \ \forall u \in \mathscr{H}_e\}$$

where the same δ can be chosen in (3) and (4).

Proof $\Rightarrow$ For any $u \in \mathscr{H}_e$ and $T \in \mathbb{R}$, $u_T \in \mathscr{H}$ and

$$\begin{aligned} \langle u | Hu \rangle_T &= \langle u_T | (Hu)_T \rangle && \text{by (3.10)} \\ &= \langle u_T | (Hu_T)_T \rangle && \text{by causality} \\ &= \langle u_T | Hu_T \rangle \\ &\geq \delta \|u_T\|^2 && \text{by (3)} \end{aligned}$$

Hence (4) holds for the same δ.

$\Leftarrow$ Let $u \in \mathscr{H}$ in (4); let $T \to \infty$ and use (3.9). ∎

The importance of the causality assumption in Lemma (2) is stressed in the following exercise.

Exercise 2 Let $H: L^2(\mathbb{R}) \to L^2(\mathbb{R})$ with $Hu = h * u$. Let $h(t) = \delta(t) + 1(t)$ $\exp(-t) + 1(-t) \exp t$, $t \in \mathbb{R}$. Show that

(a) $\text{Re}[\hat{h}(j\omega)] \geq 1$, $\forall \omega \in \mathbb{R}$;
(b) $\forall x \in L^2(\mathbb{R})$, $\langle x | h * x \rangle \geq \|x\|^2$;
(c) find some $u \in L^2$ and some $T \in \mathbb{R}$ s.t.

$$\langle u | h * u \rangle_T < 0$$

This exercise shows that when H is noncausal, it is very important to distinguish between condition (3) and condition (4). Of course, when H is causal, these conditions are equivalent. Recall that according to (4.2), $H: \mathscr{H}_e \to \mathscr{H}_e$ is said to be *passive* (*strictly passive* when $\delta > 0$) when H satisfies (4). Now let $H: \mathscr{H} \to \mathscr{H}$. When H satisfies (3) with $\delta = 0$ ($\delta > 0$, resp.), we say that H is $\mathscr{H}$ **positive** (strictly $\mathscr{H}$ **positive**, resp.). We say $\mathscr{H}$ positive to emphasize the fact that $\mathscr{H}$ positivity is tested over $\mathscr{H}$, whereas passivity is tested over $\mathscr{H}_e$. Lemma (2) says that when $H: \mathscr{H} \to \mathscr{H}$ and is causal, H is $\mathscr{H}$ positive (strictly $\mathscr{H}$ positive) if and only if H is passive (strictly passive, resp.).

5 **Remark** In the case of convolution operators, condition (3) is easily tested by Fourier methods. Condition (4) is the one required for the passivity theorem. Therefore, in certain manipulations that follow, we shall have to assure ourselves that the operators under consideration are causal.

For future reference, we must define adjoint operators.

6 Let H be linear and map $\mathscr{H}$ into $\mathscr{H}$. The map H^* defined by

7 $$\langle x | Hy \rangle = \langle H^* x | y \rangle, \qquad \forall x, y \in \mathscr{H}$$

is called the **adjoint of** H. If $H = H^*$, H is said to be **self-adjoint**.

Exercise 3 Use the bilinearity of the map $(x, y) \mapsto \langle x | y \rangle$ to show that if H, $H^*: \mathscr{H} \to \mathscr{H}$ are related by (7), then H and H^* are necessarily linear maps.

Exercise 4 Show that I and P_T are self-adjoint. Show that

$$H^{**} = H$$

8 **Lemma** Let $H: \mathscr{H} \to \mathscr{H}$ be linear. U.t.c., H is anticausal if and only if its adjoint H^* is causal.

Proof $\Rightarrow$ For all $x, y \in \mathscr{H}$, for all $T \in \mathbb{R}$, since H is anticausal

$$\langle x | (I - P_T) Hy \rangle = \langle x | (I - P_T) H (I - P_T) y \rangle$$

hence by (3.9) and the definition of the adjoint,

$$\langle H^*(I - P_T)\, x \,|\, y\rangle = \langle (I - P_T)H^*(I - P_T)\, x \,|\, y\rangle$$

Since y is arbitrary and $\mathscr{H}$ is a Hilbert space,

$$P_T\, H^*(I - P_T)x = 0, \qquad \forall x \in \mathscr{H}$$

and by linearity

$$P_T\, H^* = P_T\, H^* P_T$$

$\Leftarrow$ Retrace backward the steps of the proof above. ∎

9.2 Pattern of the noncausal multiplier technique

Keeping in mind the difficulty caused by noncausal operators, we can outline the general technique as follows.

9 **Assertion** Let $\mathscr{H}$ be a Hilbert space over the field $\mathbb{R}$. Assume that there is a multiplier M, i.e., a noncausal map $M\colon \mathscr{H} \to \mathscr{H}$. Suppose M can be factored so that

$$M = M_- M_+, \qquad M_-, M_+ \text{ mapping } \mathscr{H} \text{ into } \mathscr{H} \tag{10}$$

where M^{-1}, M_-^{-1} and M_+^{-1} are well-defined mappings from $\mathscr{H}$ into $\mathscr{H}$;

$$M_- \text{ is linear, hence } M_-^* \text{ and } (M_-^*)^{-1} \text{ well defined;} \tag{11}$$

$$M, M_+, M_-^*, \text{ and their inverses have finite gain.} \tag{12}$$

U.t.c., the L^2 stability of any one of the three feedback systems S, S_M, and S_{M+} (shown in Fig. VI.8) implies the L^2 stability of the others.

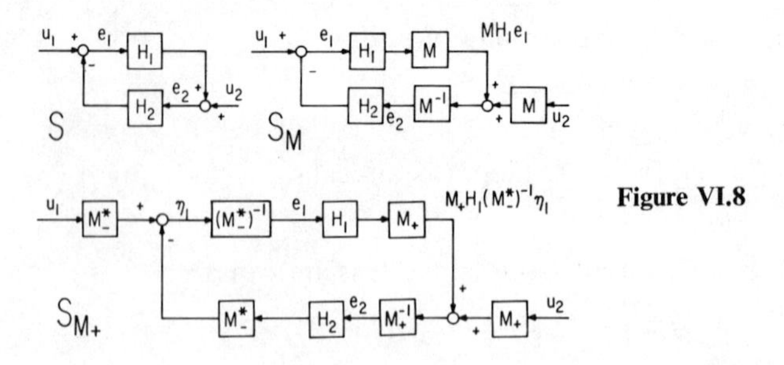

Figure VI.8

Exercise 5 Prove Assertion (9). [Use (12).]

In most applications, H_1 and H_2 are causal. Since M is noncausal, MH_1 and $H_2 M$ are noncausal. If M_+ is also causal, the operators of the feedback system S_{M+}, namely, $M_+ H_1(M_-^*)^{-1}$ and $M_-^* H_2 M_+^{-1}$, are causal. Hence in that case Lemma (2) is available to establish passivity.

The following lemma establishes an important connection between the operators MH and $M_+ H(M_-^*)^{-1}$.

15 **Lemma** Let $H: \mathscr{H} \to \mathscr{H}$ and M satisfy (10) to (12). U.t.c., the following statements are equivalent:

16 (i) $\exists \delta \geq 0$ s.t. $\langle u | MHu \rangle \geq \delta \|u\|^2, \qquad \forall u \in \mathscr{H}$

17 (ii) $\exists \delta' \geq 0$ s.t. $\langle x | M_+ H(M_-^*)^{-1} x \rangle \geq \delta' \|x\|^2, \qquad \forall x \in \mathscr{H}$

where δ and δ' are both positive or both zero.

Proof Let x and u belong to $\mathscr{H}$ and be related by $x = M_-^* u$; hence by (12) $\|x\| \leq \gamma(M_-^*)\|u\|$ and $\|u\| \leq \gamma[(M_-^*)^{-1}]\|x\|$. Therefore,

$$\langle u | MHu \rangle = \langle u | M_- M_+ Hu \rangle = \langle M_-^* u | M_+ Hu \rangle = \langle x | M_+ H(M_-^*)^{-1} x \rangle$$

The equivalence follows. ∎

From these considerations, we can state the following theorem.

20 **Theorem** Consider the system S of Fig. VI.8, where H_1 and H_2 are causal maps from $\mathscr{H}$ into $\mathscr{H}$. Suppose that for all $u_1, u_2 \in \mathscr{H}$, the solutions $e_1, e_2 \in \mathscr{H}_e$. Let there be a noncausal multiplier $M: \mathscr{H} \to \mathscr{H}$ satisfying (10), (11), and (12), and the condition that

21 $$M_+, (M_+)^{-1}, \quad M_-^*, (M_-^*)^{-1} \quad \text{are causal}$$

U.t.c., if

22 (i) $$\gamma(MH_1) < \infty$$

23 (ii) for some $\delta > 0$ $$\langle x | MH_1 x \rangle \geq \delta \|x\|^2, \qquad \forall x \in \mathscr{H}$$

24 (iii) $$\langle x | H_2 M^{-1} x \rangle \geq 0, \qquad \forall x \in \mathscr{H}$$

then S is L^2 stable.

Proof The assumptions of the passivity theorem hold for the system S_{M+}. Indeed,

25 $$\begin{aligned}\gamma[M_+ H_1(M_-^*)^{-1}] &\leq \gamma[M_- \cdot M_+ H_1(M_-^*)^{-1} M_-^*]\gamma(M_-^{-1})\gamma[(M_-^*)^{-1}] \\ &\leq \gamma(M_-^{-1}) \cdot \gamma(MH_1)\gamma[(M_-^*)^{-1}] < \infty\end{aligned}$$

where we used (22) and (12).

Applying Lemma (15) to (23) and (24) and noting the causality of the operators, we conclude that

26
$$\langle u | M_+ H_1 (M_-^*)^{-1} u \rangle_T \geq \delta' \|u\|_T^2, \qquad \forall T \in \mathbb{R}, \quad \forall u \in \mathscr{H}_e$$
$$\langle u | M_-^* H_2 M_+^{-1} u \rangle_T \geq 0 \qquad \forall T \in \mathbb{R}, \quad \forall u \in \mathscr{H}_e$$

Hence S_{M+} is L^2 stable by (5.27), and so is S by the L^2 stability equivalence established in Assertion (9). ∎

27 **Remark** Note that the operators MH_1 and $H_2 M^{-1}$ are only assumed to be $\mathscr{H}$ positive; they may or may not be passive.

Clearly, the key step in the procedure is the factorization of the multiplier M. Before developing the factorization theory, let us consider some examples. Note that in applications it is sufficient to *know* that a particular multiplier M can be factored in the manner required by Assertion (9); it is not necessary to calculate the factors M_- and M_+. The factorization theorem (62) (which is given at the end of this section) will give sufficient conditions under which the factors M_+ and M_- exist and have the required properties.

9.3 Examples

Example 1 Consider a feedback system of the form shown in Fig. III.1 and where

28
$$H_1 e_1 = g * e_1, \qquad g \in \mathscr{A}$$

29
$$(H_2 e_2)(t) = \phi[e_2(t)]$$

where $\phi: \mathbb{R} \to \mathbb{R}$, ϕ is $\nearrow$; i.e.,

30
$$[\phi(\alpha) - \phi(\beta)](\alpha - \beta) \geq 0, \qquad \forall \alpha, \beta \in \mathbb{R}$$

and for some $k < \infty$, $\phi \in$ sector $[0, k]$.

Observe that H_1 and H_2 defined by (28) and (29) are *causal* operators mapping $L_e^2(\mathbb{R})$ into $L_e^2(\mathbb{R})$.

31 **Theorem** Consider a feedback system with H_1 and H_2 satisfying (28) to (29). Suppose that there is a *noncausal* convolution operator M whose impulse response is of the form

32
$$m(t) = 1 - z(t) = 1 - \sum_{-\infty}^{+\infty} z_i \, \delta(t - t_i) - z_a(t)$$

where

33
$$\sum |z_i| < \infty, \qquad z_a(\cdot) \in L^1(\mathbb{R}) \qquad \text{and} \quad t_i \in \mathbb{R}$$

Assume that

34
$$|Z| \triangleq \sum_{-\infty}^{+\infty} |z_i| + \|z_a\|_1 < 1$$

and that there is a $\delta > 0$ such that

35
$$\mathrm{Re}[\hat{m}(j\omega)\hat{g}(j\omega)] \geq \delta > 0, \qquad \forall \omega \in \mathbb{R}$$

U.t.c., if either

36
$$z_a(\cdot) \geq 0 \qquad \text{and} \qquad z_i \geq 0, \qquad \forall i$$

or

37
$$\phi(\cdot) \text{ is an odd function}$$

then the system is L^2 stable.

38 **Remark** It follows immediately from (32) to (34) that

(a) M is a linear map;
(b) the incremental gain of M satisfies $\tilde{\gamma}(M) < 2$;
(c) M is invertible, thus $M^{-1} : L^2(\mathbb{R}) \to L^2(\mathbb{R})$, and, in fact, $\tilde{\gamma}(M^{-1}) \leq (1 - \|Z\|^{-1})$.

Proof The factorization theorem (62) establishes that the multiplier M can be factored as required. As a consequence, Theorem (31) is established if it is shown that $\gamma(MH_1) < \infty$, that the noncausal operator MH_1 is strictly $\mathscr{H}$ positive [condition (23)], and that $H_2 M^{-1}$ is $\mathscr{H}$ positive [condition (24)]. Now

$$\gamma(MH_1) \leq 2\|g\|_{\mathscr{A}} < \infty$$

(23) holds because by Parseval's theorem we have

$$\langle x | MH_1 x \rangle = (1/2\pi) \int_{-\infty}^{+\infty} \mathrm{Re}[\hat{m}(j\omega)\hat{g}(j\omega)] |\hat{x}(j\omega)|^2 \, d\omega \geq \delta \|x\|^2, \qquad \forall \in L^2(\mathbb{R})$$

The $\mathscr{H}$ positivity of $H_2 M^{-1}$ is a consequence of Lemmas (40) and (46). Hence, once the factorization is justified, the proof of Theorem (31) will be complete. ∎

0 **Lemma** If $\phi : \mathbb{R} \to \mathbb{R}$ is $\nearrow$ and belongs to some sector $[0, k]$, $k < \infty$, then, for all $x(\cdot) \in L^2(\mathbb{R})$ and all $\tau \in \mathbb{R}$,

1
$$\int_{-\infty}^{+\infty} x(t + \tau)\phi[x(t)] \, dt \leq \int_{-\infty}^{+\infty} x(t)\phi[x(t)] \, dt$$

If ϕ, in addition, is an odd function, then

2
$$\left| \int_{-\infty}^{+\infty} x(t + \tau)\phi[x(t)] \, dt \right| \leq \int_{-\infty}^{+\infty} x(t)\phi[x(t)] \, dt$$

Proof Note that $x \in L^2(\mathbb{R})$ implies that $\phi[x(\cdot)] \in L^2(\mathbb{R})$ and $\Phi[x(\cdot)] \in L^1(\mathbb{R})$, where by definition $d\Phi/dx = \phi(x)$, $\Phi(0) = 0$. Now ϕ is $\nearrow$, hence $\forall \alpha, \beta \in \mathbb{R}$

43 $$\Phi(\alpha) - \Phi(\beta) \triangleq \int_\beta^\alpha \phi(\xi)\, d\xi \leq (\alpha - \beta)\phi(\alpha) = \alpha\phi(\alpha) - \beta\phi(\alpha)$$

Letting $\alpha = x(t)$, $\beta = x(t + \tau)$, and integrating over $\mathbb{R}$, we obtain

44 $$\begin{aligned} &\int_{-\infty}^{+\infty} x(t)\phi[x(t)]\, dt - \int_{-\infty}^{+\infty} x(t+\tau)\phi[x(t)]\, dt \\ &\quad \geq \int_{-\infty}^{+\infty} \Phi[x(t)]\, dt - \int_{-\infty}^{+\infty} \Phi[x(t+\tau)]\, dt \\ &\quad = 0 \end{aligned}$$

Hence (41) follows.

Now when ϕ is odd, Φ is even, and we have, in addition to (41),

$$\begin{aligned} &\int_{-\infty}^{+\infty} \{x(t)\phi[x(t)] + x(t+\tau)\phi[x(t)]\}\, dt \\ &= \int_{-\infty}^{+\infty} (x(t)\phi[x(t)] - \{-x(t+\tau)\phi[x(t)]\})\, dt \\ &\geq \int_{-\infty}^{+\infty} \Phi[x(t)]\, dt - \int_{-\infty}^{+\infty} \Phi[-x(t+\tau)]\, dt, \qquad \text{by (43)}, \\ &= 0, \qquad \text{since } \Phi \text{ is even} \end{aligned}$$

Hence (42) follows. ∎

46 **Lemma** Let $\phi\colon \mathbb{R} \mapsto \mathbb{R}$, ϕ $\nearrow$, and $\phi \in$ sector $[0, k]$, for some $k < \infty$. Let M satisfy (32) and (33). U.t.c., if either

47 $$z_a(t) \geq 0, \qquad \forall t \in \mathbb{R}, \qquad \text{and} \qquad z_i \geq 0, \quad \forall i$$

48 $$\text{or} \quad \phi \text{ is odd}$$

then (24) holds.

Proof For convenience, let $Z\colon\; x \mapsto z * x$, $x \in L^2(\mathbb{R})$, where $z(t) = \sum z_i \delta(t - t_i) + z_a(t)$. Then $M = I - Z$. Now $\gamma(M) < 2$ and $\gamma(M^{-1}) < \infty$. Let $v \triangleq Mx$; then $v \in L^2(\mathbb{R})$ if and only if $x \in L^2(\mathbb{R})$. We obtain successively

49 $$\begin{aligned} \langle v | H_2 M^{-1} v\rangle &= \langle Mx | H_2 x\rangle, & \forall v \in L^2(\mathbb{R}) \\ &= \langle (I - Z)x | \phi[x(\cdot)]\rangle, & \forall x \in L^2(\mathbb{R}) \end{aligned}$$

and upon expansion the right-hand side becomes [all integrals are over $(-\infty, \infty)$]

$$\int x(t)\phi[x(t)]\,dt - \int (z * x)(t)\phi[x(t)]\,dt$$

$$= \int x(t)\phi[x(t)]\,dt - \sum_i z_i \int x(t - t_i)\phi[x(t)]\,dt$$

$$- \int z(\tau)\left\{\int x(t-\tau)\phi[x(t)]\,dt\right\} d\tau$$

Now by invoking Lemma (40) and either (47) or (48), we obtain

50 $$\langle v | H_2 M^{-1} v\rangle \geq (1 - \|z\|) \int x(t)\phi[x(t)]\,dt \geq 0, \qquad \forall v \in L^2(\mathbb{R})$$

where the last inequality follows from (34) and the sector condition. ∎

Example 2 Consider a system similar to that described in Theorem (31). Let H_1 be defined by (28); let $\phi: \mathbb{R} \to \mathbb{R}$ and have its slope restricted as follows. For some $\beta > 0$, $\varepsilon > 0$, and some $\alpha \in \mathbb{R}$,

51 $$\alpha < \frac{\phi(x) - \phi(y)}{x - y} \leq \alpha + \beta - \varepsilon, \qquad \forall x, y \in \mathbb{R}, \quad x \neq y$$

If the Nyquist diagram of $\hat{g}(j\omega)$ does not encircle the point $(-1/\alpha, 0)$ (in the sense of Section IV.5), then the present system can be reduced to the case of Theorem (31) by simple loop transformations.

Step 1 Apply a feedforward of $-\alpha I$ around H_2 and a feedback of $-\alpha I$ around H_1. The new nonlinearity is $H_2 - \alpha I$; its characteristic is

$$\sigma \mapsto \phi(\sigma) - \alpha\sigma, \qquad \text{and belongs to sector} \quad [0, \beta - \varepsilon]$$

The new linear subsystem is $H_1(I + \alpha H_1)^{-1}$. It is a convolution operator whose impulse response is in $\mathscr{A}$ since $g \in \mathscr{A}$ and because the Nyquist diagram does not encircle $(-1/\alpha, 0)$.

Step 2 Apply positive feeedback of $(1/\beta)I$ around the nonlinearity and a positive feedforward of $(1/\beta)I$ around the linear subsystem; the resulting nonlinearity is

52 $$(H_2 - \alpha I)[I - \beta^{-1}(H_2 - \alpha I)]^{-1} = (H_2 - \alpha I)[(\alpha + \beta)I - H_2]^{-1}\beta I$$

Note that the inverse is well defined because the nonlinear characteristic of $\beta^{-1}(H_2 - \alpha I)$ is strictly increasing and its slope is less than $(\beta - \varepsilon)/\beta < 1$. The new linear subsystem is

$$\beta^{-1}I + H_1(I + \alpha H_1)^{-1} = \beta^{-1}[I + (\alpha + \beta)H_1](I + \alpha H_1)^{-1}$$

Finally, noting that the constant factors β and β^{-1} may be canceled out without affecting the L^2 stability of the system, we end up with

53
$$\overline{H}_2 = (H_2 - \alpha I)[(\alpha + \beta)I - H_2]^{-1}$$

and

54
$$\overline{H}_1 = [I + (\alpha + \beta)H_1](I + \alpha H_1)^{-1}$$

The characteristic of $\overline{H}_2$ is strictly increasing and is in the sector $[0, \beta/\varepsilon]$. The impulse response of $\overline{H}_1$ is in $\mathscr{A}$. Hence we have the same setup as in Theorem (31).

9.4 Factorization by logarithms

55 **Lemma** Let $\mathscr{H}$ be a Hilbert space. Let M be a linear continuous map of $\mathscr{H}$ into $\mathscr{H}$. U.t.c., if M is $\mathscr{H}$ positive and M^{-1} is a well-defined linear continuous map of $\mathscr{H}$ into $\mathscr{H}$, then so is $\log M$.

It is convenient to think in terms of Banach algebras. The class $[\mathscr{H}]$ of all linear continuous maps from the Hilbert space $\mathscr{H}$ into itself constitutes an algebra; addition and scalar multiplication of such maps are defined in the usual manner. The multiplication is taken to be the composition. If, in addition, we choose the norm of such a map as the norm induced by the norm of $\mathscr{H}$, then we have

$$\|I\| = 1 \qquad \text{and} \qquad \|M_1 M_2\| \leq \|M_1\| \, \|M_2\|$$

where I is the identity map and M_1, M_2 any pair of continuous linear maps from $\mathscr{H}$ into $\mathscr{H}$. Since $\mathscr{H}$ is complete, the normed algebra $[\mathscr{H}]$ is complete; thus it is a Banach algebra.

Proof Let I be the identity map on $\mathscr{H}$; let $s \in \mathbb{C}$. By definition, the resolvent of M is the map $s \mapsto (sI - M)^{-1}$ from some subset of $\mathbb{C}$ into $\mathscr{H}$; the domain of the resolvent, $\rho(M)$, is an *open* set. Since M^{-1} is a well-defined continuous linear map from $\mathscr{H}$ into $\mathscr{H}$, $(sI - M)^{-1}$ is well defined in some open disk $B(0; r)$ centered on the origin. On the other hand, since M is continuous, the spectrum of M, $\sigma(M)$ [i.e., the set $\mathbb{C} - \rho(M)$] is in the disk $\overline{B}(0; \|M\|)$. Since M is linear, $\mathscr{H}$ positive, and continuous, $(sI - M)^{-1}$ is well defined for all $\operatorname{Re} s < 0$. Hence we can find a simple closed rectifiable curve Γ which does not touch the negative real axis (including the origin) and which encloses the spectrum of M. Let D be the domain enclosed by Γ. In D and on Γ, the function $s \mapsto \log s$ is analytic; hence $\log M$: $L^2(\mathbb{R}) \to L^2(\mathbb{R})$ is given by the Dunford–Taylor integral [Dun.1]

$$\log M = (1/2\pi j) \int_\Gamma \log s \, (sI - M)^{-1} \, ds$$ ∎

Exercise Show that $(sI - M)^{-1}$ is a well-defined continuous linear map on $\mathscr{H}$ for $|s| > \|M\|$. [*Hint*: Consider $(sI - M)^{-1} = (1/s)(I - M/s)^{-1} = (1/s)\sum_0^\infty M^n/s^n$.]

Let $\mathscr{B}$ be the class of convolution operators M such that $M: u \mapsto m * u$, where

56 $$m(t) = \sum_{-\infty}^{\infty} m_i\, \delta(t - t_i) + m_a(t)$$

with $(m_i) \in l^1$, $m_a(\cdot) \in L^1(\mathbb{R})$, and $t_i \in \mathbb{R}$, $\forall i$. Note that M is not causal in general. $M \in \mathscr{B}$ maps $L^2(\mathbb{R})$ into $L^2(\mathbb{R})$, and for all $u \in L^2(\mathbb{R})$,

57 $$\|Mu\|_2 \leq \|u\|_2 \sup_\omega \left| \sum_{-\infty}^{+\infty} m_i e^{-j\omega t_i} + \hat{m}_a(j\omega) \right| \leq \|u\|_2 \left[\sum_{-\infty}^{\infty} |m_i| + \|m_a\|_1 \right]$$

If we denote the bracket by $\|M\|$, it is easy to show that the function $\|\cdot\|$, thus defined, is norm on $\mathscr{B}$. So $M \in \mathscr{B}$ is a linear continuous map. If $M, N \in \mathscr{B}$, then the maps $M + N$, αM $(\forall \alpha \in \mathbb{C})$, MN, and NM are in $\mathscr{B}$. By Fubini's theorem, $MN = NM$, and $\|MN\| \leq \|M\|\, \|N\|$. Since the identity $I \in \mathscr{B}$, we conclude that

58 $\mathscr{B}$ is a commutative Banach algebra with a unit.

Let P_+ be a projection on $\mathscr{B}$ (hence $P_+ P_+ = P_+$) defined as follows: Since $Mu = m * u$, we have

59 $$(Mu)(t) \triangleq \int_{-\infty}^{+\infty} m(t - \tau)u(\tau)\, d\tau = \int_{-\infty}^{\infty} m(\xi)u(t - \xi)\, d\xi$$

Define $P_+ M$ by

60 $$(P_+ Mu)(t) \triangleq \int_{0-}^{\infty} m(\xi)u(t - \xi)\, d\xi = \int_{-\infty}^{t+} m(t - \tau)u(\tau)\, d\tau$$

$P_+ M$ is a causal convolution operator from $L^2(\mathbb{R})$ into $L^2(\mathbb{R})$. Let

61 $$P_- \triangleq I - P_+$$

$P_- M$ is an anticausal (or purely anticipative) convolution operator from $L^2(\mathbb{R})$ into $L^2(\mathbb{R})$.

Let $\mathscr{B}_c$ $(\mathscr{B}_a)$ be in the class of all causal (anticausal) continuous operators on $L^2(\mathbb{R})$. $\mathscr{B}_c$ and $\mathscr{B}_a$ are closed under addition, multiplication (i.e., composition of functions), and multiplication by scalars. Thus, $\mathscr{B}_c$ and $\mathscr{B}_a$ are subalgebras of $\mathscr{B}$. If $P_+ M$ and $P_- M$ have finite norms, then $P_+ M$ and $P_- M$ belong to $\mathscr{B}_c$ and $\mathscr{B}_a$, resp.

Exercise Show that if $A, B \in \mathscr{B}_c$, then $AB = BA \in \mathscr{B}_c$, $A^m B^n \in \mathscr{B}_c$ for any integers $m, n \in \mathbb{Z}_+$.

Exercise Let $A, B \in \mathbb{R}^{n \times n}$. Show that if A and B commute (i.e., $AB = BA$), then $\exp A \cdot \exp B = \exp B \cdot \exp A = \exp(A + B)$. Show, by an example, that if $AB \neq BA$, the two equalities above fail in general.

62 **Factorization Theorem** Let $\mathscr{B}$ be the Banach algebra of continuous convolution operators defined in (56). Let M be an operator in $\mathscr{B}$. If M is $\mathscr{H}$ positive and if M^{-1} is in $\mathscr{B}$, then with $\|P_+ \log M\|$ and $\|P_- \log M\|$ finite

(a) M can be factored as

63
$$M = M_- M_+, \quad \text{with} \quad M_- \in \mathscr{B}_a, \quad M_+ \in \mathscr{B}_c$$

(b) $M_+^{-1} \in \mathscr{B}_c$ and $M_-^{-1} \in \mathscr{B}_a$.

Proof Since $L^2(\mathbb{R})$ is a Hilbert space, M is $\mathscr{H}$ positive, and $M^{-1} \in \mathscr{B}$, by Lemma (55), $\log M$ is a well-defined element of $\mathscr{B}$; so are $P_+ \log M$, $P_- \log M$. Let

$$M_+ \triangleq \exp(P_+ \log M); \qquad M_- \triangleq \exp(P_- \log M)$$

Since the exponential function is analytic everywhere in $\mathbb{C}$, M_+ and M_- are continuous convolution operators in $\mathscr{B}_c$ and $\mathscr{B}_a$, resp. The same holds for their inverses because

64
$$M_+^{-1} = \exp(-P_+ \log M); \qquad M_-^{-1} = \exp(-P_- \log M)$$

Now since $M_+, M_- \in \mathscr{B}$, and $\mathscr{B}$ is a *commutative* algebra,

65
$$\begin{aligned} M_- M_+ &= \exp(P_+ \log M) \cdot \exp(P_- \log M) = \exp[(P_+ + P_-) \log M] \\ &= \exp(\log M) = M \end{aligned}$$

Similarly, we have $M_+ M_- = M$. Finally, $M_+^{-1} \in \mathscr{B}_c$ because $P_+ \log M \in \mathscr{B}_c$ and

$$M_+^{-1} = \exp(-P_+ \log M) = \sum_{n=0}^{\infty} [-P_+ \log M]^n/n! \qquad ■$$

67 **Remark** The preceding proof requires $\mathscr{B}$ to be a *commutative* algebra. Therefore, this factorization technique fails (except for special cases) in the case of convolution operators from $L_n^2(\mathbb{R})$ into $L_n^2(\mathbb{R})$, because their kernels are matrices, and the product of two matrices is, in general, not commutative. For this reason, this factorization technique fails in the multi-input–multi-output case.

9.5 Factorization by projection

The factorization theorem in the following does not require that the Banach algebra be commutative.

68 **Factorization Theorem** Let $\mathscr{B}$ be a Banach algebra with identity I. Let Π_+ be a projection on $\mathscr{B}$ i.e., $\Pi_+ : \mathscr{B} \to \mathscr{B}$ is linear and $\Pi_+ \Pi_+ = \Pi_+$). Let the projection Π_- be defined by

69 $$\Pi_- \triangleq I - \Pi_+$$

where I denotes the identity map on $\mathscr{B}$. It is assumed that

70 $$\|\Pi_+\| \leq 1 \qquad \text{and} \qquad \|\Pi_-\| \leq 1$$

Let $\mathscr{B}_+$ and $\mathscr{B}_-$ be the ranges of Π_+ and Π_-, resp. It is assumed that $\mathscr{B}_+$ and $\mathscr{B}_-$ are subalgebras (i.e., are closed under multiplication). Let $M \in \mathscr{B}$. U.t.c., if there exists a $Z \in \mathscr{B}$ such that

71 $$\|Z\| < 1$$

and

72 $$M = I - Z$$

then

(i) M can be factored as follows

73 $$M = I - Z = M_- M_+, \qquad \text{with} \quad M_-, M_+ \in \mathscr{B}$$

where M_- and M_+ are invertible in $\mathscr{B}$;

74 (ii) $$M_-, (M_-)^{-1} \in I \oplus \mathscr{B}_-$$

75 $$M_+, (M_+)^{-1} \in I \oplus \mathscr{B}_+$$

where $I \oplus \mathscr{B}_+$ ($I \oplus \mathscr{B}_-$) denotes the subspace of all elements in $\mathscr{B}$ of the form $\alpha I + M$, where $\alpha \in \mathbb{R}$, $M \in \mathscr{B}_+$ ($\mathscr{B}_-$, resp.).

76 **Comments** (I) The Banach algebra $\mathscr{B}$ is not assumed to be commutative. This is important for the multivariable case.

(II) From (71) and (72), we have $\|M\| \leq 1 + \|Z\| < 2$. If some given element N is to be factored and has a norm larger or equal to 2, then a scale factor $k > 1$ may be introduced, and the given element N may be written as $N = k(I - Z)$.

(III) There are two extremely important conditions, namely, (70) [because projections in normed spaces do not necessarily obey (70)] and the condition that $\mathscr{B}_+$ and $\mathscr{B}_-$ be subalgebras.

The proof of the factorization theorem (68) uses the following lemma.

79 **Lemma** Let $(Q_k)_1^\infty$, $(P_k)_1^\infty$, and $(N_k)_1^\infty$ be sequences in $\mathscr{B}$, $\mathscr{B}_+$, and $\mathscr{B}_-$, resp. Suppose that for $|r| < r_c$ (where $r \in \mathbb{C}$, $r_c \in \mathbb{R}$, and $r_c > 0$), the power series

$$I + \sum_1^\infty Q_k r^k = Q(r) \tag{80}$$

$$I + \sum_1^\infty P_k r^k = P(r) \tag{81}$$

$$I + \sum_1^\infty N_k r^k = N(r) \tag{82}$$

converge. [Consequently, Q, P, N are analytic functions of r in $B(0; r_c)$, taking values in $\mathscr{B}$, $I \oplus \mathscr{B}_+$, and $I \oplus \mathscr{B}_-$, resp.] U.t.c., if these functions are related by $Q = PN$, then the sequence $(Q_k)_1^\infty \subset \mathscr{B}$ determines *uniquely* the sequences $(P_k)_1^\infty \subset \mathscr{B}_+$ and $(N_k)_1^\infty \subset \mathscr{B}_-$.

Proof In $Q = PN$, replace each function by its power series; then using a well-known theorem of analytic functions, we equate coefficients and obtain

$$Q_1 = P_1 + N_1$$

whence

$$P_1 = \Pi_+ Q_1, \qquad N_1 = \Pi_- Q_1$$

and

$$Q_k = P_k + N_k + \sum_{i=1}^{k-1} P_{k-i} N_i, \qquad k = 1, 2, \ldots$$

whence

$$P_k = \Pi_+(Q_k - \sum_{i=1}^{k-1} P_{k-i} N_i), \qquad k = 1, 2, \ldots$$

and a similar relation for N_k. Thus, the P_k's and N_k's are successively determined uniquely in terms of the Q_k's. ∎

Proof of the Factorization Theorem (68)

Step I Consider for $|r| \le 1$, the following equations

$$P = f_+(P) \triangleq I + r\Pi_+(ZP) \tag{84}$$

$$N = f_-(N) \triangleq I + r\Pi_-(NZ) \tag{85}$$

Note that to simplify notations, we wrote P for $P(r)$ and N for $N(r)$. The functions f_+ and f_- are contractions on $\mathscr{B}$; indeed, for any $P_1, P_2 \in \mathscr{B}$,

$$\|f_+(P_1) - f_+(P_2)\| = \|r\Pi_+[Z(P_1 - P_2)]\| \le |r| \, \|Z\| \, \|P_1 - P_2\| \tag{86}$$

where in the first step we used the linearity of Π_+ and the distributive law in $\mathscr{B}$; in the second step we used (70). Since $|r| \cdot \|Z\| < 1, f_+$ is a contraction on $\mathscr{B}$. A similar proof holds for f_-.

Thus, P and N can be calculated by iteration starting with $P_0 = N_0 = I$; thus, again using linearity and the distributive law,

87 $$P = I + \sum_1^\infty P_k r^k, \qquad N = I + \sum_1^\infty N_k r^k$$

with $P_{k+1} \triangleq \Pi_+(ZP_k)$, $N_{k+1} \triangleq \Pi_-(N_k Z)$, $k = 0, 1, 2, \ldots$. Also, for all k, $P_k \subset \mathscr{B}_+$, $N_k \subset \mathscr{B}$; $P \in I \oplus \mathscr{B}_+$, $N \in I \oplus \mathscr{B}_-$. The solutions P and N are analytic functions in $B(0; \|Z\|^{-1})$. Also

88 $$\|P\| \le (1 - |r| \ \|Z\|)^{-1}$$

and similarly for $\|N\|$.

Step II From Eq. (84) and (85), recalling that $\Pi_+ + \Pi_- = I$, we obtain

89 $$(I - rZ)P = I - r\Pi_-(ZP)$$

90 $$N(I - rZ) = I - r\Pi_+(NZ)$$

Since by assumption $\|Z\| < 1$, for $|r| < \|Z\|^{-1}$, $(I - rZ)^{-1} \in \mathscr{B}$ and is given the power series $\sum_0^\infty Z^k r^k$ convergent in $B(0; \|Z\|^{-1})$. Now, using (70) and (88),

$$\|r\Pi_-(ZP)\| \le |r| \ \|Z\| \ \|P\| \le \frac{|r| \ \|Z\|}{1 - |r| \ \|Z\|}$$

the same bound holds for $\|r\Pi_+(NZ)\|$. Therefore, the elements $I - r\Pi_-(ZP)$ and $I - r\Pi_+(NZ)$ of $\mathscr{B}$ are invertible in $\mathscr{B}$ for $|r| < \|Z\|^{-1}/2$. Their inverses are given by power series convergent in $B(0; \|Z\|^{-1}/2)$. The inverses take values in $I \oplus \mathscr{B}_-$ and $I \oplus \mathscr{B}_+$. Hence we have from (89) and (90)

91 $$(I - rZ)^{-1} = P[I - r\Pi_-(ZP)]^{-1} = [I - r\Pi_+(NZ)]^{-1} N$$

Since, in these two equalities, the five power series involved have, as common domain of convergence, the disk $B(0; \|Z\|^{-1}/2)$, the uniqueness guaranteed by Lemma (79) gives

$$P = [I - r\Pi_+(NZ)]^{-1}, \qquad N = [I - r\Pi_-(ZP)]^{-1}$$

and

92 $$(I - rZ)^{-1} = PN$$

Now in (92), $(I - rZ)^{-1}$, P, and N are represented by power series convergent for $|r| < \|Z\|^{-1}$; hence setting $r = 1$, we obtain

93 $$I - Z = N^{-1}P^{-1} = M_- M_+$$

with $M_- \triangleq N^{-1}$, $M_+ \triangleq P^{-1}$. All the properties of M_- and M_+ have been established in the course of the derivation. ∎

94 **Application** Consider now the application of this factorization theorem to the following special case: Let $\mathscr{A}_2$ be the Banach algebra defined in Section V. 9.2; namely, $\mathscr{A}_2$ consists of generalized functions $f(\cdot)$ of the form

95
$$f(t) = \sum_{i=-\infty}^{\infty} f_i \, \delta(t - t_i) + f_a(t)$$

where $t_i \in \mathbb{R}$ with $t_i < 0$ ($=0$, >0 resp.) for $i < 0$ ($=0$, >0 resp.);

$$\sum_{i=-\infty}^{\infty} |f_i| < \infty$$

$$f_a(\cdot) \colon \mathbb{R} \to \mathbb{R}, \qquad \text{and} \qquad f_a(\cdot) \in L_1(\mathbb{R})$$

Let $\mathscr{A}_2^{n \times n}$ denote the set of $n \times n$ matrices whose elements belong to $\mathscr{A}_2$. If $F(\cdot)$ of the form

96
$$F(t) = \sum_{i=-\infty}^{\infty} F_i \, \delta(t - t_i) + F_a(t)$$

is an element of $\mathscr{A}_2^{n \times n}$, we define its norm by

97
$$\|F\|_{\mathscr{A}_2} = \sum_{i=-\infty}^{\infty} |F_i| + \int_{-\infty}^{\infty} |F_a(t)| \, dt$$

where $|\cdot|$ is any *induced* norm on $\mathbb{R}^{n \times n}$. Finally, we define the product of two elements in $\mathscr{A}_2^{n \times n}$ to be their convolution. Under these conditions, one can easily verify that $\mathscr{A}_2^{n \times n}$ is a Banach algebra, that $I \cdot \delta(t)$ is the identity element of $\mathscr{A}_2^{n \times n}$, and that $\mathscr{A}_2^{n \times n}$ is not a commutative algebra unless $n = 1$.

Let $\mathscr{A}^{n \times n}$ be the subset of $\mathscr{A}_2^{n \times n}$ consisting of elements $F(\cdot)$ that satisfy

98
$$F_i = 0 \quad \forall i < 0, \qquad F_a(t) = 0 \quad \forall t < 0$$

Then $\mathscr{A}^{n \times n}$ is a subalgebra of $\mathscr{A}_2^{n \times n}$ and contains the identity element. Similarly, let $\mathscr{A}_-^{n \times n}$ be the subset of $\mathscr{A}_2^{n \times n}$ consisting of elements $F(\cdot)$ that satisfy

99
$$F_i = 0 \quad \forall i > 0, \qquad F_a(t) = 0 \quad \forall t > 0$$

Then $\mathscr{A}_-^{n \times n}$ is also a subalgebra of $\mathscr{A}_2^{n \times n}$, and it too contains the identity element. If we think of $\mathscr{A}_2^{n \times n}$ as the set consisting of the impulse responses of stable n-input-n-output systems, then $\mathscr{A}^{n \times n}$ consists of all causal impulse responses in $\mathscr{A}_2^{n \times n}$, while $\mathscr{A}_-^{n \times n}$ consists of all anticausal impulse responses in $\mathscr{A}_2^{n \times n}$.

Next, let $\Pi_+ : \mathscr{A}_2^{n \times n} \to \mathscr{A}_2^{n \times n}$ and $\Pi_- : \mathscr{A}_2^{n \times n} \to \mathscr{A}_2^{n \times n}$ be the mappings defined by $(\Pi_+ F)(t) = \sum_{i=0}^{\infty} F_i \, \delta(t - t_i) + F_{a+}(t)$ and $(\Pi_- F)(t) = \sum_{i=-\infty}^{-1} F_i \, \delta(t - t_i) + F_{a-}(t)$

where

$$F_{a+}(t) = \begin{cases} F_a(t) & t \geq 0 \\ 0 & t < 0 \end{cases}; \qquad F_{a-}(t) = \begin{cases} F_a(t) & t < 0 \\ 0 & t \geq 0 \end{cases}$$

It is routine to verify that Π_+ maps $\mathscr{A}_2^{n\times n}$ into $\mathscr{A}^{n\times n}$, that $\Pi_+^{\ 2} = \Pi_+$ (so that Π_+ is indeed a projection), and that $\mathscr{A}^{n\times n}$ is the range of Π_+. Similarly, Π_- maps $\mathscr{A}_2^{n\times n}$ into $\mathscr{A}_-^{n\times n}$, $\Pi_-^{\ 2} = \Pi_-$, and $\mathscr{A}_-^{n\times n}$ is the direct sum of the identity operator and the range of Π_-. Also, in view of the definition (97) of the norm on $\mathscr{A}_2^{n\times n}$, it is clear that

$$\|\Pi_+ F\|_{\mathscr{A}_2} \leq \|F\|_{\mathscr{A}_2}, \ \|\Pi_- F\|_{\mathscr{A}_2} \leq \|F\|_{\mathscr{A}_2} \qquad \forall F \in \mathscr{A}_2^{n\times n}$$

so that

$$\|\Pi_+\| \leq 1, \quad \|\Pi_-\| \leq 1$$

Thus all the hypotheses needed to apply the factorization theorem (68) are satisfied. Hence we have the following

101 **Theorem** Let $M \in \mathscr{A}_2^{n\times n}$, and suppose $M = I - Z$ where $\|Z\|_{\mathscr{A}_2} < 1$. Then M can be expressed in the form

$$M = M_- * M_+ \tag{102}$$

where M_-, M_+ are invertible in $\mathscr{A}_2^{n\times n}$,

$$M_-, M_-^{-1} \in \mathscr{A}_-^{n\times n} \qquad \text{and} \qquad M_+, M_+^{-1} \in \mathscr{A}_+^{n\times n} \tag{103}$$

104 **Remark** In factoring by logarithms, as in (62), the projections P_+ and P_- could have norms larger than 1, but the Banach algebra had to be commutative. In (101) the projections Π_+ and Π_- must have norms less than or equal to 1, but the Banach algebra need not be commutative.

10 Relation between the passivity theorem and the small gain theorem

We have derived a form of the Popov criterion by applying the small gain theorem (see V.8), and also by applying the passivity theorem (see VI.6.1). This suggests that these two theorems are related. It should be stressed that they are *not* equivalent. Indeed, referring to the general formulation of Sections III.1 and III.2, we see that the small gain theorem requires only a *normed space structure* (L_n^1, L_n^2, L_n^∞, ...), whereas the passivity theorem requires an inner-product space structure (usually, a Hilbert space, with L^2 as the prototype). We shall see below that further assumptions are required in order that the "equivalence" hold.

The intuitive idea behind the relation between passivity and small gain is supplied by linear circuit theory. Indeed, consider a *linear time-invariant n*-port and let it be described by its impedance matrix Z. If $\hat{v}$ and $\hat{\imath}$ represent the Laplace transforms of its port voltages and currents, we have

1 $$\hat{v} = Z\hat{\imath}$$

The n-port may also be described by its scattering matrix S, which relates the incident wave $\hat{a}$ to the reflected (scattered) wave $\hat{b}$:

2 $$\hat{b} = S\hat{a}$$

where, using the standard normalization of the 1-ohm transmission line,

3 $$\hat{v} = \hat{b} + \hat{a}, \qquad \hat{\imath} = \hat{a} - \hat{b}$$

Hence

4 $$S = (Z - I)(I + Z)^{-1}$$

It is also physically obvious that if the linear time-invariant n-port is passive (hence Z is a passive operator; positive semidefinite, as they say in circuit theory), then the reflected wave $\hat{b}$ carries an amount of energy no larger than the incident wave $\hat{a}$, and conversely. Thus,

5 $$Z \text{ is passive} \Leftrightarrow \gamma(S) \leq 1$$

This suggestion from linear time-invariant n-port theory extends to the general framework of Section 3. It is made precise in the following lemma.

7 **Lemma** Let $H: \mathscr{H}_e \to \mathscr{H}_e$. Assume that

8 $$(I + H)^{-1}: \mathscr{H}_e \to \mathscr{H}_e$$

is well defined.

Define $S: \mathscr{H}_e \to \mathscr{H}_e$ by

9 $$S = (H - I)(I + H)^{-1}$$

U.t.c.,

(a) H is passive with the constant $\beta = 0$, i.e.,

10 $$\langle Hx | x \rangle_T \geq 0, \qquad \forall x \in \mathscr{H}_e, \quad \forall T \in \mathscr{T}$$

if and only if S has a gain ≤ 1, i.e.,

11 $$\|Sy\|_T{}^2 \leq \|y\|_T{}^2, \qquad \forall y \in \mathscr{H}_e, \quad \forall T \in \mathscr{T}$$

(b) H has a finite gain γ with the additive constant $\beta = 0$, i.e.,

12 $$\|Hx\|_T \leq \gamma \|x\|_T; \qquad \forall x \in \mathscr{H}_e, \quad \forall T \in \mathscr{T}$$

and H is strictly passive, i.e., there is a $\delta > 0$ s.t.

13 $$\langle Hx | x \rangle_T \geq \delta \|x\|_T{}^2, \qquad \forall x \in \mathscr{H}_e, \quad \forall T \in \mathscr{T}$$

if and only if S has a gain smaller than 1, i.e., for some $\gamma' \in (0, 1)$,

14 $$\|Sy\|_T{}^2 \leq (1 - \gamma')\|y\|^2{}_T, \qquad \forall y \in \mathscr{H}_e, \quad \forall T \in \mathscr{T}$$

Exercise 1 Since, in (4), Z is a linear operator, show that $S = (I + Z)^{-1}(Z - I)$. [*Hint*: Calculate the difference between this expression and that of (4); exhibit the places where linearity is used.] Show, by example, that in the nonlinear case, $(H - I)(I + H)^{-1} \neq (I + H)^{-1}(H - I)$.

15 **Comment** The lemma establishes that if (8) holds, then whenever the "impedance" operator H is passive, then the corresponding "scattering" operator S has a gain ≤ 1, and conversely; also whenever the "impedance" operator H has finite gain and is strictly passive, then the corresponding "scattering" operator S has a gain smaller than 1. In contrast to the usual derivations found in circuit theory texts, the "impedance" operator and the "scattering" operator are neither assumed to be linear nor time invariant.

Before proving lemma (7), let us establish a few *identities*. Given any $y \in \mathscr{H}_e$, define $x \in \mathscr{H}_e$ by

16 $$x \triangleq (I + H)^{-1}y$$

As a consequence,

17 $$Sy = (H - I)x \qquad \text{and} \qquad y = (I + H)x$$

Hence

18 $$\|Sy\|_T{}^2 = \|Hx\|_T{}^2 + \|x\|_T{}^2 - 2\langle x | Hx \rangle_T$$

and

19 $$\|y\|_T{}^2 = \|Hx\|_T{}^2 + \|x\|_T{}^2 + 2\langle x | Hx \rangle_T$$

Thus, for all $y \in \mathscr{H}_e$, for all $T \in \mathscr{T}$,

20 $$\|Sy\|_T{}^2 = \|y\|_T{}^2 - 4\langle x | Hx \rangle_T.$$

Proof of Lemma (7) (a) The required equivalence of (10) and (11) follows immediately from the identity (20).

(b) $\Rightarrow$ Using (12) and (16) in (13), we obtain

$$4\langle x | Hx \rangle_T \geq 4\delta \|x\|_T{}^2 \geq 4\delta(1 + \gamma)^{-2}\|y\|_T{}^2 \geq \gamma' \|y\|_T{}^2$$

where γ' is chosen to satisfy $0 < \gamma' < \max[1, 4\delta(1 + \gamma)^{-2}]$. Using this last inequality in (20) yields (14).

$\Leftarrow$ Assumption (14) and (20) give

$$4\langle x | Hx \rangle_T \geq \gamma' \|y\|_T{}^2 = \gamma'[\|Hx\|_T{}^2 + \|x\|_T{}^2 + \langle 2x | Hx \rangle_T]$$

Since $\gamma' \in (0, 1)$, we obtain

$$\langle x | Hx \rangle_T \geq \gamma'' \|x\|_T^2$$

where $\gamma'' \triangleq \gamma'/(4 - 2\gamma') > 0$. So (14) implies that H is strictly passive in the sense of (13).

Eliminate y from (14) by (18) and (19) and rearrange terms to obtain

$$\gamma' \|Hx\|_T^2 \leq (4 - 2\gamma') \|Hx\|_T \, \|x\|_T - \gamma' \|x\|_T^2$$

The finite-gain condition (12) follows if we choose $\gamma = (4 - 2\gamma')/\gamma'$. ∎

Exercise 2 Suppose H is given as a black box; devise block diagrams for S. (*Hint*: $S = 2H(I + H)^{-1} - I; S = (H - I)(\frac{1}{2}I) \cdot [I + (H - I)(\frac{1}{2}I)^{-1}$; watch out that in the nonlinear case, $H \cdot (2I) \neq 2IH$.)

Exercise 3 To appreciate the importance of assumption (8), construct an example where $H: \mathscr{H}_e \to \mathscr{H}_e$ has finite gain and is strictly passive but where $I + H$ does not have an inverse. (*Hint*: Take $\mathscr{T} = \{0\}$, $\mathscr{H} = \mathbb{R}$; recall Chapter I.)

Exercise 4 Show that if (8) holds and if H is incrementally passive, then S has an incremental gain ≤ 1.

To exhibit the relation between the small gain theorem and the passivity theorem, we consider a system $\mathscr{S}$ described by

$$u_1 = e_1 + H_2 e_2 \qquad u_2 = e_2 - H_1 e_1 \tag{24}$$

where $u_1, u_2, e_1, e_2 \in \mathscr{H}_e$ and H_1, H_2 map $\mathscr{H}_e$ into itself. We apply successively the loop transformation theorem (III.6.3). These transformations are described as follows:

Forward subsystem	*Feedback subsystem*
H_1	H_2
Apply feedback with gain -1;	Apply feedforward with gain -1:
$H_1(I + H_1)^{-1}$	$H_2 - I$
Multiply *output* by 2:	Multiply input by $\frac{1}{2}$:
$2H_1(I + H_1)^{-1}$	$(H_2 - I) \cdot (\frac{1}{2}I)$
Apply feedforward with gain -1:	Apply feedback with gain -1:
$2H_1(I + H_1)^{-1} - I$ $= (H_1 - I)(I + H_1)^{-1}$ $\triangleq S_1$	$(H_2 - I)(\frac{1}{2}I)[I + (H_2 - I)(\frac{1}{2}I)]^{-1}$ $= (H_2 - I)(I + H_2)^{-1}$ $\triangleq S_2$

It can be checked that in the process, the inputs have been changed to $u_1 - u_2$ and $u_1 + u_2$, respectively. Thus, we obtain the system $\tilde{\mathscr{S}}$ shown in Fig. VI.9 The loop transformation theorem (III.6.3) yields the conclusion that, provided

Figure VI.9

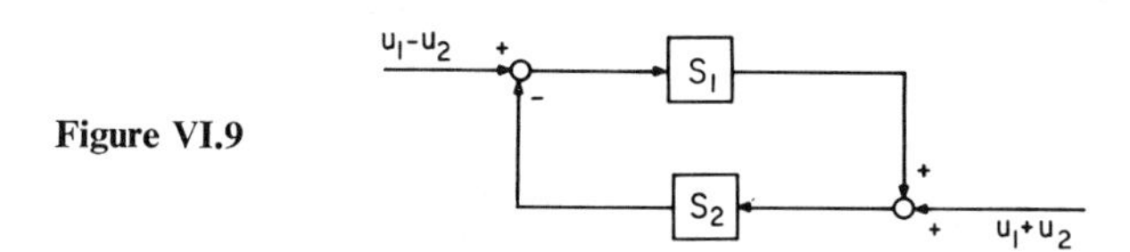

$(I + H_1)^{-1}$ and $(I + H_2)^{-1}$ are well-defined maps from $\mathscr{H}_e$ into $\mathscr{H}_e$, *the system* $\mathscr{S}$ *described by* (24) *is* $\mathscr{H}$ *stable if and only if* $\tilde{\mathscr{S}}$ *is stable.*

We make now two observations:

(a) If H_1 satisfies (10) (is passive) and if H_2 satisfies (12) (finite gain) and (13) (strictly passive), then, by Lemma (7), $\gamma(S_1) \leq 1$ and $\gamma(S_2) \leq (1 - \gamma') < 1$. So by the small gain theorem (III.2.1), $\tilde{\mathscr{S}}$ is $\mathscr{H}$ stable; so is $\mathscr{S}$ by virtue of the loop transformations.

(b) If $\gamma(S_1) \leq 1$ and $\gamma(S_2) \leq 1 - \gamma' < 1$, then H_1 satisfies (10) and H_2 satisfies (12) and (13); therefore, by the passivity theorem (VI.5.10), $\mathscr{S}$ is $\mathscr{H}$ stable; so is $\tilde{\mathscr{S}}$ by virtue of the loop transformations.

Note that we have *not* shown that the small gain theorem and the passivity theorem are equivalent; i.e., whenever the $\mathscr{H}$ stability of a system can be established by one of the theorems, it can be established by the other. In the first place, the passivity theorem requires an inner-product space structure, whereas the small gain theorem requires only a normed space structure. It would seem that $(I + H_1)^{-1}$ and $(I + H_2)^{-1}$ be well defined *maps* from $\mathscr{H}_e$ into $\mathscr{H}_e$ is also required. However, if $(I + H_1)^{-1}$ and $(I + H_2)^{-1}$ are interpreted as the *inverse relation* of $I + H_1$ and $I + H_2$, then the conclusion still holds.

In the next section, we consider the problem of finding conditions under which $I + H$ has an inverse.

11 Invertibility of $I + H$

Throughout our study of feedback systems, we encounter equations of the form

$$u = (I + H)e$$

If $I + H$ is known to be invertible in some space, say, $\mathscr{H}$, the conclusion follows that for any $u \in \mathscr{H}$, the equation has a unique solution in $\mathscr{H}$. Note also that in order to legitimately apply the loop transformation theorem, we need to know that a map of the form $(I + KH_1)$ is invertible. We give below two theorems that guarantee the invertibility of such maps. Both theorems require an inner-product space structure.

1 **Theorem** Let $\mathscr{H}$ be a Hilbert space. Let $F\colon \mathscr{H}_e \to \mathscr{H}_e$. We assume that F is incrementally passive and has finite incremental gain; more precisely, there is a $\tilde{\delta} > 0$ and a $\tilde{\gamma} < \infty$ s.t.

$$\langle Fx - Fx' \,|\, x - x' \rangle_T \geq \tilde{\xi} \|x - x'\|_T^{\,2}, \qquad \forall x, x' \in \mathscr{H}_e, \quad \forall T \in \mathscr{T} \tag{2}$$

$$\|Fx - Fx'\|_T \leq \tilde{\gamma} \|x - x'\|_T \tag{3}$$

Under these conditions,

(i) F is a bijection from $\mathscr{H}_e$ onto $\mathscr{H}_e$; equivalently, F^{-1} is a well-defined map from $\mathscr{H}_e$ *onto* $\mathscr{H}_e$;
(ii) F^{-1} has a finite incremental gain: $\tilde{\gamma}(F^{-1}) \leq 1/\tilde{\xi}$;
(iii) F^{-1} satisfies the condition

$$\langle F^{-1}z - F^{-1}z' \,|\, z - z' \rangle_T \geq \tilde{\delta} \|F^{-1}z - F^{-1}z'\|_T^{\,2}, \qquad \forall z, z' \in \mathscr{H}_e, \quad \forall T \in \mathscr{T} \tag{4}$$

Exercise 1 Show that (2) and (3) imply that $\tilde{\gamma} \geq \tilde{\delta}$.

Exercise 2 Show that (3) implies that F is nonanticipative, and (4) implies that F^{-1} is nonanticipative.

We could express the idea of (3) by saying that for all $T \in \mathscr{T}$, the causal map $F\colon \mathscr{H}_e \to \mathscr{H}_e$ is globally, uniformly (in T), Lipschitz continuous in $P_T \mathscr{H}_e$, with the Lipschitz constant $\tilde{\gamma}$. Similarly, conclusion (ii) says that for all $T \in \mathscr{T}$, the causal map $F^{-1}\colon \mathscr{H}_e \to \mathscr{H}_e$ is globally, uniformly, Lipschitz continuous in $P_T \mathscr{H}_e$, with the Lipschitz constant $1/\tilde{\delta}$.

Proof (i) From Exercise 1, $\tilde{\gamma} \geq \tilde{\delta}$. Pick any $z \in \mathscr{H}_e$ and a nonzero scalar α; then the equation $z = Fx$ is equivalent to

$$x = \alpha z + x - \alpha F x \triangleq f(x, z) \tag{5}$$

If we set α equal to $\alpha_0 \triangleq \tilde{\delta}/\tilde{\gamma}^2$, we claim that f defined in (5) is a contraction. Indeed, $\forall T \in \mathscr{T}, \ \forall x, x' \in \mathscr{H}_e$

$$\begin{aligned} \|f(x, z) - f(x', z)\|_T^{\,2} &= \|x - x' - \alpha(Fx - Fx')\|_T^{\,2} \\ &= \|x - x'\|_T^{\,2} - 2\alpha\langle x - x' \,|\, Fx - Fx' \rangle_T \\ &\quad + \alpha^2 \|Fx - Fx'\|_T^{\,2} \\ &\leq \|x - x'\|_T^{\,2}[1 - 2\alpha\tilde{\delta} + \alpha^2\tilde{\gamma}^2] \end{aligned} \tag{6}$$

where we used (2) and (3). Minimizing the right-hand side of (6) with respect to α, we see that the minimum $k_0^{\,2} = 1 - (\tilde{\delta}^2/\tilde{\gamma}^2)$ is reached when $\alpha = \tilde{\delta}/\tilde{\gamma}^2$.

Thus, k_0, the contraction constant, is <1 and independent of T. Consequently, given any $z \in \mathscr{H}_e$, there is one and only one $x \in \mathscr{H}_e$ such that $z = Fx$; equivalently, F^{-1} is a well-defined function mapping $\mathscr{H}_e$ onto $\mathscr{H}$.

(ii) From (2)

$$\|Fx - Fx'\|_T \geq \tilde{\delta}\|x - x'\|_T, \qquad \forall x, x' \in \mathscr{H}_e, \quad \forall T \in \mathscr{T}$$

with $z \triangleq Fx$ and $x = F^{-1}z$, we have

7 $$\|F^{-1}z - F^{-1}z'\|_T \leq (1/\tilde{\delta})\|z - z'\|_T, \qquad \forall z, z' \in \mathscr{H}, \quad \forall T \in \mathscr{T}$$

Finally, (iii) is immediate from (2), by replacing x and x' by $F^{-1}z$ and $F^{-1}z'$, resp. ∎

8 **Corollary** Let F be a nonanticipative *linear* map from $\mathscr{H}_e \to \mathscr{H}_e$ which has finite gain. U.t.c., if F is strictly passive, then F^{-1} is a nonanticipative, linear, strictly passive map from $\mathscr{H}_e$ into $\mathscr{H}_e$ s.t.

$$\langle F^{-1}z | z\rangle_T \geq \tilde{\delta}\|F^{-1}z\|_T, \qquad \forall z \in \mathscr{H}_e, \quad \forall T \in \mathscr{T}$$

Proof By linearity, assumptions (2) and (3) reduce to those of the corollary. ∎

The following theorem shows that the requirement of finite incremental gain in Theorem (1) can be replaced by a continuity requirement.

10 **Theorem** Let $\mathscr{H}$ be a Hilbert space and $P_T\mathscr{H}_e$ be complete for all $T \in \mathscr{T}$. Let F map $\mathscr{H}_e$ into $\mathscr{H}_e$. For each $T \in \mathscr{T}$, let $P_T F$ be a continuous map of $P_T\mathscr{H}_e$ into $P_T\mathscr{H}_e$. U.t.c., if F is strictly incrementally passive, i.e., there is a $\delta > 0$ s.t.

11 $$\langle Fx - Fx' | x - x'\rangle_T \geq \delta\|x - x'\|_T^2, \qquad \forall x, x' \in \mathscr{H}_e, \quad \forall T \in \mathscr{T}$$

then

(a) F is a bijection of $\mathscr{H}_e$ onto $\mathscr{H}_e$, and
(b) F^{-1} has an incremental gain smaller or equal to δ^{-1}.

12 **Comments** In feedback systems, Theorem (10) is used as follows. Suppose that H: $\mathscr{H}_e \to \mathscr{H}_e$ and that, for all T, $P_T H$: $P_T\mathscr{H}_e \to P_T\mathscr{H}_e$ is *continuous.* U.t.c.,

(a) if H is *incrementally passive*, then $(I + H)$ is a bijection of $\mathscr{H}_e$ onto $\mathscr{H}_e$, and $(I + H)^{-1}$ has an incremental gain smaller or equal to 1;

(b) if H is *strictly incrementally passive* (with constant δ_H), then $(I + H)$ is a bijection of $\mathscr{H}_e$ onto $\mathscr{H}_e$, and $(I + H)^{-1}$ has an incremental gain smaller or equal to $(1 + \delta_H)^{-1}$.

Exercise 3 Give an example of a map $H: \mathscr{H}_e \to \mathscr{H}_e$ s.t. H has finite incremental gain, $H: P_T \mathscr{H}_e \to P_T \mathscr{H}_e$ is continuous, and is *strictly passive* (and *not* incrementally passive), but which does not have an inverse.
[*Hint*: Take $\mathscr{H}_e = \mathbb{R}$, $\mathscr{T} = \{0\}$ so H is given by its graph in $\mathbb{R}^2$. Choose H so that for some $y \in \mathbb{R}$, $(I + H)x = y$ has several solutions; hence $(I + H)^{-1}$ can at best be a relation, not a function. Use Chapter I.]

Proof From (11) and Schwarz's inequality,

$$\|Fx - Fx'\|_T \|x - x'\|_T \geq \langle Fx - Fx' | x - x' \rangle_T \geq \delta \|x - x'\|_T{}^2$$

Hence we have

$$\|Fx - Fx'\|_T \geq \delta \|x - x'\|_T, \qquad \forall x, x' \in \mathscr{H}_e \tag{12a}$$

which shows that F is injective (one to one) on $\mathscr{H}_e$. Therefore, F^{-1} is a well-defined function on $\mathscr{R}(F)$, the range of F, and, from (12a),

$$\|F^{-1}y - F^{-1}y'\|_T \leq (1/\delta)\|y - y'\|_T, \qquad \forall y, y' \in \mathscr{R}(F), \quad \forall T \in \mathscr{T} \tag{13}$$

Thus, F^{-1} has finite incremental gain on $\mathscr{R}(F)$. It is easy to show that the continuity of F and (13) imply that $\mathscr{R}(P_T F)$ is closed (see Exercise 4, in the following.)

It remains to show that $\mathscr{R}(F) = \mathscr{H}_e$. To simplify the calculations below, let $\delta = 1$ in (11) and define $H: \mathscr{H}_e \to \mathscr{H}_e$ by

$$Fx \triangleq (I + H)x \qquad \text{or} \qquad F \triangleq I + H \tag{14}$$

Thus, H is continuous on $P_T \mathscr{H}_e$, and (11) with $\delta = 1$ becomes

$$\langle Hx - Hx' | x - x' \rangle_T \geq 0, \qquad \forall x, x' \in \mathscr{H}_e, \quad \forall T \in \mathscr{T} \tag{15}$$

i.e., H is *incrementally* passive. Let $S: \mathscr{R}(F) \to \mathscr{H}_e$ be defined by

$$S \triangleq (H - I)(I + H)^{-1} \tag{16}$$

so if y and x are related by $y = Fx$, we have

$$y = Fx \Leftrightarrow y = x + Hx \Leftrightarrow Sy = Hx - x \tag{17}$$

Since H is incrementally passive, then $S: \mathscr{R}(F) \to \mathscr{H}_e$ has an incremental gain ≤ 1; see Exercise 4, Section 10. Thus, we have

$$\|Sy - Sy'\|_T{}^2 \leq \|y - y'\|_T{}^2, \qquad \forall y, y' \in \mathscr{R}(F), \quad \forall T \in \mathscr{T} \tag{20}$$

Now it is well known that [Min. 1] a map $P_T S$ from the closed set $\mathscr{R}(P_T F) \subset P_T \mathscr{H}_e$ into $P_T \mathscr{H}_e$ and which satisfies a global Lipschitz condition like (20) can be extended to a map $\bar{S}: P_T \mathscr{H}_e \to P_T \mathscr{H}_e$ and still preserve (20).

Define the map $B: \mathscr{H}_e \to \mathscr{H}_e$ defined by $B: y \mapsto \frac{1}{2}(y - \bar{S}y)$. Now on $\mathscr{R}(F)$,

21 $$B = \tfrac{1}{2}(I - S) = \tfrac{1}{2}[I - (H - I)(I + H)^{-1}] = \tfrac{1}{2}[(I + H) - (H - I)](I + H)^{-1} = (I + H)^{-1} = F^{-1}$$

In other words, $FB = I$ on $\mathscr{R}(F)$. We are going to show that B is the inverse F on all of $\mathscr{H}_e$, i.e., that $\mathscr{R}(F) = \mathscr{H}_e$. Pick any $\bar{y} \in \mathscr{H}_e$ and define

22 $$\bar{x} \triangleq B\bar{y}$$

We claim that $F\bar{x} = \bar{y}$. Equivalently, $FB\bar{y} = \bar{y}$ for any $\bar{y} \in \mathscr{H}_e$; i.e., B is the inverse of F on all of $\mathscr{H}_e$. The proof is by contradiction. Suppose that for the chosen $\bar{y} \in \mathscr{H}_e$ there is some $T \in \mathscr{T}$ such that

23 $$\|\bar{y} - F\bar{x}\|_T > 0$$

Since H is continuous on $P_T\mathscr{H}_e$, there is an $\eta > 0$ such that

24 $$\|x - \bar{x}\|_T > \eta \Rightarrow \|Hx - H\bar{x}\|_T \leq (\tfrac{1}{2})\|\bar{y} - F\bar{x}\|_T$$

Choose $x_0 = \bar{x} + \lambda(\bar{y} - F\bar{x})$ with $\lambda > 0$ and small enough so that $\|x_0 - \bar{x}\|_T < \eta$. Given that particular x_0, define y_0 by

$$y_0 = Fx_0 = x_0 + Hx_0$$

Therefore, we have $\bar{y}_0 \in \mathscr{R}(F)$ and $By_0 = x_0$. We obtain successively, using (21) and expanding the scalar products,

25 $$\begin{aligned}&\langle y_0 - \bar{y} - (By_0 - B\bar{y}) | (By_0 - B\bar{y})\rangle_T \\ &= \langle \tfrac{1}{2}(y_0 - \bar{y}) + \tfrac{1}{2}(\bar{S}y_0 - \bar{S}\bar{y}) | \tfrac{1}{2}(y_0 - \bar{y}) - \tfrac{1}{2}(\bar{S}y_0 - \bar{S}\bar{y})\rangle_T \\ &= \tfrac{1}{4}\|y_0 - \bar{y}\|_T^2 - \tfrac{1}{4}\|\bar{S}\bar{y}_0 - \bar{S}\bar{y}\|_T^2 \geq 0\end{aligned}$$

where the last inequality follows by (20). Now by $By_0 = x_0$ and by (22), (25) becomes

27 $$\langle y_0 - \bar{y} - (x_0 - \bar{x}) | x_0 - \bar{x}\rangle_T \geq 0$$

Now on the one hand, $y_0 = Fx_0 = (I + H)x_0$, and by the choice of x_0,

$$x_0 - \bar{x} = \lambda(\bar{y} - F\bar{x}) = \lambda(\bar{y} - \bar{x} - H\bar{x})$$

(27), then becomes, after noting that $\lambda > 0$

$$\langle Hx_0 - \bar{y} + \bar{x} | \bar{y} - \bar{x} - H\bar{x}\rangle_T \geq 0$$

Adding and subtracting $H\bar{x}$ and noting that $F\bar{x} = \bar{x} + H\bar{x}$, we obtain

$$\langle Hx_0 - H\bar{x} - (\bar{y} - F\bar{x}) | \bar{y} - F\bar{x}\rangle_T \geq 0$$

or equivalently,

30 $$\langle Hx - H\bar{x} | \bar{y} - F\bar{x}\rangle_T \geq \|\bar{y} - F\bar{x}\|_T^2$$

Finally, by Schwarz's inequality and (24), (30) becomes

$$(\tfrac{1}{2})\|\bar{y} - F\bar{x}\|_T{}^2 \geq \|\bar{y} - F\bar{x}\|_T{}^2$$

This shows that the supposition (23) leads to a contradiction. Hence $B \triangleq \frac{1}{2}(I - \bar{S})$; $\mathscr{H}_e \to \mathscr{H}_e$ is the inverse of $F = I + H$ on $\mathscr{H}_e$ and $\mathscr{R}(F) = \mathscr{H}_e$. Thus, $F = (I + H)$ is a bijection of $\mathscr{H}_e$ onto $\mathscr{H}_e$. Part (b) of the theorem follows from the above and (13). ∎

Exercise 4 Show that $P_T F$ continuous and (13) imply that $\mathscr{R}(P_T F)$ is a closed set in $P_T \mathscr{H}_e$. [*Hint*: Consider a convergent sequence in $\mathscr{R}(P_T F)$; use (13) and the continuity of $P_T F$].

12 Instability theorems

In this section, we derive an instability counterpart to the Popov criterion of Section 6. As in Section V.9.1, the present results are based on an orthogonal decomposition of L^2, and we make use of some of the theorems from Section V.9.1.

We begin with a general result that illustrates the method.

1 **Theorem** Consider a feedback system represented by the equations

$$e_1 = u_1 - He_2 \tag{2}$$

$$e_2 = u_2 + Ge_1 \tag{3}$$

where $e_1, e_2, u_1, u_2: \mathbb{R}_+ \to \mathbb{R}^n$; $G, H: L^2_{ne}(\mathbb{R}_+) \to L^2_{ne}(\mathbb{R}_+)$, and suppose that corresponding to each u_1, u_2 in $L_n{}^2(\mathbb{R}_+)$, there exists a unique pair (e_1, e_2) in $L^2_{ne}(\mathbb{R}_+) \times L^2_{ne}(\mathbb{R}_+)$ such that (2) and (3) are satisfied. Suppose further that

4 G is causal and linear, and satisfies assumptions (V,9.6) and (V.9.7)

$$He = 0 \Rightarrow e = 0 \tag{5}$$

There is some $\delta \in \mathbb{R}$ such that

$$\langle e | Ge \rangle_T \geq \delta \|e_T\|^2, \qquad \forall e \in M \tag{6}$$

where M is defined by Eq. (V.9.5), and $\varepsilon \in \mathbb{R}$ such that

$$\langle e | He \rangle_T \geq \varepsilon \|(He)_T\|^2, \qquad \forall e \in L_e{}^2 \tag{7}$$

U.t.c., if M is not all of L^2, and if

$$\delta + \varepsilon > 0 \tag{8}$$

then $y_1 = Ge_1 \notin L^2$ whenever $u_1 = 0$, $u_2 \neq 0$, and $u_2 \in M^\perp$.

Proof [As in Theorem (V.9.10) if M is not all of L^2, then $M^\perp$ is a nontrivial subspace of L^2.] Let $u_1 = 0$, $u_2 \neq 0$, and $u_2 \in M^\perp$. Suppose by way of contradiction that $Ge_1 \in L^2$. Then this implies that $e_1 \in M$. Now we have

9
$$\begin{aligned}\langle e_1 | Ge_1 \rangle_T + \langle e_2 | He_2 \rangle_T &= \langle e_1 | e_2 - u_2 \rangle_T + \langle e_2 | u_1 - e_1 \rangle_T \\ &= -\langle e_1 | u_2 \rangle_T + \langle e_2 | u_1 \rangle_T = 0\end{aligned}$$

since $u_1 = 0$ and $u_2 \in M^\perp$. But, on the other hand, we get from (6) and (7) that

10
$$\langle e_1 | Ge_1 \rangle_T + \langle e_2 | He_2 \rangle_T \geq \delta \| e_{1T} \|^2 + \varepsilon \| (He_2)_T \|^2 = (\delta + \varepsilon) \| e_{1T} \|^2$$

Since $\delta + \varepsilon > 0$, (9) and (10) can be simultaneously satisfied only if $e_1 = 0$. But this implies, on the one hand, that $Ge_1 = 0$ and, on the other hand, that $He_2 = 0$, whence $e_2 = 0$ by (5). Finally, since $e_1 = Ge_1 + u_2$, the conditions $e_1 = 0$, $e_2 = 0$, and $u_2 \neq 0$ lead to a contradiction. Hence $Ge_1 \notin L^2$.

Next, we consider the instability counterpart to Theorem (6.5).

11 **Theorem** Consider a system described by (2) and (3), where u_1, u_2, e_1, e_2: $\mathbb{R}_+ \to \mathbb{R}$. The subsystem G is linear and causal and is represented by

12
$$(Ge)(t) = (g * e)(t) \triangleq y(t)$$

where

13
$$g(\cdot) \text{ is absolutely continuous.}$$

[This implies that $g(\cdot) \in L_e^1$, that is $\dot{g}$ measurable except possibly for an impulse at $t = 0$, and that $\dot{g}_T(\cdot) \in \mathscr{A}$ for all $T < \infty$.] Further, $g(\cdot)$ is Laplace transformable; $\hat{g}(\cdot)$ can be analytically continued to the region $\{s\colon \operatorname{Re} s \geq 0\}$; and $\hat{g}(\cdot)$ is meromorphic in this region. Also, we assume that

14
$$\text{the maps } \omega \mapsto \hat{g}(j\omega) \text{ and } \omega \mapsto j\omega\hat{g}(j\omega) \text{ are bounded on } \mathbb{R}.$$

The subsystem H is represented by

15
$$(He)(t) = \phi[e(t)]$$

where ϕ: $\mathbb{R} \to \mathbb{R}$ is continuous and $\phi \in$ sector $[0, k]$. Suppose finally that corresponding to each u_1, u_2 in L^2, there exists a pair (e_1, e_2) in $L_e^2 \times L_e^2$ satisfying (2) and (3). U.t.c., if $\hat{g}(\cdot)$ has at least one pole in the region $\{s\colon \operatorname{Re} s > 0\}$, if there exist real numbers $q \geq 0$ and $r > 0$ such that

16
$$\operatorname{Re}[(1 + jq\omega)\hat{g}(j\omega)] + 1/k \geq r > 0, \qquad \forall \omega \in \mathbb{R}$$

and if

17
$$\phi(x) = 0 \Rightarrow x = 0$$

then the system under study is L^2 unstable.

Proof If $u_1 = 0$, the feedback system can be modified as shown in Fig. VI.10

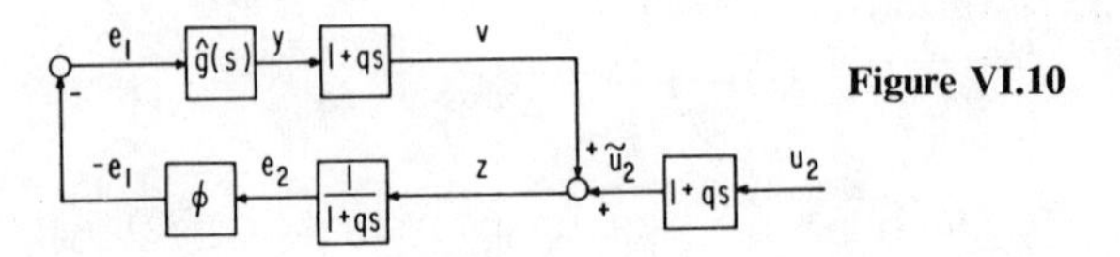

Figure VI.10

With this transformation, the system equations can be rewritten as

$$z(t) = [(g + q\dot{g}) * e_1](t) + \tilde{u}_2(t) = v(t) + u_2(t) \tag{18}$$

$$e_1(t) = -\phi[e_2(t)] \tag{19}$$

$$z(t) = e_2(t) + q\dot{e}_2(t) \tag{20}$$

Let H_1 and H_2 be the mappings defined by $H_1\colon e_1 \mapsto u$ and $H_2\colon z \mapsto -e_1$. Then we know from Example 6 that the operator H_2 satisfies (7) with $\varepsilon = 1/k$. The operator H_1 is a convolution operator with kernel $h_1 \triangleq g + q\dot{g}$. In view of the assumptions on g and $\dot{g}$, we see that the operator H_1 satisfies conditions (V.9.6) and (V.9.7). Hence the preimage of L^2 under H_1, say M_1, is a closed subspace of L^2. Also, since $\hat{g}$ has a singularity in the region $\{s\colon \operatorname{Re} s > 0\}$, we see that M_1 is a proper subspace of L^2. Now it is easy to verify by Parseval's equality that if $x(\cdot)$ and $[h_1 * x(\cdot)]$ belong to L^2, then

$$\langle x | h_1 * x \rangle \geq \inf_{\omega \in \mathbb{R}} \{\operatorname{Re} \hat{h}_1(j\omega)\} \cdot \|x\|^2 \tag{21}$$

Making use of the causality of H_1 and invoking Lemma (9.2), we conclude from (21) that

$$\begin{aligned} \langle x | H_1 x \rangle_T &\geq \inf_{\omega \in \mathbb{R}} \{\operatorname{Re} \hat{h}_1(j\omega)\} \cdot \|x_T\|^2 \\ &= \inf_{\omega \in \mathbb{R}} \{\operatorname{Re}[(1 + jq\omega)\hat{g}(j\omega)]\} \cdot \|x_T\|^2, \qquad \forall x \in L_e^2 \end{aligned}$$

So if (16) holds, then the mapping H_1 satisfies (6) with $\delta = r - 1/k$. Finally, we have $\delta + \varepsilon = r > 0$. Thus, we see from Theorem (1) that there exists a $\tilde{u}_2 \in L^2$ such that the corresponding $y \notin L^2$. For this $\tilde{u}_2$, let $u_2 = \mathscr{L}^{-1}\{[1/(1 + qs)]\tilde{u}_2(s)\}$. Then $u_2 \in L^2$ but the corresponding $y \notin L^2$, and hence the system is L^2 unstable. ∎

Notes and references

Theorem (1.3) was established in Youla *et al.* [You.1] for the linear case. The formal framework of Section 3 is to be found in Sandberg [San.8], Zames [Zam.3], and Willems [Wil.5]. In Section 4, Examples 1, 2, and 3 are well known in the circuit theory literature. Example 5 is based on an observation of Cho and Narendra [Cho.1]. Examples 6 and 7 can be found in Sundareshan and Thathachar [Sun.1]. The passivity theorems were developed by Sandberg [San.8], Zames [Zam.3], and Cho and Narendra [Cho.1]. The first treatment of the Popov criterion, which considered distributed systems, is found in Desoer [Des.3], and its generalization to the multivariable case is due to Lee and Desoer [Lee.1]. The discrete-time case development follows [Kri.1]. Theorem (8.8) is a sharpened version of the well-known paper of Zames and Freedman [Zam.6]; the improvement is due to Ramarajan and Thathachar [Ram.1]. The multiplier theory has been applied by many researchers. The idea of using noncausal multipliers is due to O'Shea [O'Sh.1]. The factorization technique using logarithms is originally due to Zames and Falb [Zam.5] and is found in its present form in Sundareshan and Thathachar [Sun.3]. The example involving monotone nonlinearities is due to Zames and Falb [Zam.5]. The second factorization technique can be found in Willems [Wil.5]. The application to multivariable systems using L^2 norms is due to Vidyasagar. The relationship between the passivity theorem and the small gain theorem pervades the circuit theory literature in the linear case. The development of Section 10 is based on Anderson [And.4]. Theorem (11.1) is based on Sandberg [San.11], and Theorem (11.10) on Browder [Bro.6]. The extension theorem used in the proof of (10.10) is in Minty [Min.1]. The instability results of Section 12 are due to Takeda and Bergen [Tak.1].

A INTEGRALS AND SERIES

A.1 Regulated functions

In system theory there is one particularly useful class of piecewise continuous functions, namely, the regulated functions. We define them below and state some of their properties.

1 Let $(E, \|\cdot\|)$ be a complete normed linear space, i.e., a Banach space. Let I be an interval in $\mathbb{R}$. The mapping $f: I \to E$ is said to be a *step function* iff there exists a *finite* partition of I, i.e.,

$$I = \bigcup_{i=0}^{k} [x_i, x_{i+1}] \qquad \text{with} \quad x_i < x_{i+1}, \quad \forall_i,$$

such that f is constant on each *open* interval (x_i, x_{i+1}). (*Note*: If $I = \mathbb{R}$, $x_0 = -\infty$, $x_k = \infty$.)

2 Let I be an interval in $\mathbb{R}$ and E be a Banach space. A function $f: I \to E$ is said to be **regulated** iff, for all $x \in I$, f has one-sided limits. More precisely, let the closure of I be $[\alpha, \beta]$; then, for all $x \in I$ distinct from β, for $h \to 0$,

3 $$\lim_{h>0} f(x+h) \triangleq f(x+) \qquad \text{exists} \quad (\text{hence } \|f(x+)\| \text{ is finite})$$

and for all $x' \in I$ distinct from α, for $h \to 0$,

4 $$\lim_{h>0} f(x'-h) \triangleq f(x'-) \qquad \text{exists} \quad (\text{hence } \|f(x-)\| \text{ is finite})$$

5 **Theorem** A function f: $I \to E$ is regulated if and only if, over all *compact* subintervals of I, it is the limit of a uniformly convergent sequence of step functions. (Recall that an interval is compact if and only if it is closed and bounded.)

It is immediate that if f: $I \to E$ is continuous, then it is regulated; also if f: $I \to R$ is monotonic, then it is regulated.

6 **Corollary** If f is regulated, then it can only have a denumerable number of discontinuities. Example: f: $(0, 1) \to R$ where $t \mapsto \text{sgn}[\sin(\varepsilon^{1/t})]$.

7 **Corollary** If f: $I \to E$ is regulated, then f is bounded on every *compact* subinterval of I.

8 **Corollary** Let f_i: $I \to E_i$ be regulated functions, where each E_i is a Banach space, $i = 1, 2, \ldots, n$. Let g: $\prod_{i=1}^{n} E_i \to F$ (where F is a Banach space) be *continuous*, then the composite function

$$t \mapsto g[f_1(t), f_2(t), \ldots, f_n(t)]$$

is regulated from I to F.

An immediate consequence of Corollary (8) is that if f and g are regulated functions from I to $\mathbb{R}$, so are $t \mapsto f(t) + g(t)$, $t \mapsto f(t)g(t)$, and $t \mapsto f(t)/g(t)$, where for the last one it is required that $g(t) \neq 0$, $\forall t \in I$.

Exercise 1 Give examples to show the following: Suppose that f: $I \to R$ and $g: f(I) \to \mathbb{R}$. U.t.c.,

(i) if f and g are regulated, then $g \circ f$ is not necessarily regulated;
(ii) if f is continuous and g regulated, then $g \circ f$ is not necessarily regulated.

9 The indefinite integral of a regulated function f is easily defined. Let f: $[a, b] \to E$, then, by definition,

10 $$\phi(t) = \int_a^t f(\tau)\, d\tau \triangleq \lim \int_a^t f_\nu(\tau)\, d\tau$$

where the f_ν's are step functions, which converge uniformly to f over (a, t).

11 Clearly, ϕ has a derivative everywhere, except at the points of discontinuity of f, but at such points, say t', ϕ has a well-defined right derivative and left derivative:

12
$$\phi'(t'+) = f(t'+) \qquad \text{and} \qquad \phi'(t'-) = f(t'-)$$

13 A function f: $[a, b] \to R$ is said to be **absolutely continuous** on $[a, b]$ iff, for any $\varepsilon > 0$, there is a $\delta > 0$ such that

$$\sum_{i=1}^{n} |f(\alpha_i) - f(\beta_i)| < \varepsilon$$

for every finite collection of subintervals (α_i, β_i) of $[a, b]$ with

$$\sum_{i=1}^{n} |\alpha_i - \beta_i| < \delta$$

14 **Special Cases** (I) By choosing the collection above to consist of one subinterval, we see that if f is absolutely continuous on $[a, b]$, then it is uniformly continuous on $[a, b]$.

(II) If f obeys a Lipschitz condition on $[a, b]$, then it is absolutely continuous on $[a, b]$.

(III) If f is absolutely continuous on $[a, b]$, then it is of bounded variation on $[a, b]$.

(IV) If f: $[a, b] \to \mathbb{R}$ is the integral of a regulated function, then f is absolutely continuous.

(V) There are classical examples of monotonically increasing functions that are continuous but not absolutely continuous.

The importance of absolutely continuous functions lies in the following theorem [McS.1, p. 208].

15 **Theorem** If f: $[a, b] \to \mathbb{R}$ is absolutely continuous, then

(a) its derivative $f'(x)$ exists and is finite almost everywhere, and

(b) if we set $\dot{f}(x) = f'(x)$, where f' is defined, and zero elsewhere, then we have

$$f(x) = \int_a^x \dot{f}(\xi)\, d\xi + f(a), \qquad \forall x \in [a, b]$$

Conversely, if f is of the form

$$f(x) = \int_a^x g(\xi)\, d\xi + f(a), \qquad \forall x \in [a, b]$$

where g is integrable on $[a, b]$, then f is absolutely continuous on $[a, b]$.

A.2 Integrals

We state in the following a number of properties of the Lebesgue integral that are used in the main development. For readers acquainted with Lebesgue integration, this will be a review. For readers who have not gone through a detailed development of the Lebesgue integral, they need only know that

(1) The Lebesgue integral is an extension of the usual Riemann integral; the class of Lebesgue integrable functions includes the class of Riemann integrable functions (which includes continuous functions, piecewise-continuous functions, regulated functions etc.).

(2) The analytical properties of Lebesgue integrable functions are simpler than those of Riemann integrable functions. The logic of the main development will not fail if such readers take the properties in the following as axiomatic.

One of the most important analytical properties of the Lebesgue integral is the following theorem.

1 **Dominated Convergence Theorem** [Ros. 1, p. 76] Let g be integrable on an interval I finite or infinite. Let $\{f_n\}_0^\infty$ be a sequence of functions on I such that $\forall n$, $|f_n(x)| \leq g(x)$, $\forall x \in I$. If, for almost all $x \in I$, as $n \to \infty$, $f_n(x)$ tends to a limit called $f(x)$, then

$$\int_I f(x)\,dx = \lim_{n\to\infty} \int_I f_n(x)\,dx \qquad \text{and} \qquad \lim \int |f - f_n|\,dx = 0$$

2 **Hölder's Inequality** [Roy. 1, p. 95] Let $f, g\colon \mathbb{R} \to \mathbb{R}$. Let p and q be non-negative extended real numbers (i.e., $1 \leq p,\, q \leq \infty$) with $1/p + 1/q = 1$. If $f \in L^p$ and $g \in L^q$, then

(a) $fg \in L^1$

(b) $\|fg\|_1 \leq \|f\|_p \, \|g\|_q$.

When $p = 2$, the Hölder inequality becomes the *Schwartz inequality*.

3 **Minkowski Inequality** [Roy. 1, p.5] For $p \in [1, \infty]$, $f, g \in L^p$ implies that

$$\|f + g\|_p \leq \|f\|_p + \|g\|_p$$

4 **Fact** Let $f\colon \mathbb{R} \to \mathbb{R}$ and $1 \leq p < \infty$. If $f \in L^p$ and if f is *uniformly continuous* on $\mathbb{R}$, then $|f(t)| \to 0$ as $|t| \to \infty$. (Note that $\dot{f} \in L^\infty \Rightarrow f$ is uniformly continuous.)

5 **Fact** If $f\colon \mathbb{R} \to \mathbb{R}$ and $f \in L^1 \cap L^\infty$, then for $p \in [1, \infty]$, $f \in L^p$.

6 **Fact** Let f: $[a, b] \to \mathbb{R}$, where $\infty < a < b < \infty$. If for some $p \in [1, \infty]$, $f \in L^p[a, b]$, then $f \in L^1[a, b]$.

Give an example to show that the converse is not true.

7 **Fact** [McS.1, p. 227] If f: $\mathbb{R} \to \mathbb{R}$ and $f \in L^1$, then

$$\lim_{h \to 0} \int_{-\infty}^{+\infty} |f(t+h) - f(t)| \, dt = 0$$

8 **Tonelli's Theorem** [McS.1, p. 145] Let m and n be positive integers. Let f: $\mathbb{R}^m \times \mathbb{R}^n \to \mathbb{R}$ be locally integrable on $\mathbb{R}^m \times \mathbb{R}^n$. If

(a) for all $x \in \mathbb{R}^m$, except for a set E of measure zero, the function $y \mapsto |f(x, y)|$ is integrable over $\mathbb{R}^n$,

(b) the *iterated* integral

$$\int_{\mathbb{R}^m - E} \left[\int_{\mathbb{R}^n} |f(x, y)| \, dy \right] dx < \infty$$

then

(i) $(x, y) \mapsto f(x, y)$ is integrable over $\mathbb{R}^m \times \mathbb{R}^n$

(ii)
$$\int_{\mathbb{R}^m - E} \left[\int_{\mathbb{R}^n} f(x, y) \, dy \right] dx = \int_{\mathbb{R}^m \times \mathbb{R}^n} f(x, y) \, dx \, dy$$

9 **Remarks** (1) The absolute value sign in assumption (b) is essential; see counterexample [McS.1, p. 144].

(2) Roughly speaking, the theorem says that if one *iterated* integral of the *absolute value* of f exists, then it is equal to the double integral of f. By symmetry, the double integral is equal to each of the iterated integrals.

(3) In applications, one establishes via Tonelli's theorem the existence of the double integral by studying one of the iterated integrals, i.e., by establishing inequality (b).

Indefinite integrals

10 **Theorem** Let I be an interval (finite or infinite) of $\mathbb{R}$. A function F: $I \to \mathbb{R}$ is the indefinite integral of some integrable function f if and only if F is absolutely continuous. Also, $\dot{F} = f$ a.e., on I.

Exercise 1 If $\dot{f} \in L^1$, then $\lim_{t \to \infty} f(t)$ exists (and is finite).

A.3 Series

In our work we use sequences $n \mapsto x_n$, where $x_n \in \mathbb{R}$ or $\mathbb{R}^n$ or $\mathbb{R}^{n \times n}$, etc. So it is simpler to think in terms of sequences which take values in a normed space E. The norm in E is denoted by $|\cdot|$. In most cases, E will be complete, i.e., a Banach space.

Given a sequence $(x_n)_0^\infty$ (i.e., the function $n \mapsto x_n$, from $\mathbb{Z}_+$ to E), we define the nth partial sum s_n by

1
$$s_n = x_0 + x_1 + \cdots + x_n$$

2 We say that **the series** $\sum_0^\infty x_n$ **converges** to s iff $\lim s_n = s$. (This is convergence in terms of the norm of E.)

3 For the case where the normed space E is complete, we say that the **series** $\sum_0^\infty x_n$ converges **absolutely** if and only if the series of *positive* real numbers $\sum_0^\infty |x_n|$ converges.

To discuss the convolution of sequences, we need a theorem analogous to Tonelli's. Instead of functions of two variables, we have double sequences.

4 **Theorem** Let $(m, n) \mapsto a_{mn}$ be a double sequence in E (i.e., a function mapping $\mathbb{Z}_+ \times \mathbb{Z}_+$ into E). If

$$\sum_{m=0}^{\infty} |a_{mn}| \qquad \text{converges for} \qquad n = 0, 1, 2, \ldots$$

and

$$\sum_{n=0}^{\infty} \sum_{m=0}^{\infty} |a_{mn}| < \infty$$

then

$$\sum_{m,n=0}^{\infty} a_{mn} = \sum_{n=0}^{\infty} \left(\sum_{m=0}^{\infty} a_{mn} \right) = \sum_{m=0}^{\infty} \left(\sum_{n=0}^{\infty} a_{mn} \right)$$

The two expressions on the right are called *repeated series.*

5 **Theorem** (Hölder's inequality for sequences) Let $x = (x_1, x_2, \ldots)$, $y = (y_1, y_2, \ldots)$ be sequences in E, i.e., $x, y\colon \mathbb{Z}_+ \to E$. Let $p, q \in [1, \infty]$ with $p^{-1} + q^{-1} = 1$. If $x \in l^p$ and $y \in l^q$, then

$$\sum_{k=0}^{\infty} |x_k y_k| < \infty$$

(i.e., the scalar product $x^T y = \sum_0^\infty x_k y_k$ converges absolutely in E), and

6
$$\sum_{k=0}^{\infty} |x_k y_k| \le \|x\|_p \|y\|_q$$

For convolution of sequences, see Appendix C. 4.

B FOURIER TRANSFORMS

We collect in the following some basic results that are frequently used in our work.

B.1 L^1 Theory

Theorem If $f\colon \mathbb{R} \to \mathbb{R}$ and $f \in L^1$, and if $\hat{f}(j\omega) \triangleq \int_{-\infty}^{+\infty} f(t)\varepsilon^{-j\omega t}\, dt$, then

(a) $\omega \mapsto \hat{f}(j\omega) \triangleq \int_{-\infty}^{+\infty} f(t)\varepsilon^{-j\omega t}\, dt$ is *uniformly continuous* on $\mathbb{R}$,
(b) $\hat{f} \in L^\infty$
(c) $|\hat{f}(j\omega)| \to 0 \quad$ as $\quad |\omega| \to \infty$ (Riemann–Lebesgue)
(d) $\max_{\omega \in \mathbb{R}} |\hat{f}(j\omega)| \leq \|f\|_1$
(e) $f(t) = (1/2\pi) \int_{-\infty}^{\infty} \hat{f}(j\omega)\varepsilon^{j\omega t}\, d\omega \qquad$ almost everywhere in $\mathbb{R}$.
(f) if, in addition, f is of bounded variation in a neighborhood of t, then

$$\tfrac{1}{2}[f(t+0) - f(t-0)] = (1/2\pi) \lim_{\Omega \to \infty} \int_{-\Omega}^{+\Omega} \hat{f}(j\omega)\varepsilon^{j\omega t}\, d\omega$$

B.2 L^2 Theory

1 **Theorem** Let $f: \mathbb{R} \to \mathbb{R}$ and $f \in L^2$. If

$$\hat{f}_N(j\omega) \triangleq \int_{-N}^{+N} f(t)\varepsilon^{-j\omega t}\, dt, \qquad N = 1, 2, \ldots \tag{2}$$

then

(a) as $N \to \infty$,

$$\hat{f}_N \xrightarrow{L^2} \hat{f} \qquad \text{where} \quad \hat{f} \in L^2$$

(b) $(\|f\|_2)^2 = (1/2\pi)(\|\hat{f}\|_2)^2$
(c) as $N \to \infty$,

$$(1/2\pi)\int_{-N}^{N} \hat{f}(j\omega)\varepsilon^{j\omega t}\, d\omega \xrightarrow{L^2} f(t)$$

3 **Remarks** (a) The convergence in (a) and (c) is convergence with respect to the L^2 norm. It is not pointwise convergence (e.g., the Gibbs phenomenon).

(b) The Fourier transform maps L^2 *onto* L^2, and the L^2 norms of f and $\hat{f}$ are equal except for the factor of $1/(2\pi)^{1/2}$.

(c) $f \in L^1 \not\Rightarrow \hat{f} \in L^1$ (e.g., $f(t) = 1$ for $|t| \le 1$ and zero elsewhere).
(d) $f \in L^2 \not\Rightarrow \hat{f} \in L^\infty$.
(e) $f \in L^2 \not\Rightarrow \hat{f} \in L^1$.

4 **Parseval Theorem** If $f, g \in L^2$, then

(a) $\widehat{f * g} = \hat{f}\hat{g}$
(b) $\int_{-\infty}^{+\infty} f(t)g(t)\, dt = (1/2\pi)\int_{-\infty}^{+\infty} \hat{f}^*(j\omega)\hat{g}(j\omega)\, d\omega$
(c) $\|f\|_2 = [(1/2\pi)^{1/2}]\|\hat{f}\|_2$

5 **Theorem** (Sandberg) (a) If f and $\dot{f} \in L^2$, then $\hat{f} \in L^1$.
(b) If $\hat{f}$ and $\dot{\hat{f}} \in L^2$, then $f \in L^1$.

Proof $f, \dot{f} \in L^2$ imply that $\hat{f} \in L^2$ and $j\omega\hat{f}(j\omega) \in L^2$. Thus,

$$\begin{aligned}
\int |\hat{f}(j\omega)|\, d\omega &= \int (1 + \omega^2)^{-1/2}[(1 + \omega^2)^{1/2}\, |\hat{f}(j\omega)|]\, d\omega \\
&\le \left(\int \frac{d\omega}{1 + \omega^2}\right)^{1/2} \left[\int (1 + \omega^2)\, |\hat{f}(j\omega)|^2\, d\omega\right]^{1/2} \\
&= (\pi)^{1/2}(\|\hat{f}\|_2{}^2 + \|\omega\hat{f}(j\omega)\|_2{}^2)^{1/2} < \infty.
\end{aligned}$$

∎

Exercise 1 If f and $\dot{f} \in L^2$, show that $f \in L^\infty$ and $|f(t)| \to 0$ as $t \to \infty$. (*Hint*: Consider the integral of $f\dot{f}$, ...)

Exercise 2 If $f \in L^2$ and $tf \in L^2$, then $f \in L^1$.

B.3 Laplace transform

The Laplace transform has simpler properties than the Fourier transform because it considers only functions that are identically zero for $t < 0$. Except for immediate consequences of the Fourier theory, the most interesting results are Theorems (4) and (5).

1 If f: $\mathbb{R}_+ \to \mathbb{R}$ is locally integrable, its Laplace transform is defined by

$$\hat{f}(s) = \int_0^\infty f(t)e^{-st}\,dt, \qquad s = \sigma + j\omega$$

where the domain of definition of $\hat{f}$ depends on the convergence of the integral.

We use $\mathscr{L}(f)$ to denote the Laplace transform of f.

2 **Fact** If the integral converges absolutely for $s = s_0$, then $s \mapsto \hat{f}(s)$ is analytic for all s such that Re $s >$ Re s_0.

3 **Fact** If $f \in L^1(\mathbb{R}_+)$ [or $L^2(\mathbb{R}_+)$ or $L^\infty(\mathbb{R}_+)$], then $s \mapsto \hat{f}(s)$ is analytic in Re $s > 0$.

In the case of distributions (generalized functions) and of L^2 functions, one can give a necessary and sufficient condition as follows.

4 **Theorem** [Sch.1] Let $\hat{f}$ be an analytic function defined on some half-plane Re $s > \sigma_0$. U.t.c., $\hat{f}$ is the Laplace transform of a distribution with support on $\mathbb{R}_+$ if and only if $|\hat{f}(s)|$ is bounded, for $\sigma =$ Re s sufficiently large, by a polynomial in $|s|$.

The degree of the polynomial depends on the distribution; for example, $\mathscr{L}[\delta^{(n)}] = s^n$.

5 **Theorem** A function $\hat{f}$ is the Laplace transform of a function f: $\mathbb{R}_+ \to \mathbb{R}$ with $f \in L^2$ if and only if

(a) $\hat{f}$ is analytic for $\sigma > 0$,
(b) for some $M < \infty$ (which depends on $\hat{f}$),

$$\int_{-\infty}^{+\infty} |\hat{f}(\sigma + j\omega)|^2\,d\omega \leq M, \qquad \text{for all} \quad \sigma > 0$$

C CONVOLUTION

C.1 Introduction

Given two functions u and h mapping $\mathbb{R}_+$ into $\mathbb{R}$, we may compute (under some conditions) their **convolution** $u * h$ which is defined by the integral

$$(u * h)(t) = \int_0^t h(t - \tau)u(\tau)\, d\tau = y(t), \qquad \text{for} \quad t \geq 0 \tag{1}$$

The main reasons for using the convolution as a mathematical representation for linear time-invariant systems are the following:

(a) Under very mild conditions, L. Schwartz has proved that any linear time-invariant system is represented by a convolution with a kernel, which is a distribution (generalized function);

(b) It allows consideration under the same framework of lumped-parameter systems, distributed systems, and systems with transportation lags [Sch.1, p. 162].

2 The simplest case is where $h(\cdot)$ is the impulse response of a linear, time-invariant, nonanticipative system whose transfer function $\hat{h}(s)$ is a *rational* function of s with $|\hat{h}(s)| \to 0$ as $|s| \to \infty$. Note that u.t.c.,

(A) $\hat{h}(s)$ has all its poles in the open left half-plane if and only if $h \in L^1$. If (A) holds, then

(i) h decays exponentially, i.e., for some $h_m < \infty$, and some $\alpha > 0$,

$$|h(t)| \leq h_m \varepsilon^{-\alpha t}, \qquad \forall t \in \mathbb{R}_+$$

(ii) $\dot{h}(t) = h(0+)\delta(t) + h_1(t)$

where $h_1(\cdot)$ decays exponentially; $h(0+)$ is possibly zero. Indeed, $h(0+) = \lim_{s \to \infty} s\hat{h}(s)$.

(iii) $u \in L^1 \Rightarrow y \in L^1 \cap L^\infty$, $\dot{y} \in L^1$; furthermore, y is continuous and $y(t) \to 0$ as $t \to \infty$. $u \in L^2 \Rightarrow y \in L^2 \cap L^\infty$, $\dot{y} \in L^2$; furthermore, y is continuous and $y(t) \to 0$ as $t \to \infty$.

(iv) For $1 \leq p \leq \infty, u \in L^p \Rightarrow y$ and $\dot{y} \in L^p$; furthermore, y is continuous.
Statements (i) and (ii) are obvious; (iii) and (iv) require Theorem (C.2.14).

Exercise 1 If, in addition, for some integer $m > 1$, $\lim_{|s| \to \infty} s^{m+1}\hat{h}(s) = c$, a constant. State additional conclusions that you can draw. [*Hint*: Consider $h, \dot{h}, \ldots, h^{(m)}$.]

C.2 Convolution of functions

L^1 Theory

1 **Theorem** Let $u, v, w \colon \mathbb{R}_+ \to \mathbb{R}$. If $u, v, w \in L^1$, then

2 $$u * w \in L^1 \qquad \text{and} \qquad \|u * w\|_1 \leq \|u\|_1 \cdot \|w\|_1$$

3 $$u * w = w * u \qquad \text{and} \qquad (u * v) * w = u * (v * w)$$

4 **Comment** The linear space L^1, together with the convolution as a product, constitutes an algebra, because the addition, scalar multiplication, and multiplication obey all the required axioms (see Appendix D). Furthermore, it is a Banach algebra, because $\|u * w\|_1 \leq \|u\|_1 \cdot \|w\|_1$ and because L^1 is complete. In view of (3), it is a *commutative* Banach algebra which, however, does not have a unit.

Exercise 1 Discuss the system-theoretic implications of Theorem (1). Consider the zero-state response of interconnections of linear time-invariant subsystems whose impulse response is in L^1.

Proof The key tool in the derivation is Tonelli's theorem. All integrals below are on $\mathbb{R}_+$; so we omit the limits on integral signs. Let us bound

5 $$|(w * u)(t)| = \left|\int w(t-\tau)u(\tau)\,d\tau\right| \le \int |w(t-\tau)|\,|u(\tau)|\,d\tau$$

where the last integral may take the value ∞ for some t. Anyway, let us calculate $\|w * u\|_1$:

6 $$\int |(w * u)(t)|\,dt \le \int\left[\int |w(t-\tau)|\,|u(\tau)|\,d\tau\right] dt$$

Consider the other iterated integral

7 $$\int\left[\int |w(t-\tau)|\,|u(\tau)|\,dt\right] d\tau$$

8 $$= \int |u(\tau)| \left[\int |w(t-\tau)|\,dt\right] d\tau$$

9 $$= \|u\|_1 \|w\|_1 < \infty$$

The inequality (6) is immediate; however, at this stage the right-hand side might be infinite. (7) is simply the iterated integral in reverse order, which is then evaluated by (8) and found to be finite in (9). By Tonelli's theorem, since the iterated integral (7) is finite, so is the integral (6). Therefore, conclusion (2) is established. Conclusion (3) follows from (2) and Tonelli's theorem. ∎

10 **Corollary** Let $W: \mathbb{R}_+ \to \mathbb{R}^{n\times n}$ and $u: \mathbb{R}_+ \to \mathbb{R}^n$. If all elements of W and of u are in L^1, then

11 $$\|W * u\|_1 \le \|W\|_1 \|u\|_1$$

where

12 $$\|u\|_1 = \int |u(t)|\,dt, \qquad \|W\|_1 = \int |W(t)|\,dt$$

with $|u(t)|$ designating some $\mathbb{R}^n$ norm of $u(t)$, and $|W(t)|$ the corresponding induced matrix norm in $\mathbb{R}^{n\times n}$.

13 **Remark** If $u, w \in L^1$, then

(a) $w * u$ need not be bounded (on $\mathbb{R}_+$) nor continuous,

(b) $w * u$ need not go to zero as $t \to \infty$,

(c) $\widehat{w * u} = \hat{w}\hat{u}$ is bounded, uniformly continuous, and goes to zero as $\omega \to \infty$,

(d) $\widehat{w * u}$ need not be in L^1.

Exercise 2 Let $f\colon \mathbb{R}_+ \to \mathbb{R}$ and $f\colon t \mapsto (1+t)^{-1}(t)^{-1/2}$. Let $g\colon \mathbb{R}_+ \to \mathbb{R}$ with $g(t) = f(1-t)$ for $t \in (0, 1)$ and zero elsewhere. Show that $f * g \notin L^\infty(\mathbb{R}_+)$. Let $\phi(t) = \sum_{n=2}^{\infty} 2^{-n} f(t-n)$. Show that $g * \phi$ does not go to zero as $t \to \infty$ and that $\forall T > 0$, $\exists t' \geq T$ such that $|(g * \phi)(t')| \geq T$.

L^p Theory

14 **Theorem** Let $u, w\colon \mathbb{R}_+ \to \mathbb{R}$ and $p \in [1, \infty]$. If $u \in L^p$ and $w \in L^1$, then

15
$$\|w * u\|_p \leq \|w\|_1 \|u\|_p$$

Proof Consider $1 < p < \infty$; then we have

$$|(w * u)(t)| \leq \int |w(t-\tau)|^{1/p}| \; |u(\tau)| \cdot |w(t-\tau)|^{1/q} \, d\tau$$

The first factor is in L^p [by Theorem (1)], and the second is in L^q; hence by Hölder's inequality,

$$|(w * u)(t)| \leq \left[\int |w(t-\tau)| \; |u(\tau)|^p \, d\tau\right]^{1/p} \left[\int |w(t-\tau)|^{q/q} \, d\tau\right]^{1/q}$$

Note that the last factor is bounded by $\|w\|_1^{1/q}$. Taking L^p norms of both sides,

$$\begin{aligned} \|w * u\|_p &\leq \|w\|_1^{1/q} \left\{\int \left[\int |w(t-\tau)| \; |u(\tau)|^p \, d\tau\right] dt\right\}^{1/p} \\ &\leq \|w\|_1^{1/q} \|w\|_1^{1/p} \|u\|_p = \|w\|_1 \|u\|_p \end{aligned}$$

where we used again Theorem (1).

For $p = 1$, (15) becomes the known inequality (2). For $p = \infty$, (15) is immediate since we can pull the essential supremum of u out of the convolution integral. ∎

16 **Remarks** (I) Inequality (15) of Theorem (14) extends to the matrix–vector case as in Corollary (10).

(II) In Theorem (14), $w * u$ need not be bounded, nor continuous nor tend to zero as $t \to \infty$.

(III) If $w \in L^1$ and $u \in L^2$, then we have a sharper bound (II.6.7)

$$\|w * u\|_2 \leq \max_\omega |\hat{w}(j\omega)| \; \|u\|_2$$

Furthermore, it can be shown that [Tit. 1, Boc.1]

$$\widehat{w * u} = \hat{w}\hat{u}$$

(IV) Inequality (15) is sharp only for $p = 1, \infty$, because then $\|w\|_1$ is the induced norm of the map $u \mapsto w * u$ from L^∞ into L^∞ (II.6.3).

Exercise 3 If $w \in L^1$ and $u \in L^\infty$, then

(a) $w * u$ is uniformly continuous. [*Hint*: Use Fact (A.2.4).]
(b) $w * u$ need not go to zero as $t \to \infty$. (*Hint*: Think of some step response!)

Exercise 4 If $w \in L^2$ and $u \in L^2$, then

(a) $\widehat{w * u} = \hat{w}\hat{u} \in L^1$;
(b) $w * u \in L^\infty$, $w * u$ is uniformly continuous, and $(w * u)(t) \to 0$ as $t \to \infty$.

Exercise 5 Let us impose more restrictions on w. Let $w \in L^1 \cap L^\infty$; hence $w \in L^p$ for $1 \leq p \leq \infty$.

U.t.c., if $u \in L^1$, then $w * u \in L^1 \cap L^\infty$ is uniformly continuous and goes to zero as $t \to \infty$; if $u \in L^2$, then $w * u \in L^2 \cap L^\infty$ is uniformly continuous and goes to zero as $t \to \infty$ (observe that $\widehat{w * u} \in L^1$).

Exercise 6 Verify in detail that Theorem (14) applies when $u(t) \in \mathbb{R}^n$ and $W(t) \in \mathbb{R}^{n \times n}$. Be sure to justify every step by invoking properties of norms, induced norms, etc.

C.3 Convolution of a measure and a function

Models of physical systems involve often impulse responses which include impulses. So instead of considering its impulse response w, we think in terms of its step response μ. For example, if w consists of a sum of a locally integrable function w_1 and impulses

$$w(t) = w_1(t) + \sum_0^\infty \alpha_k \delta(t - t_k), \qquad 0 \leq t_1 < t_2 < t_3 \cdots \tag{1}$$

then the corresponding μ defined by

$$\mu(t) = \int_{0-}^{t+} w(t')\, dt' \tag{2}$$

includes steps of size α_k at t_k, $k = 0, 1, \ldots$. The upper limit is designated $t+$ because we require that μ be continuous from the right. The function μ defined by (2) is a special case of a *measure* on $\mathbb{R}_+$. In particular, the measure of the interval $(a, b]$ is given by $\mu(b) - \mu(a)$. In the standard manner [Roy.1], the integral of the measurable function $f: \mathbb{R}_+ \to \mathbb{R}$ is defined and denoted by

$$\int f \, d\mu \triangleq \mu(f)$$

Let

3 $$\|\mu\| \triangleq \sup |\mu(f)|$$

where the supremum is taken over all $f: \mathbb{R}_+ \to \mathbb{R}$ which are continuous, have compact support and such that $\sup_{t \geq 0} |f(t)| \leq 1$.

4 The measure μ is said to be **bounded** iff $\|\mu\| < \infty$.

Exercise 1 In case μ is defined by (2) in terms of w given by (1), show that

$$\|\mu\| = \int_0^\infty |w_1(t)| \, dt + \sum_0^\infty |\alpha_k|$$

The convolution of a function $g: \mathbb{R}_+ \to \mathbb{R}$ with the measure μ is denoted by $(\mu * g)$ and is defined by

5 $$(\mu * g)(t) = \int_{0-}^{t+} g(t - \tau) \, d\mu(\tau)$$

For example, for the measure μ defined by (1) and (2),

$$(\mu * g)(t) = \int_0^t w_1(t - \tau) g(\tau) \, d\tau + \sum_0^k \alpha_j g(t - t_j)$$

where k is the largest integer such that $t_j \leq t$.

The following result can be proven (Die.2).

6 **Theorem** Let μ be a bounded measure on $\mathbb{R}_+$,

(a) If $p \in [1, \infty]$ and $g \in L^p(\mathbb{R}_+)$, then $\mu \in g$ is defined almost everywhere and

7 $$\|\mu * g\|_p \leq \|\mu\| \, \|g\|_p$$

(b) If g is continuous, then $\mu * g$ is defined everywhere and is continuous.
(c) If g is continuous and $\to 0$ as $t \to \infty$, then so does $\mu * g$.

C.4 Convolution of sequences

Let $a = (a_0, a_1, a_2, \ldots)$ and $b = (b_0, b_1, b_2, \ldots)$ be sequences of real numbers, i.e., functions from $\mathbb{Z}_+$ to $\mathbb{R}$. The convolution of a and b is defined to be the sequence

1 $$a * b = (\gamma_0, \gamma_1, \gamma_2, \ldots)$$

where

2 $$\gamma_n = \sum_{k=0}^{n} a_{n-k} b_k, \qquad n = 0, 1, 2, \ldots$$

It is a fact that the convolution of two l^1 sequences is an l^1 sequence. More precisely, we have the following theorem.

3 **Theorem** (Apostol) If a and b are l^1 sequences and if

4 $$\sum_0^\infty a_k = \alpha \qquad \text{and} \qquad \sum_0^\infty b_k = \beta$$

then

5 $$a * b \in l^1$$

and, with γ_n defined by (2),

6 $$\sum_0^\infty \gamma_n = \alpha\beta; \qquad \sum_0^\infty |\gamma_n| \le \left(\sum_0^\infty |a_k|\right)\left(\sum_0^\infty |b_j|\right)$$

Since Hölder's inequality holds for sequences, we have the following theorem.

7 **Theorem** Let a and b be sequences and $p \in [1, \infty]$. If $a \in l^p$ and $b \in l^1$, then

8 $$\|a * b\|_p \le \|a\|_p \|b\|_1$$

9 **Remark** The conclusions (5) and (8) still hold if a and b are sequences that take values in $\mathbb{R}^{n \times n}$ or in any normed space, provided that in the latter case, the product of two elements is defined and that $\|ab\| \le \|a\| \, \|b\|$ for all a, b. Indeed, careful examination of the definitions and of the proofs shows that, with the general definition of convergence in normed spaces (A.2.2) and the properties of the norm, every step of the proof is valid.

D ALGEBRAS

The purpose of this appendix is to introduce certain general definitions and facts concerning algebras, to discuss in detail the algebras $\mathscr{A}$ and $\mathscr{A}^{n \times n}$, and, finally, to state some useful inversion theorems.

D.1 Algebras

1 A **linear space** is, by definition, a set V of elements together with a field $\mathbb{K}$ and two operations; an *addition* (i.e., a map $V \times V \to V$) is defined on V, and it is *associative*, *commutative*, has a *zero vector* θ, and every $v \in V$ has an *inverse* $-v$ (under addition); a *scalar multiplication* (i.e., a map $V \times \mathbb{K} \to V$) is defined, and it is associative, distributes with respect to addition, and $1v = v$, $\forall v \in V$.

2 If in addition to scalar multiplication we have a multiplication, we obtain an algebra. More precisely, we say that A is an **algebra over the field** $\mathbb{K}$ iff

(1) A is a *linear space* over $\mathbb{K}$ (hence an addition and a scalar multiplication are defined in A);

(2) a multiplication, i.e., a map $(x, y) \mapsto xy$ from $A \times A \to A$, is defined and is *associative*

$$(xy)z = x(yz) = xyz, \qquad \forall x, y, z \in A$$

(3) multiplication *distributes* over addition

$$x(y+z) = xy + xz \qquad (y+z)x = yx + zx, \qquad \forall x, y, z \in A$$

(4) multiplication and scalar multiplication commute

$$(\alpha x)(\beta y) = (\alpha\beta)xy, \qquad \forall \alpha, \beta \in \mathbb{K}, \quad \forall x, y \in A$$

3 **Notes** (a) Another way of expressing conditions (3) and (4) is to say that multiplication is a *bilinear* map from $A \times A$ into A (over the field $\mathbb{K}$).

(b) If the multiplication is commutative, the algebra is said to be **commutative**.

(c) An algebra A need not have a **unit element**, i.e., an element e such that $ex = xe = x$, $\forall x \in A$.

(d) If, in addition, A is a Banach space over $\mathbb{K}$ (i.e., a complete normed linear space over $\mathbb{K}$) and if $\|xy\| \le \|x\| \, \|y\|$, $\forall x, y \in A$, then A is said to be a **Banach algebra**. If A has a unit element e, the norm is usually scaled so that $\|e\| = 1$.

4 **Examples** 1. The set of all $n \times n$ matrices with elements in $\mathbb{K}$ with the usual operations is an example of a *noncommutative* algebra with a unit element (the identity matrix).

2. Ditto for the class of all continuous linear maps from E into E, where E is any normed linear space. (Multiplication here is the composition of linear maps.)

3. Let $A = L^1(\mathbb{R})$ with the convolution taken to be the product. This is a commutative algebra without unit. [The unit is $\delta(t)$, which is not an element of $L^1(\mathbb{R})$.]

4 Let $\mathscr{A}$ have elements of the form

$$g(t) = \begin{cases} g_a(t) + \sum_{i=0}^{\infty} g_i \delta(t - t_i), & \text{for } t \ge 0 \\ 0, & \text{for } t < 0 \end{cases} \tag{5}$$

where

$$g_a \in L^1(\mathbb{R}_+); \qquad g_i \in \mathbb{R}, \quad \forall i \quad \text{and} \quad \sum_{i=0}^{\infty} |g_i| < \infty; \quad 0 = t_0, 0 < t_i, \forall i$$

On $\mathscr{A}$, addition is defined pointwise, and scalar multiplication by real numbers is defined in the usual manner. The product of two elements $f, g \in \mathscr{A}$ is defined to be their convolution. More precisely, let g be given by (5) and f be given by

$$f(t) = f_a(t) + \sum_{k=0}^{\infty} f_k \,\delta(t - t_k') \tag{6}$$

Then the convolution $f * g$ is the function

$$\begin{aligned}(f * g)(t) = (f_a * g_a)(t) &+ \sum_{t_i \le t} g_i f_a(t - t_i) + \sum_{t_i' \le t} f_i g_a(t - t_i') \\ &+ \sum_{t_i + t_k' \le t} g_i f_k \,\delta[t - (t_i + t_k')]\end{aligned} \tag{7}$$

Exercise 1 Use the completeness of L^1 and the properties of $\mathscr{A}$ to show that the second and third terms of (7) are in L^1. Finally, prove that if $f, g \in \mathscr{A}$, then $f * g = g * f \in \mathscr{A}$.

By Exercise 1, $\mathscr{A}$ is closed under this multiplication, so that $\mathscr{A}$ is a *commutative* algebra (over $\mathbb{R}$) with a unit element, namely, $\delta(t)$. Define a norm on $\mathscr{A}$ by

$$\|g\|_{\mathscr{A}} = \|g_a\|_1 + \sum_{0}^{\infty} |g_i| \tag{8}$$

Then it is easy to show that

$$\|f * g\|_{\mathscr{A}} \le \|f\|_{\mathscr{A}} \|g\|_{\mathscr{A}} \tag{9}$$

and

$$\|\delta\|_{\mathscr{A}} = 1 \tag{10}$$

Thus, with the norm (8), $\mathscr{A}$ is a normed algebra which can be shown to be complete [Hil.1]. In other words, $\mathscr{A}$ is a *commutative Banach algebra* with a unit.

Exercise 2 Let $f \in L^p(\mathbb{R}_+)$, where $1 \le p \le \infty$, and let $w \in \mathscr{A}$. Show that, for any $p \in [1, \infty]$, $f * w \in L^p$ and that

$$\|f * w\|_p \le \|f\|_p \|w\|_{\mathscr{A}}$$

Exercise 3 Let $f \in L^2(\mathbb{R}_+)$ and $w \in \mathscr{A}$. Show that $f * w \in L^2$ and

$$\|f * w\|_2 \le \|f\|_2 \sup_{\omega} |\hat{w}(j\omega)|$$

Generalize to the case where $f \in L_n^2(\mathbb{R}_+)$ and $w \in \mathscr{A}^{n \times n}$. [Use Theorem (II.6.7).]

Extensions

11 Let $\sigma \in \mathbb{R}$. Define the **algebra** $\mathscr{A}(\sigma)$ as consisting of elements of the form (5) where now we require that

$$t \mapsto g_a(t)\varepsilon^{-\sigma t} \in L^1(\mathbb{R}_+) \tag{12}$$

and

$$\sum_0^\infty |g_k|\varepsilon^{-k\sigma} < \infty \tag{13}$$

The norm in $\mathscr{A}(\sigma)$ is taken to be (abusing notations!)

$$\|g\|_{\mathscr{A}(\sigma)} = \|g_a(t)\varepsilon^{-\sigma t}\|_1 + \|g_k\varepsilon^{-\sigma t_k}\|_1 \tag{14}$$

Exercise 4 Show that $\mathscr{A}(\sigma)$ is closed under the convolution defined by (7).

Exercise 5 Show that if $g \in \mathscr{A}(\sigma)$, then its Laplace transform $\hat{g}(s)$ has the following properties:

(a) $\hat{g}$ is holomorphic in the *open* right half-plane $\operatorname{Re} s > \sigma$.
(b) $\hat{g}$ is bounded on $\operatorname{Re} s \geq \sigma$; in fact, $\sup_{\operatorname{Re} s \geq \sigma}|\hat{g}(s)| \leq \|g\|_{\mathscr{A}(\sigma)}$;
(c) The function $\omega \mapsto \hat{g}(\sigma + j\omega)$ is continuous and bounded on $\mathbb{R}$.

15 **Definition** Let $\sigma \in \mathbb{R}$ and $\mathscr{A}^n(\sigma)$ be the set of all ordered n tuples $g = (g_1, g_2, \ldots, g_n)$ such that $g_i \in \mathscr{A}(\sigma)$ for $i = 1, 2, \ldots, n$. Similarly, let $\mathscr{A}^{n\times n}(\sigma)$ be the set of all $n \times n$ matrices $G = (g_{ij})$ $(i, j_i = 1, 2, \ldots, n)$ such that all $g_{ij} \in \mathscr{A}(\sigma)$.

Exercise 6 Show that $\mathscr{A}^{n\times n}(\sigma)$ is a noncommutative Banach algebra with a unit element.

Exercise 7 Let $H \in \mathscr{A}^{n\times n}$ be viewed as defining a map of L_n^∞ into itself, namely, $H\colon u \mapsto H * u$. Pick in $\mathbb{R}^n$ the l^∞ norm, namely, $|x(t)| = \max_i |x_i(t)|$. Show that the induced norm of H is

$$\|H\| = \max_i \sum_{j=1}^n \|h_{ij}(\cdot)\|_{\mathscr{A}}$$

where h_{ij} is the (i, j) element of H.

D.2 Ideals

1 Given a commutative algebra A, I is said to be an **ideal** of A iff

(a) I is a linear space $\subset A$;
(b) $i \in I \Rightarrow ix \in I$, $\forall x \in A$.

2 The algebra A and the empty set $\varnothing$ are ideals of A; they are said to be **trivial ideals of** A. An ideal I of A is said to be a **proper ideal of** A iff $I \neq \varnothing$ and $I \neq A$; i.e., I is a nonempty proper subset of A.

Example 1 Consider the commutative algebra of all $n \times n$ *diagonal* matrices with elements in $\mathbb{R}$. Show that $I \triangleq$ set of all diagonal matrices X with $x_{11} = 0$ is an ideal.

Example 2 $L^1(\mathbb{R}_+)$ is an ideal of the algebra $\mathscr{A}$ defined above.

Example 3 Let $A = \{f \in L^1(\mathbb{R})$; convolution product$\}$. Show that

$$I = \{f \in A \mid \hat{f}(j\omega)_0 = 0, \qquad \text{for some fixed } \omega_0\}$$

is an ideal of A.

Example 4 Consider the algebra $\mathscr{A}$ of Example 4 above. Show that $I = \{f \in \mathscr{A} : \hat{f}(s_0) = 0$ for some fixed s_0 with $\operatorname{Re} s_0 \geq 0\}$ is an ideal of $\mathscr{A}$.

3 **Theorem** Let A be a commutative algebra with unit element e; let I be a *proper* ideal of A. If $x \in I$, then x has no inverse in A; equivalently,

$$xy \neq e, \qquad \forall y \in A$$

Proof (by contradiction) Suppose that some $x \in I$ has an inverse x^{-1}; thus $xx^{-1} = e$. Now for *any* $y \in A$, $x^{-1}y \in A$ and, since I is an ideal, $x(x^{-1}y) \in I$. On the other hand, by associativity,

$$x(x^{-1}y) = (xx^{-1})y = ey = y$$

Thus, the product of x with every element of A will cover A. This contradicts the assumption that I was proper. ∎

D.3 Inverses in $\mathscr{A}$

The main result is due to Hille and Phillips.

1 **Theorem** Let $g \in \mathscr{A}$; then g has an inverse in $\mathscr{A}$ if and only if

2
$$\inf_{\operatorname{Re} s \geq 0} |\hat{g}(s)| > 0$$

Exercise 1 Suppose that $g \in L^1 \subset \mathscr{A}$. Show that (2) is never satisfied. (*Hint*: Use Riemann–Lebesgue.)

Proof $\Rightarrow$ Call x the inverse of g: $g * x = \delta$. Since $g, x \in \mathscr{A}$,

$$\hat{g}(s)\hat{x}(s) = 1 \qquad \forall s \quad \text{with} \quad \operatorname{Re} s \geq 0$$

Now $x \in \mathscr{A}$; so $\sup_{\text{Re}\, s \geq 0} |\hat{x}(s)| \leq \|x\|_{\mathscr{A}} < \infty$. Hence

$$|\hat{g}(s)| = |\hat{x}(s)|^{-1} \geq \|x\|_{\mathscr{A}}^{-1} \qquad \forall s \quad \text{with} \quad \text{Re}\, s \geq 0$$

$\Leftarrow$ For a complete proof, refer to Hille and Phillips. ∎

It is illuminating to observe that if there were an $s_0 \in \mathbb{C}$ with $\text{Re}(s_0) \geq 0$ such that $\hat{g}(s_0) = 0$, then g would be in a *proper* ideal of $\mathscr{A}$, hence would not have an inverse in $\mathscr{A}$. Therefore, to guarantee that g have an inverse in $\mathscr{A}$, we must have $|\hat{g}(s)| > 0$, $\forall s \in \mathbb{C}$ with $\text{Re}\, s \geq 0$. Similarly, if in $\text{Re}\, s \geq 0$, there were a sequence of points s_k with $|s_k| \to \infty$ with $|\hat{g}(s_k)| \to \infty$, we would contradict the boundedness in $\text{Re}\, s \geq 0$ of the Laplace transform of g^{-1}.

3 **Corollary** Let $G \in \mathscr{A}^{n \times n}$; then G has an inverse in $\mathscr{A}^{n \times n}$, if and only if

$$\inf_{\text{Re}\, s \geq 0} |\det \hat{G}(s)| > 0 \tag{4}$$

Proof Follows immediately from the fact that $\hat{f}, \hat{g} \in \hat{\mathscr{A}} \triangleq \mathscr{L}(\mathscr{A})$ implies that $s \mapsto \hat{f}(s)\hat{g}(s) \in \hat{\mathscr{A}}$, and from Cramer's rule. ∎

Exercise 2 Extend Theorem (1) and Corollary (3) to $\mathscr{A}(\sigma)$ and $\mathscr{A}^{n \times n}(\sigma)$.

Discrete-time case

There is a discrete-time analogue to Theorem (1) above. The setup is as follows. Consider all *one-sided* sequences, in particular those in $l_1 \triangleq \{g = (g_0, g_1, g_2, \ldots) | g_i \in \mathbb{R}, \sum_0^\infty |g_i| \triangleq \|g\| < \infty\}$. The linear space l^1 becomes a commutative algebra with a unit if one uses convolution of sequences as the multiplication. By Theorem (C.4.3), l^1 is closed under this multiplication.

Exercise 3 Verify that with the multiplication, l^1 is an algebra over $\mathbb{R}$, according to definition (1.2). If $g \in l^1$, define

$$\tilde{g}(z) \triangleq \sum_0^\infty g_k z^{-k}$$

It is easy to prove the following theorem.

5 **Theorem** If $g \in l^1$, then

(a) $z \mapsto \tilde{g}(z)$ is an analytic function of z for $|z| > 1$;
(b) $\theta \mapsto \tilde{g}(\varepsilon^{j\theta})$ is uniformly continuous on $[0, 2\pi]$;
(c) $|\tilde{g}(z)| \leq \|g\|$, $\forall |z| \geq 1$;
(d) as $|z| \to \infty$, $\tilde{g}(z) \to g_0$.

The analogue to Theorem (1) is Wiener's theorem (Wie.1).

6 **Theorem** Let $g = (g_0, g_1, g_2, \ldots)$ be a (*one-sided*) sequence in l^1 with $g_0 \neq 0$. U.t.c., g has an inverse in l^1 if and only if the curve

7 $$\theta \mapsto \tilde{g}(\epsilon^{j\theta}), \qquad \text{the image in } \mathbb{C} \text{ of the interval } [0, 2\pi],$$

8 does not go through the origin and does not encircle it.

The theorem can be stated as: Let $g \in l^1$; then g has an inverse in l^1 if and only if $\inf_{|z| \geq 1} |\tilde{g}(z)| > 0$.

The equivalence between (6) and (8) is immediate in view of (d) of Theorem (5) and the principle of the argument.

Exercise 4 Instead of the algebra l^1, consider the algebra $l^1(\rho)$. Let $0 < \rho \in \mathbb{R}$; then $l^1(\rho) \triangleq \{g = (g_0, g_1, \ldots) | g_i \in \mathbb{R}, \sum_0^\infty |g_k| \rho^{-k} < \infty\}$. Check that it is a commutative algebra with a unit and write down the inversion theorem corresponding to (6).

E BELLMAN-GRONWALL LEMMA

1 **Lemma** Let

(i) $f, g, k; \mathbb{R}_+ \to \mathbb{R}$ and locally integrable;
(ii) $g \geq 0, k \geq 0$;
(iii) $g \in L_e^{\infty},$;
(iv) gk is locally integrable on $\mathbb{R}_+$.

U.t.c., if $u\colon \mathbb{R}_+ \to \mathbb{R}$ satisfies

$$u(t) \leq f(t) + g(t) \int_0^t k(\tau)u(\tau)\, d\tau, \qquad \forall t \in \mathbb{R}_+ \tag{2}$$

then

$$u(t) \leq f(t) + g(t) \int_0^t k(\tau)f(\tau)\left[\exp \int_\tau^t k(\tau_1)g(\tau_1)\, d\tau_1\right] d\tau, \qquad \forall t \in \mathbb{R}_+ \tag{3}$$

4 **Special Case** Let $k\colon \mathbb{R}_+ \to \mathbb{R}$ locally integrable on $\mathbb{R}_+$ and $k \geq 0$; if

$$u(t) \leq c + \int_0^t k(\tau)u(\tau)\, d\tau, \qquad \forall t \geq 0 \tag{5}$$

then

6 $$u(t) \leq c \exp\left[\int_0^t k(\tau)\, d\tau\right], \qquad \forall t \geq 0$$

Proof (The standard proof uses differentiations and an integrating factor $k(t) \exp[-\int_0^t k(\tau)g(\tau)\, d\tau]$.) Let us prove it directly. Consider the integral equation,

7 $$y(t) = f(t) + g(t) \int_0^t k(\tau)y(\tau)\, d\tau, \qquad y(0) = f(0)$$

Its solution is

8 $$y(t) = f(t) + g(t) \int_0^t k(\tau)f(\tau)\left[\exp \int_\tau^t k(t')g(t')\, dt'\right] d\tau$$

Subtracting (2) and (7) and defining ζ, we obtain

9 $$\zeta(t) \triangleq y(t) - u(t) \geq g(t) \int_0^t k(\tau)[y(\tau) - u(\tau)]\, d\tau$$

which is of the form

$$\zeta(t) \geq (T\zeta)(t)$$

Hence

$$\zeta \geq T\zeta \leq T^2\zeta \geq \cdots \geq T^n\zeta, \qquad \forall n \in \mathbb{Z}_+$$

Now

$$(T^n\zeta)(t) = g(t) \int_0^t k(\tau_1)g(\tau_1) \int_0^{\tau_1} k(\tau_2)g(\tau_2) \int_0^{\tau_2} k(\tau_3)g(\tau_3) \cdots$$

$$\int_0^{\tau_{n-1}} k(\tau_n)\zeta(\tau_n) \quad d\tau_1 \quad d\tau_2 \cdots d\tau_n$$

10 $$= g(t) \int_0^t [(n-1)!]^{-1}\left[\int_0^t k(\tau_1)g(\tau_1)\, d\tau_1\right]^{n-1} k(\tau)\zeta(\tau)\, d\tau$$

Let

11 $$m(t) \triangleq \int_0^t k(\tau)g(\tau)\, d\tau$$

Note that $m(\cdot)$ is continuous and $m(t) \geq 0$, for $t \geq 0$; so the bracket in (10) is no larger than $[m(t)]^{n-1}$ because $k(\tau)g(\tau) \geq 0$, $\forall \tau$ by (ii). Hence (10) becomes

$$\zeta(t) \geq -g(t) \frac{[m(t)]^{n-1}}{(n-1)!} \int_0^t k(\tau)|\zeta(\tau)|\, d\tau$$

For any *fixed* t, as $n \to \infty$, we obtain

12 $$\zeta(t) \geq 0$$

where we used (iii). Finally, assertion (3) follows from (12), (9), and (8). ∎

For the discrete case, we have the following lemma.

13 **Lemma** Let $(u_k)_0^\infty$, $(f_k)_0^\infty$, $(h_k)_0^\infty$ be real-valued sequences on $\mathbb{Z}_+$. Let

14 $$h_k \geq 0, \qquad \forall k \in \mathbb{Z}_+$$

U.t.c., if

15 $$u_k \leq f_k + \sum_{0 \leq i < k} h_i u_i, \qquad k = 0, 1, 2, \ldots$$

then

16 $$u_k \leq f_k + \sum_{0 \leq i < k} \Big[\prod_{i < j < k} (1 + h_j) h_i f_i\Big], \qquad k = 0, 1, 2, \ldots$$

where $\prod_{i<j<k}(1 + h_j)$ is set equal to 1 when $i = k - 1$.

Proof By direct substitution in (15), using (14), we see that

$$\begin{aligned} u_1 &\leq f_1 + h_0 f_0 \\ u_2 &\leq f_2 + (1 + h_1)h_0 f_0 + h_1 f_1 \\ u_3 &\leq f_3 + (1 + h_1)(1 + h_2)h_0 f_0 + (1 + h_2)h_1 f_1 + h_2 f_2 \end{aligned}$$

The proof of (16) is easily obtained by induction. ∎

Note that

(a) if for some constant h_M, $h_i \leq h_M$, $\forall i$, then

$$u_k \leq f_k + h_M \sum_{0 \leq i < k} (1 + h_M)^{k-i-1} f_i$$

(b) if for some constant f_M, $f_i \leq f_M$, $\forall i$, then

$$u_k \leq f_M \prod_{0 \leq i < k} (1 + h_i)$$

REFERENCES

And.1 Anderson, B. D. O., The small gain theorem, the passivity theorem and their equivalence, *J. Franklin Inst.* **293** (2), 105–115 (Feb. 1972).

Apo.1 Apostol, T. M., "Mathematical Analysis," Addison-Wesley, Reading, Massachusetts, 1957.

Bak.1 Baker, R. A., and Vakharia, D. J., Input–output stability of linear time-invariant systems, *IEEE Trans. Automat. Contr.* **AC-15** (3), 316–319 (June 1970).

Bar.1 Barman, J. F., Well posedness of feedback systems and singular perturbations, Ph.D. thesis, Univ. California, Berkeley, 1973.

Ber.1 Bergen, A. R., Iwens, R. P., and Rault, A. J., On input–output stability of nonlinear feedback systems, *IEEE Trans. Automat. Contr.* **AC-11**, 742–745 (Oct. 1966).

Boc.1 Bochner, S., and Chandrasekharan, R. S., "Fourier Transforms," Princeton Studies 17, Princeton, Univ. Press, Princeton, New Jersey, 1949.

Bou.1 Bourkabi, N., "Fonctions d'une variable réelle," Livre IV, Chaps. 1–3, 2nd ed., Hermann, Paris, 1958.

Bou.2 Bourbaki, N., "Fonctions d'une variable réelle," Livre IV, Chaps. 4–7, 2nd ed., Hermann, Paris, 1961.

Bra.1 Brauer, F., Nonlinear differential equations with forcing terms, *Proc. Amer. Math. Soc.* **15**, 758–765 (1964).

Bro.1 Brockett, R. W., and Forys, L. J., On the stability of systems containing a time-varying gain, *Proc. 2nd Allerton Conf.*, Univ. of Illinois, Urbana, Illinois, 413–430 (1964).

Bro.2 Brockett, R. W., and Willems, J. L., Frequency domain stability criteria, Pts. I and II, *IEEE Trans. Automat. Contr.* **AC-10**, 225–261, 407–413, (July and Oct. 1965).

Bro.3 Brockett, R. W., The status of stability theory for deterministic systems, *IEEE Trans. Automat. Contr.* **AC-11** (3), 586–607 (July 1966).

Bro.4 Brockett, R. W., Path integrals, Liapunov functions, and quadratic minimization, *Proc. 4th Allerton Conf. on Circuits and System Theory*, 685–697 (1966).

Bro.5 Brockett, R. W., and Lee, H. B., Frequency domain instability criteria for time-varying and nonlinear systems, *Proc. IEEE* **55**, (5), 604–618. (May 1967).

Bro.6 Browder, F. E., The solvability of nonlinear functional equations, *Duke Math. J.* **30**, 557–560 (1963).

Cal.1 Callier, F. M., and Desoer, C. A., A graphical test for checking the stability of a linear time-invariant feedback system, *IEEE Trans. Automat. Contr.* **AC-17**, 773–780 (Dec.1972).

Cal.2 Callier, F. M., and Desoer, C. A., Necessary and sufficient conditions for the stability of n-input n-output convolution feedback systems with a finite number of unstable poles, *IEEE Trans. Automat. Contr.* **AC-18** (3), 295–298 (June 1973).

Che.1 Chen. C. T., L^p-stability of linear time-varying feedback systems, *J. SIAM Contr.* **6** (2), 186–193 (May 1968).

Cho.1 Cho, Y. S., and Narendra, K. S., Stability of nonlinear time-varying feedback systems, *Proc. 5th Allerton Conf.*, **249**–258 (1967).

Chu.1 Chu, S. C., and Metcalf, F. T., On Gronwall's inequality, *Proc. Amer. Math, Soc* **18** (3), 439–440 (June 1967).

Cop.1 Coppel, W. A., "Stability and Asymptotic Behavior of Differential Equations," Heath, Boston, Massachusetts, 1965.

Cor.1 Corduneanu, C., Problems globaux dans la théorie des èquations intégrales de Volterra, *Annali di Matematica Pura et Applicata* (*IV*) **67**, 349–364.

Dah.1 Dahlquist, G., Stability and error bounds in the numerical integrations of ordinary differential equations, *Trans. Roy. Inst. Tech.* (Sweden), No. 130 (1959).

Dav.1 Davis, J. H., Encirclement conditions for stability and instability of feedback systems with delays, *Int. J. Contr.* **15**, 793–799 (April 1972).

Dav.2 Davis, J. H., Fredholm operators, encirclements and stability Criteria, *J. SIAM Contr.* **10**, 608–622 (Nov. 1972).

Des.1 Desoer, C. A., and Thomasian, A. J., A note on zero-state stability of linear systems, *Proc. Allerton Conf.* 50–52 (1963).

Des.2 Desoer, C. A., A general formulation of the Nyquist criterion," *IEEE Trans. Circuit Theory* **CT-12** (2), 230–234 (June 1965).

Des.3 Desoer, C. A., A generalization of the Popov criterion," *IEEE Trans. Automat. Contr.* **AC-10** (2), 182–184 (April, 1965).

Des.4 Desoer, C. A., and Wong, K. K., Small signal behavior of nonlinear lumped networks, *Proc. IEEE* **56** (1), 14–23 (Jan. 1968).

Des.5 Desoer, C. A., and Wu, M. Y., Stability of multiple-loop feedback linear time-invariant systems, *J. Math. Anal. Appl.* **23**, (1), 121–130 (July 1968).

Des.6 Desoer, C. A., and Wu, M. Y., Stability of linear time-invariant systems, *IEEE Trans. Circuit Theory* **CT-15**, 245–250 (Sept. 1968).

Des.7 Desoer, C. A., Slowly varying system $\dot{x} = A(t)x$, *IEEE Trans. Automat. Contr.* **AC-14** (6), 780–781 (Dec. 1969).

Des.8 Desoer, C. A., Slowly varying system $x_{i+1} = A_i x_i$, *Electron. Lett.* **6** (11), 339–340, 1970.

Des.9 Desoer, C. A., and Wu, M. Y., Input–output properties of multiple-input multiple output discrete systems, Pt. I, *J. Franklin Inst.* **290** (1), 11–24 (July 1970).

Des.10 Desoer, C. A,. and Vidyasagar, M., General necessary conditions for input–output stability, *Proc. IEEE* **59** (8), 1255–1256 (Aug. 1971).

Des.11 Desoer, C. A., and Haneda, H., The measure of a matrix as a tool to analyze algorithms for circuit analysis, *IEEE Trans. Circuit Theory* **CT**-19 (5), 480–486 (Sept. 1972).

Des.12 Desoer, C. A., and Callier, F. M., Convolution feedback systems, *J. SIAM Contr.* **10**, 737–746 (Nov. 1972).

Des.13 Desoer, C. A., and Schulman, J. D., Cancellations in multivariable continuous-time and discrete-time feedback systems treated by greatest common divisor extraction, *IEEE Trans. Automat. Contr.* **AC-18** (4), 401–402 (Aug. 1973).

Des.14 Desoer, C. A., "Notes for a second course on linear systems," Van Nostrand Reinhold, New York, 1970.

Dew.1 Dewey, A. G., and Jury, E. I., A stability inequality for a class of nonlinear feedback systems, *IEEE Trans. Automat. Contr.* **AC-11** (1), 54–62 (Jan. 1966).

Die.1 Dieudonné, J., "Foundations of Modern Analysis," Academic Press, New York, 1960.

Die.2 Dieudonné, J., "Treatise on Analysis," Vol. II, Academic Press, New York, 1970.

Dun.1 Dunford, N., and Schwarz, J. T., "Linear Operators. Part I: General Theory," Interscience Publishers, Inc., New York, 1958

Edw.1 Edwards, R. E., "Functional Analysis," Holt, Rinehart & Winston, New York, 1965.

Est.1 Estrada, R. F., and Desoer, C. A., Passivity and stability of systems with a state representation, *Int. J. Contr.* **13** (1), 1–26 (Jan. 1971).

Flu.1 Flügge-Lotz, I., "Discontinuous and Optimal Control," McGraw-Hill Book Co., New York, 1968.

Fre.1 Freedman, M., and Zames, G., Logarithmic variation criteria for the stability of systems with time-varying gains, *J. SIAM Contr.* **6** (3), 487–507 (Aug. 1968).

Gof.1 Goffman, C., and Pedrick, G., "First Course on Functional Analysis," Prentice-Hall, Englewood Cliffs, N. J., 1964.

Gol.1 Goldberg, R. R., "Fourier Transforms," Cambridge Univ. Press, London and New York, 1961.

Hah.1 Hahn, W., "Stability of Motion," Springer-Verlag, New York, 1967.

Hil.1 Hille, E., and Phillips, R. S., Functional analysis and semi-groups, *Amer. Math. Soc. Coll. Publ.*, **XXXI**, New Providence (1957).

Hol.1 Holtzman, J. M., Contraction maps and equivalent linearization, *Bell Sys. Tech. J.* **46** (10), 2405–2435 (Dec. 1967).

Hol.2 Holtzman, J. M., The use of the contraction mapping theorem with derivatives in a Banach space, *Q. Appl. Math*, **26** (3), 462–465 (Oct. 1968).

Hol.3 Holtzman, J. M., "Nonlinear System Theory," Prentice-Hall, Englewood Cliffs, New Jersey, 1970.

Hou.1 Householder, A. S., "The Theory of Matrices in Numerical Analysis," Blairdell, New York, 1964.

Hsu.1 Hsu, C. H., and Chen, C. T. A proof of the stability of multivariable systems, *Proc. IEEE* **56** (11), 2061–2062 (1968).

Joh.1 Johnson, C. D., A note on control systems with one nonlinear element, *IEEE Trans. Automat. Contr.* **AC-11** (1), 122–124 (Jan. 1966).

Kri.1 Krikorian, J. S., Jr., A l^2-stability criterion with frequency domain interpretation for a class of nonlinear discrete systems, *IEEE Trans. Automat. Contr.* **AC-17** (3), 365–368 (June 1972).

Lee.1 Lee, C. T., and Desoer, C. A., Stability of single-loop nonlinear feedback systems, *Proc. 3rd Allerton Conf.*, 259–269 (1965).

McS.1 McShane, S., "Integration," Princeton Univ. Press, Princeton, New Jersey, 1944.

Min.1 Minty, G. J., Monotone (nonlinear) operators in Hilbert space, *Duke Math. J.* **29**, 341–346 (1962).

Nar.1 Narendra, K. S., and Goldwyn, R. M., A geometrical criterion for the stability of certain nonlinear nonautonomous systems, *IEEE Trans. Circuit Theory* **CT-11** (3) 406–408 (Sept. 1964).

O'Sh.1 O'Shea, R. P., A combined frequency-time domain criterion for autonomous linear systems, *IEEE Trans. Automatic Control* **AC-11**, 3, 1966.

Pal.1 Paley, R. E. A. C., and Wiener, N., Fourier transforms, *Amer. Math, Soc. Coll. Publ.* **XIX**, New Providence (1934).

Per.1 Perkins, W. R., Sensitivity analysis *in* "Feedback Systems," (J. B. Cruz, ed.), McGraw-Hill, New York, 1972.

Pop.1 Popov, V. M., "Some Properties of the Control Systems with Irreducible Matrix-Transfer Functions," Seminar on Differential Equations and Dynamical Systems, Lecture Notes in Mathematics 144, Springer-Verlag, New York, 1970.

Ram.1 Ramarajan, S., and Thathachar, M. A. L., L^2-stability of time-varying systems with global conditions on the time-varying gain, *Int. J. Syst. Sci.* **3** (4), 385–394 (Dec. 1972).

Ros.1 Rosenbrock, H. H., "State Space and Multivariable Theory," Wiley-Interscience New York, 1970.

Roy.1 Royden, H. L., "Real Analysis," The Macmillan Co., New York, 1963.

Sae.1 Saeks, R., Causality in Hilbert space, *SIAM Rev.* **12** (3), 357–383 (July 1970).

Sae.2 Saeks, R., "Resolution Space, Operators Systems," Springer-Verlag, New York, 1973.

San.1 Sandberg, I. W., On the properties of systems that distort signals (I and II), *Bell Sys. Tech. J.* **42**, 2033–2047 (Sept. 1963); and *Bell Sys. Tech. J.* **43**, 91–112 (Jan. 1964).

San.2 Sandberg, I. W., On truncation techniques in the approximate analysis of periodically time-varying networks, *IEEE Trans. Circuit Theory* **CT-11** (2), 195–201 (June 1964).

San.3 Sandberg, I. W., On the $\mathscr{L}_2$-boundedness of solutions of nonlinear functional equations, *Bell Sys. Tech. J.* **43**, 1581–1599 (July 1964).

San.4 Sandberg, I. W., A frequency domain condition for stability of feedback systems containing a single time-varying nonlinear element, *Bell Sys. Tech. J.* **43**, 1601–1608, Pt. II (July 1964).

San.5 Sandberg, I. W., Feedback-domain criteria for the stability of nonlinear feedback systems, *Proc. NEC*, 737–740 (1964).

San.6 Sandberg, I. W., On the boundedness of solutions of nonlinear integral equations, *Bell Sys. Tech. J.* **44** (1), 439–453 (Mar. 1965).

San.7 Sandberg, I. W., A stability criterion for linear networks containing time-varying capacitors, *IEEE Trans. Circuit Theory* **CT-12** (1), 2–12 (Mar. 1965).

San.8 Sandberg, I. W., Some results on the theory of physical systems governed by nonlinear functional equations, *Bell Sys. Tech, J.* **44**, 871–898 (May–June 1965).

San.9 Sandberg, I. W., An observation concerning the application of the contraction mapping fixed-point theorem and a result concerning the norm-boundedness of solutions of nonlinear functional equations, *Bell Sys. Tech. J.* **44**, 1809–1812 (1965).

San.10 Sandberg, I. W., Some stability results related to those of V. M. Popov, *Bell Sys. Tech. J.* **46**, 2133–2148 (Nov. 1965).

San.11 Sandberg, I. W., Conditions for the causality of nonlinear operators defined on a function space, *Q. of Appl. Math.* **XXIII** (1), 87–91 (Apr. 1965).

San.12 Sandberg, I. W., On the stability of liner systems containing a time-varying element with restricted rate of variation, *IEEE Int. Conv. Rec.* (U.S.A.) **14**, Pt. 7 173–182, 1966.

San.13 Sandberg, I. W., On generalizations and extensions of the Popov criterion, *IEEE Trans. Circuit Theory* **CT-13** (1), 117–118 (Mar. 1966).

Sch.1 Schwartz, L., "Théorie des Distributions," (rev. ed.), Hermann, Paris, 1966.

Sko.1 Skoog, R. A., and Blankenship, G. L., Generalized pulse-modulated feedback systems: norms, gains, Lipschitz constants, and stability, *IEEE Trans. Automat. Contr.* **AC-15** (3), 300–315 (June 1970).

Sun.1 Sundareshan, M. K., and Thathachar, M. A. L., L_2-stability of linear time-varying systems-conditions involving noncausal multipliers, *IEEE Trans. Automat. Contr.* **AC-17** (4), 504–510 (Aug. 1972).

Sun.2 Sundareshan, M. K., and Thathachar, M. A. L., Time domain criteria for the L^2-stability of nonstationary feedback systems, *IEEE Trans. Automat. Contr.* **AC-18** (1), 80–81 (Feb. 1973).

Sun.3 Sundareshan, M. K., and Thathachar, M. A. L., Generalized factorizability conditions for stability multipliers, *IEEE Trans. Automat. Contr.* **AC-18** (183–184 (Apr. 1973).

Tak.1 Takeda, S., and Bergen, A. R., Instability of feedback systems by orthogonal decomposition of L_2, *IEEE Trans. Automat. Contr.* (to appear).

Tha.1 Thathachar, M. A. L., Srinath, M. D., and Krishna, G., Stability with nonlinearity in a sector, *IEEE Trans. Automat. Contr.* **AC-11** (2), 311–312 (Apr. 1966).

Tho.1 Thomasian, A. J., "The Structure of Probability Theory with Applications," McGraw-Hill, New York, 1969.

Tit.1 Titmarsh, E. C., "Theory of Fourier Integrals," Oxford Univ. Press, New York, 1938.

Vid.1 Vidyasagar, M., Input–output stability of a broad class of linear time-invariant multivariable feedback systems, *J. SIAM Contr.* **10**, 203–209 (Feb. 1972).

Vid.2 Vidyasagar, M., L_p-stability of time-varying linear feedback systems, *IEEE Trans. Automat. Contr.* **AC-17**, 412–414 (June 1972).

Vid.3 Vidyasagar, M., Some applications of the spectral radius concept to nonlinear feedback stability, *IEEE Trans. Circuit Theory* **CT-19**, 608–615 (Nov. 1972).

Wan.1 Wang, S. H., "Design of Linear Multivariable Systems," Ph. D. Thesis, Univ, of California, Berkeley, 1971.

Wie.1 Wiener, N., "The Fourier Integral and Certain of Its Applications," Cambridge Univ. Press, 1933 London and New York.

Wil.1 Willems, J. C., Stability, instability, invertibility and causality, *J. SIAM Contr.* **7**, 645–671 (Nov. 1969).

Wil.2 Willems, J. C., Some results on the L^p-stability of linear time-varying systems, *IEEE Trans. Automat. Contr.* **AC-14** 660–665 (Dec. 1969).

Wil.3 Willems, J. C., and Brockett, R. W., Some new rearrangement inequalities having application in stability analysis, *IEEE Trans. Automat. Contr.* **AC-13**, 539–549 (Oct. 1968).

Wil.4 Willems, J. C., A survey of stability of distributed parameter systems, *in* "*Control of Distributed Parameter Systems*," publ. by the ASME for the JACC, Aug. 1969.

Wil.5 Willems, J. C., "The Analysis of Feedback Systems," MIT Press, Cambridge Massachusetts, 1971.

Wol.1 Wolovich, W. A., The determination of state-space representations for linear multivariable systems, Second IFAC Symp. Multivariable Tech. Contr. Syst., Düsseldorf, Germany, October 1971.

Wu.1 Wu, M. Y., and Desoer, C. A., L^p-stability ($1 \leq p \leq \infty$) of nonlinear time-varying feedback systems, *J. SIAM Contr.* **7**, (2) 356–364 (May 1969).

Wu.2 Wu, M. Y., and Desoer, C. A., Input–output properties of multiple-input multiple-output discrete systems: Pt. II, *J. Franklin Inst.* **290** (2) 85–101 (Aug. 1960).

Yos.1 Yoshizawa, T., "Stability Theory by Liapunov's Second Method," Maruzen, Tokyo, 1966.

Yos.2 Yosida, K., "Functional Analysis," Academic Press, New York, 1965.

You.1 Youla, D. C., Castriota, L. J., and Carlin, H. J., Bounded real scattering matrices and the foundations of linear passive network theory, *IRE Trans. Circuit Theory* **CT-4** (1), 102–124 (Mar. 1959).

Zam.1 Zames, G., On the stability of nonlinear time-varying feedback systems, *Proc. NEC* **20**, 725–730 (1964).

Zam.2 Zames, G., Nonlinear time-varying feedback systems—conditions for L_∞ boundedness derived using conic operators on exponentially weighted spaces, *Proc. 3rd Allerton Conf.* (Oct. 1965).

Zam.3 Zames, G., On the input–output stability of nonlinear time-varying feedback systems, Pt. I and II, *IEEE Trans. Automat. Contr.* **AC-11** (2), 228–238 (Apr. 1966); and **3**, 465–477 (July 1966).

Zam.4 Zames, G., and Falb, P. L., On the stability of systems with monotone and odd monotone nonlinearities, *IEEE Trans. Automat. Contr.* **AC-12** (2), 221–222 (Apr. 1967).

Zam.5 Zames, G., ad Falb., P. L. Stability conditions for systems with monotone and slope restricted nonlinearities, *J. SIAM Contr.* **6**, (1), 89–108 (Feb. 1968).

Zam.6 Zames, G., and Kallman, R. R., On spectral mappings, higher order circle criteria, and periodically varying systems, *IEEE Trans. Automat. Contr.* **AC-15** (6), 649–652, (Dec. 1970).

Zub.1 Zubov, V. I., "Methods of A. M. Lyapunov and their Application," Noordhoof, Groningen, Netherlands, 1964.

INDEX

R

S

T

U

Z

ELECTRICAL SCIENCE

A Series of Monographs and Texts

Editors

Henry G. Booker
UNIVERSITY OF CALIFORNIA AT SAN DIEGO
LA JOLLA, CALIFORNIA

Nicholas DeClaris
UNIVERSITY OF MARYLAND
COLLEGE PARK, MARYLAND

Joseph E. Rowe. Nonlinear Electron-Wave Interaction Phenomena. 1965

Max J. O. Strutt. Semiconductor Devices: Volume I. Semiconductors and Semiconductor Diodes. 1966

Austin Blaquiere. Nonlinear System Analysis. 1966

Victor Rumsey. Frequency Independent Antennas. 1966

Charles K. Birdsall and William B. Bridges. Electron Dynamics of Diode Regions. 1966

A. D. Kuz'min and A. E. Salomonovich. Radioastronomical Methods of Antenna Measurements. 1966

Charles Cook and Marvin Bernfeld. Radar Signals: An Introduction to Theory and Application. 1967

J. W. Crispin, Jr., and K. M. Siegel (eds.). Methods of Radar Cross Section Analysis. 1968

Giuseppe Biorci (ed.). Network and Switching Theory. 1968

Ernest C. Okress (ed.). Microwave Power Engineering:
Volume 1. Generation, Transmission, Rectification. 1968
Volume 2. Applications. 1968

T. R. Bashkow (ed.). Engineering Applications of Digital Computers. 1968

Julius T. Tou (ed.). Applied Automata Theory. 1968

Robert Lyon-Caen. Diodes, Transistors, and Integrated Circuits for Switching Systems. 1969

M. Ronald Wohlers. Lumped and Distributed Passive Networks. 1969

Michel Cuenod and Allen E. Durling. A Discrete-Time Approach for System Analysis. 1969

K. Kurokawa. An Introduction to the Theory of Microwave Circuits. 1969

H. K. Messerle. Energy Conversion Statics. 1969

George Tyras. Radiation and Propagation of Electromagnetic Waves. 1969

Georges Metzger and Jean-Paul Vabre. Transmission Lines with Pulse Excitation. 1969

C. L. Sheng. Threshold Logic. 1969

Dale M. Grimes. Electromagnetism and Quantum Theory. 1969

Robert O. Harger. Synthetic Aperture Radar Systems: Theory and Design. 1970

M. A. Lampert and P. Mark. Current Injection in Solids. 1970

W. V. T. Rusch and P. D. Potter. Analysis of Reflector Antennas. 1970

Amar Mukhopadhyay. Recent Developments in Switching Theory. 1971

A. D. Whalen. Detection of Signals in Noise. 1971

J. E. Rubio. The Theory of Linear Systems. 1971

Keinosuke Fukunaga. Introduction To Statistical Pattern Recognition. 1972

Jacob Klapper and John T. Frankle. Phase-Locked and Frequency-Feedback Systems: Principles and Techniques. 1972

Kumpati S. Narendra and James H. Taylor. Frequency Domain Criteria for Absolute Stability. 1973

Daniel P. Meyer and Herbert A. Mayer. Radar Target Detection: Handbook of Theory and Practice. 1973

T. R. N. Rao. Error Coding for Arithmetic Processors. 1974

C. A. Desoer and M. Vidyasagar. Feedback Systems: Input-Output Properties. 1975

A
B 5
C 6
D 7
E 8
F 9
G 0
H 1
I 2
J 3